THE WORD
WIZARD

Uniform with this edition

SAILING AWAY

Poems from our Fall 2003 National Poetry Contest
for young Canadians, aged 13 to 18 years

ACKNOWLEDGEMENTS

We are grateful for the efforts of the following
individuals in making this anthology possible:

Diane Wolf, Andy Nystrom,
Bryony Wynne-Jones and Tracy Playfair

THE WORD WIZARD

(AB, BC & SK)

A book of verse
from young Canadians
aged 7 to 12 years

Wendy K. Burgess
Editor

Peter B. Jones
Publisher

Poetry Institute of Canada
(Canadian Poetry Institute Inc.)

Victoria, British Columbia, Canada

ISBN 1-896965-42-3

Published by
Poetry Institute of Canada
P.O. Box 5577, Victoria, B.C.
V8R 6S4

Printed in Canada

INTRODUCTION

Poetry Institute of Canada, Young Writers, was established in 1995.

Its aim is to encourage and promote creative writing in children, and to make reading and writing poetry enjoyable and fun. This year again, has proved to be a great success.

When selecting poems, imagination and expression of ideas and feelings, are given as much importance as good use of language. The young writer's age is also taken into consideration.

Without the co-operation and enthusiasm of school teachers and parents this book of fine poems would not have been possible. It represents a new generation of young voices. They speak on a wide range of subjects, from home and social life, to school, world politics and the environment.

The high standard of work and effort by the children whose work appears in these pages, is a reflection of the teaching skills and encouragement shown in schools today.

CONTENTS

The Word Wizard
National School Prize Winners

1st Prize: $500
Whitefield Christian Academy, Scarborough, ON

2nd Prize: $100
Knob Hill Junior Public School, Scarborough, ON
Malden Central Public School, Amherstburg, ON
Swanavon School, Grande Prairie, AB

School Runners-Up
Margaret Twomey Public School, Marathon, ON
Branksome Hall, Toronto, ON
River Elm School, Winnipeg, MB

Student Winners
(AB, BC & SK)
1st: Jayleen Chivers (Nicomekl Elementary School, BC)
Runners-Up: Erica Stark (Woodlands Elementary School, AB)
Eric Stein (Langley Fundamental Elementary School, BC)
Alexandre Perrault (Wondertree Centre, BC)

Student Winner

My Grandfather's Garden

In my grandfather's garden
Tomatoes and beans reach up to the sky.
Pansies and hydrangeas grow lovely
And welcome friends passing by.

His garden is like a smile -
Each tomato, marigold, or rose
Calling out to those who pass -
Like a friendship it gently grows.

My grandfather in his garden
Does not seem so old.
Among the rows of plants and trees
He can carry a heavy load.

There are photos I have seen
Of him in a younger day.
A lifetime of growing lovely things
Are in his memories so far away.

There are perfect geraniums growing.
My grandfather is cutting the grass.
He lets me water the fruit trees.
Friends and strangers wave as they pass.

In my grandfather's garden
Tomatoes and beans reach up to the sky...

Jayleen Chivers (age 9)
Nicomekl Elementary School
Langley, BC

Runners-Up

Together

There once was a little boy,
Lost and scared.
Trying to find someone,
Someone who cared.
Cared about the bullied, depressed, the cold.
Cared about the sad, the mad, and the old.
He wished for sunlight in dark, sad places.
He wish for peace between the races.
He didn't think twice about his own fate;
He thought about those who might think hope too late.
He hoped that someone would triumph, succeed,
He wished to find someone, who would do this good deed,
Of not tolerating the violence, that brings shame and tears,
But upholding the peace that should wipe away fears.
Come one everybody; try to be like that boy
And we'll take away the qualms and bring in the joys
So let's join as one and around the world unite.
Let's forget our differences
And together we'll make this place right!!!

Erika Stark (age 11)
Woodlands Elementary School, Calgary, BC

———

The Sadness of War

Often I've fought in wars,
On the sea and the land and the air.
Often I've come close to death,
But with my good friends I share.

The moments of valour and courage,
The moments of fear and pain,
The moments of hatred and bloodshed,
And the moments of capture and shame.

In the prison camps of Auschwitz,
My brave friend suffered great pain.
They greatly tortured and beat him,
And that's where his good body was lain.

Until one day when my comrades,
Who were courageous, trustworthy, and brave,
Defeated the enemy Nazis,
And came to Auschwitz to save.

I told how the Nazis' cruel torture,
Never made my companion bend.
The memory of my long lost partner will go on,
My brave, true, and faithful friend.

Eric Stein (age 10)
Langley Fundamental Elementary School, Langley, BC

8

Runner-Up

Blood and Industry

The human strikes down a tree with an axe
The earth cries out in pain
The human demands an ongoing tax
The earth laments in vain

The human kills with pleasure
The bear will kill when maimed
By slaughter in great measure
Nothing can be gained

We scar the earth with metal beasts
We kill all in our path
Many a line of creatures ceased
In our bloody wrath

We wreak balance, upset its scales
And still we will not stop
Justice tries to live, and fails
This mess, we will not mop

We try to flatten mountains
We dump waste to and fro
Toxic water spouts from fountains
Good thing some folks say "no"

Industry, in its blind greed
Cares not for nature's grace
I must work with all speed
To block this iron mace

Alexandre Perrault (age 12)
Wondertree Centre
Vancouver, BC

Untitled

Help me now
For my
Cries are unheard.
Even though a glimmer
Of hope still resides.
Many people don't see
Me though I'm standing
Right there,
Nor do they care
That I'm
Dying from where:
My water is dirty,
The air is not clean
M y
Face is burning
From the sun

Help me!
I am Mother Earth

Rhiannon King (age 12)
Lansdowne Middle School

~//~

The Dull, Boring, Mean Teacher

Screech, squeak... "Sshh,"
The teacher
Growled
As the chalk again
Screeched, and
Squeaked,
Wailed across the blackboard
Whisper, whisper
"In the hall young man"
Scribble, scribble, peck
"The note on my desk, now,"
"Hmm interesting"
The note contains
"She's mean"
Phone call home
Rinngg!! Rinngg!!
"You are dismissed," (finally)
While we put
Our stuff away
We hear
Screech, squeak... "Sshh,"
"Can't you guys be quieter?"

Leanne Braun (age 12)
Hillcrest Community School

Wildfires

Wildfires are terrifying and fearsome!
Sometimes they are out of control.
Firefighters fight the flaming beast with
water and retardant
It ruins landscapes from pretty views
It destroys trees and wildlife, too.
The smokey, massive fire burns its path
into ash!

Daniel Carney (age 11)
Sherwood Park Elementary School

~//~

Poem to my Unborn Child

The world is tough these days
Work is assigned every day
School is a war zone
And bullies take over the playground
each day.

Don't let friends put you down from
your life, be a hero and be yourself.

Your troubles tempt you
You need a break
You ask for help
But they turn away.

Don't let friends put you down, be a hero,
be yourself.

Now when the abuse is over
You get ready to rest
But something comes up
And you have to stay up late

Don't let your friends put you down,
be a hero, be yourself.

So this is the end
I wish you good luck
Your road is ahead of you
Choose wisely,
My child!

Don't let friends put you down
from your life, be a hero, be yourself.

Patrick Grzelak (age 12)
Immaculate Conception School

Where's all my Stuff?

I lost my bat?
Where's my hat?
Where's my house?
What about my mouse?
I lose everything?
I lost my toy door
When I was only four!
And now I lost my new bat and even
  my best hat!
I lose everything in my long losing life.

Mohamed A. Al-Sehly (age 9)
Edmonton Islamic School

~//~

Sunset

Shining in the cool winter night,
I spy a lovely sunset, so bright.
Glowing through my house on the hill,
I watch it through my window sill.

Chirping birds, flying way up high,
Soaring through the dark black sky.
My sick grandmother is in bed,
I look at the sky, as it turns red.

As the sun drops behind the ocean,
Clouds are moving in slow motion.
The clouds clear out and out come the stars,
As I hear a band playing guitars.

All of a sudden the sky is light,
Oh, what a beautiful sight.
Listening to the waves rushing around,
Ringing in my ears such a nice sound.

Glittering, sparkling white snow,
Falling from the sky so slow.
Watching the snowflakes slowly drift down,
I hear the choir in the town.

My grandmother wakes up feeling swell,
Rushing to her room I give a yell.
"Mom" she came running into the room,
I glance out the window and out came
  the moon.

Janelle Bilodeau (age 10)
Notre Dame Elementary School

Big Cats

Cats are sometimes big
Cats are very very smart
Purring, meowing

Aidan Rosswood
David Oppenheimer Elementary School

~//~

Bear

Breathing quite loudly
While trotting on the white ice
Slowly he goes on
Until he finds fish
When he does it is dinner
But it's not easy

Branden Domoslai (age 10)
Notre Dame Elementary School

~//~

Good

Good,
Peace, rainbow,
Loving, laughing, hugging
wars, tanks, rifles, cannons,
killing, cutting, hurting
evil

Jason Liu (age 7)
David Oppenheimer Elementary School

~//~

Shining Star

After the sun's descent
In the pure black sky
Like a pearl in the night
Behind the northern lights
It comes out to play so bright
As the sun ascends into the sky
You fade away to sleep

Alex McGregor (age 10)
Notre Dame Elementary School

Flowers

Flowers oh flowers they smell so sweet.
Smelling them is really a treat.
Their colours so beautiful.
The colours so sweet.

Maddison Tyler (age 8)
Glenmore Christian Academy

~//~

Fire

Fire is like a furious lion.
It doesn't stop fighting until its appetite
    is full
Fire scars the land, like how a lion scars
    his enemies.
Fire is fast like when a lion runs.
Fire is like a furious lion... it doesn't stop.

Christopher Brierly (age 11)
Sherwood Park Elementary School

~//~

Fall

I'm looking out my window
up into the sky
when a single leaf
slowly flutters by,
It has turned the crimson/red
that all leaves do in Fall
when you're wishing it was Summer
but it isn't that at all,
When school books are piled high
waiting to be read
and you must rise at seven
when you want to stay in bed,
It has been a dry hot Summer
and clouds had gone to hide
but now rain on my window
tells me to stay inside,
All these silent signs
tell me Fall is here at last
and Summer's just
a mere thing of the past.

Marianne Brimmell (age 11)
St. Patrick's Elementary School

Birds

flying, chirping, birds,
robins, cockatiels, herons,
there are many birds.

Derek Kwan (age 8)
David Oppenheimer Elementary School

~//~

The Day Has Come

Pine trees whisper silent songs
In the very dead of a moonlit night

I wonder what goes on in
placid shadows
Where the lonely moon's stare
cannot reach

Cold feet dance on dewy grass
Dew drops like diamonds, strewn upon
the silver lawn

Can people hear the cricket symphony?
Strands of music wafting 'round the
dancing trees and I

On the crest of the hill's black silhouette
I see the golden glow of the sun,
Peering over the still sleeping mountain

The crisp new dawn arrives in silence
Pushing the last of the night into the
corners of the sky

Slowly, the sky fades from the
starry black
To a playful blue, waiting to share the
many secrets of the day ahead

"The day has come!" cry the little birds
As the sun mercifully warms their
downy wings

I smile as the little chorus of birds grows
To welcome the shining sun and the life
it brings

"The day has come!" I whisper
"The day has come at last!"

Taylor Bachand (age 11)
Dallas Elementary School

Favourite Foods Sonnet

I have a list of favourite food
That are really dandy
Most of them taste *So So* good!
They're almost as good as candy!
Ice cream is like a dream
What I also like is pizza
The sweet and sour nectarine
And the bread like pita
Red fresh strawberries
And grain wheat bread
Sweet red cherries
And tasty strawberry spread
These are some foods that are tasty
And I really like sugary pastries.

Paolo Balce (age 12)
Immaculate Conception School

~//~

A Child's Love

When you hear about child poverty,
you think it's just rumours.
Well it's not.

When you walk down the street,
you see kids begging for food
with no home or nothing to eat.

Some will give a penny or two,
but seriously what's it gonna do?
A penny a day won't keep you alive
for the rest of your life,
but a family will.

That's all a kid wants in life,
a loving family who cares for them.
We throw lots of food away,
but some kids would risk their life
just to get that last bite of sandwich.

Next time you throw out food,
think about all the kids who have nothing.
Sure there's orphanages in the world,
but how long until they fill up?
That's not a real home.

Take a minute out of your time
and think how lucky you are!

Emily Thomason (age 12)
Kidston Elementary School

Untitled

I had a frog that hid in a log
Along came a dog.
Looked in the log and saw the frog.
What are you doing in there frog?
Hiding from the hog.

Carter Cochrane (age 7)
Notre Dame School

~//~

Leaves are Red

Leaves are red.
Ted likes red and yellow.
Yellow is mellow.
Green is the best.
Thanks Ted
For reminding me
That I like red.

Cydnee York (age 7)
Notre Dame School

~//~

Whirling Leaves

In fall

The leaves are bright colours
Red, yellow, brown, green.

A wonderful sight
to watch
Seasons changing
Fall
Turning into
winter
Bright colours flying
around
the sky
Geese
flying
south
for the winter
trees...bare
winter comes

Haley Garnett (age 10)
Deep Cove Elementary School

13

Let's Play Laces!

I have a dog. She's a Border Collie.
Her name is Laces.
She likes to hide in different places.
She runs around in my back yard,
Catching her is really hard.
She lays down in the long grass,
You can hardly see her.
She is a sneaky lass.
Ta ta for now.

Claire Cameron (age 7)
Glenmore Christian Academy

~//~

My Dog Popcorn

My dog Popcorn, I named him that
He's so funny and he's so fat.
He likes walking and he knows tricks
When I hug him he always licks!

He's like a cat because he eats fish
Sometimes he eats from the kitty's dish.
I love Popcorn so very much
In fact, this much!
Xoxoxoxoxoxoxoxoxoxoxoxoxo

Jayme Sauer (age 6)
Glenmore Christian Academy

~//~

My Pillow

My fluffy, cuddly pillow is as soft
   as it can be,
Heavier than a feather, much lighter
   than a tree.
When I wake up my pillow is warm
To give me comfort even in a storm.
Then one night I had a bad dream,
My pillow was there by a stream.
My pillow almost fell in, I caught it
   in time, then I awoke
And found my pillow safe as can be,
Heavier than a feather,
Much lighter than a tree.

Lindsay Dober (age 10)
St. Patrick's Elementary School

Colour Poem

Gold is...
Gold is as strong as bright glowing lights,
Gold is as sharp as a knife
Gold is as heavy as steel,
Gold is as flashy as lightning,
Gold is as shiny as a diamond,
Gold is as beautiful as the leaves in fall,
Gold is as soft as butter,
Gold is as hard to bend as silver,
Gold is beautiful, very beautiful.

Oscar Kapsa (age 8)
David Oppenheimer School

~//~

It's Time for Winter

It's a time when fall has ended,
It's time for old winter clothes
   to be mended,
It's a time when your hands freeze,
It's a time for a cold winter breeze.

It's time for a snowfall,
It's a time when snowmen call,
It's a time to pull on coats,
It's a time when ice freezes castle moats.

It's time to go inside now,
It's time to put away the farmer's plow,
It's time to go around the fire,
It's time because we are so tired.

It's time to go outside now, I think,
It's time for our eyes to freeze
   before we even blink,
It's time to go to the skating pond,
It's time to share a great bond.

It's time to skate around,
It's time to fall to the ground,
It's time to get hot chocolate,
It's time for candles to be lit.

It's time to go home in the van,
It's time to think about getting a sun tan,
It's time to say "goodbye,"
It's time for spring to start, oh my!

Samantha Hauca (age 9)
St. Vincent School

14

The Storm

Dark huge puffy clouds blowing from
   the west,
It looks like a storm is coming our way.
Thunder crashing, lightning flashing
   the storm has begun.
Hail pelting the rooftops,
   giant puddles, sewer drains full,
   almost over-flowing.
Hail turns to rain, rain turns to a
   light shower.
The sun creeps out from behind the clouds,
The rain completely stops and the clouds
   blow away
   to reveal up in the sky the splendour
   of the rainbow after the storm.

Meagan Popowich (age 10)
Notre Dame Elementary School

~//~

The Special Place

There they go again
Dancing in the wind,
Dashing past the delicious blackberries
And bolting through the dried grass.
There's the smell of fresh hay in the air,
The sound of hooves clicking
   against the ground.
I see two images in the field,
   running and rearing.
The taste of blackberries tickles
   my taste buds,
Squirting purple juice everywhere.
I feel the softness of the horse's
   neck on my sweaty face.
The wind is calling my name
   and tugging at my shirt.
Then in the distance I see the horses'
   manes swishing in the wind
I hear a neigh and the sneezes of horses,
And the sounds of them slurping
   up water from an old rusty tub.

This is the kind of place I like.
I feel safe and comfortable.
I would like to live here one day.
Of course, with animals.

Sadie Liberty (age 11)
Meadowridge School

Mystery Redhead?

Whose hair is red?
Who would rather have the colour of lead?
Who finally dyes her hair green,
   and all her classmates make a scene?
Who loves her friend Diana,
   and her country Canada?

Carmela Elisabeth Desireau (age 11)
Calgary French & International School

~//~

Snow Flakes

Snow flakes
   falling
   falling
   from the sky
It's a winter wonderland
   as the cars go by
Snow flakes
   falling
   falling
   from the sky
It's a winter wonderland
   as the children pass by.

Rose Leishman (age 9)
Deep Cove Elementary School

~//~

The Whispering Wind

On a dark cold night,
Not a sound to hear,
The whispering wind takes flight.

Through wings of seagulls,
Through the sky,
Can you hear its softest sigh?

Up, around and over the moon,
And over mountains, snowy white,
The wind goes home to end its flight.

Tomorrow night, if you dare,
Watch the wind come out of its lair.

Kennedy Doyle (age 9)
St. Vincent School

Autumn

I smell leaves
I hear birds singing
I taste pumpkin pie
I see a bear in my yard
I touch apple trees

Alexandra Dehnel (age 6)
St. Joseph School

~//~

Wild Fires

Fire makes children cry.
Fire doesn't care if you're a superstar or...
Just a poor old guy.
And if you're not prepared,
It will swish by...
And in seconds make fire the
Despair of your life!!!

Mehrdad Momeni (age 10)
Sherwood Park Elementary School

~//~

Spring

The sun is shining
the trees are green
the wind blowing in my hair
I like spring,
do you?
I like the air
so fresh and clean
I like the dry leaves
rubbing together
don't you?
I like the sound
of birds singing
the grass
the colour of gold
I like the flowers blooming
and vines hanging
do you?
Yes, I do
I like spring.

Deion Harris (age 8)
Captain Cook Elementary School

Rabbits

Rabbits
Adorable, soft,
Hopping, jumping, playing
Carnivore, mean, unfriendly, chasing,
Walking, running, hunting,
Tiger.

Angela He (age 8)
David Oppenheimer Elementary School

~//~

Sunset of the Pantheon

The sun's light still etches
The sky, though the fiery marble
has already
Sunken behind the
Hallowed hills.

The water is dappled a salmon hue
By the last fingers of light, fingers
That stretch out to stroke and caress the
Water with its radiant fingertips.

The azure blue dome that is the sky,
that curves overhead,
Is a flawless ceramic bowl, its lip
Disappearing beyond the horizon,
forever out of reach.
The azurite glaze is shot through
with streaks of
Pink-orange fire, and fades into a
periwinkle mist.

There are bright, gleaming gashes rent
In the fabric of the dome, carved by the
Wings of a marauding angel.

Then the silver crescent
of the arriving moon
Slips into the sky, and the roof blackens,
The rents fade, the fires wane.
The glazes darken, and
the lights of heaven shine
Through, a sprinkle of
Diamonds against the midnight velvet
that makes up
The tapestry of the night sky.

Krystina Bojanowski (age 12)
Meadowridge School

The Dream World

In these days of high-tech gizmos,
   everything is swirled;
Sometimes I just need to escape into
   my imaginary world.
Where you can always feel,
   the crisp autumn breeze,
And a sweater wrapped around you,
   from your head-tips to your knees.
Where every feeling in your hearts,
   shows up on your teeth,
Where everyone is showing,
   their feelings underneath.
Where there's music in your fingertips,
   and passion in your heart,
Where the wise are appreciated,
   not just the cute and smart.
Where the fears of tomorrow,
   seem to wash away,
Where you can feel the gentle sun
   drops, savouring every ray.
Where you breathe in the solid maples,
   glowing brightly in your soul
Remembering when you planted them
   in the majestic leaf-filled hole.
You can shout out all your secrets,
   letting the truth take its path,
Never feeling any suffering,
   never feeling any wrath.
Skin is not a difference, we're people
   all the same,
Feelings of achieving, reaching goals
   that you aim.
Lying in the water, only hearing
   soaring wings,
Feeling all the colours, and souls
   of everything.
No flashing lights, no commercials,
   no "new"! or "fat-free"!
Desiring every shrivelled flower,
   and every willowing tree.
You can feel the wind lifting you,
   no matter how low you are,
Watching the shadows of the moonlight,
   falling on the misty stars.
Now mother earth's done so much more,
   but please don't raise your brow,
Sometimes I think we're living there,
   just some way, somehow!

Zoë Field (age 10)
Charles Dickens Elementary School

~//~

Untitled

Honey
Liquid, thick
Flowing, swirling, sticking
Oozing out to earth
Lava

Jeanie Lim (age 11)
Parkcrest School

~//~

Flowers

Flowers here, flowers there,
Flowers everywhere.
Flowers in the air,
Flowers on my kite.
Flowers on the ground.
Books about flowers,
Posters of flowers too.
Flowers for a gift,
Flowers for my birthday.
Flowers are different colours,
Flowers smell very nice.
Do you like flowers?

Manrose Mann (age 7)
Windebank Elementary School

~//~

Autumn Leaves

Air is crisp and cool,
Under the trees the leaves fall,
Twinkling sunset through the trees,
Up and away the leaves fly,
Makes the summer go away,
Nice fragrant smell.

Leaves get raked up and carried away,
Everyone is happy,
Almost all children love
   to play with leaves,
Violet covered sky in the evening,
Everything is gold yellow, cherry red
   and brown,
Soon the cold winter will come.

Tena Martens (age 10)
Hillcrest Community School

Untitled

blue is...
blue is as bright as the sky
blue is as beautiful as the clouds,
blue is dark as water

Michelle Hoy (age 10)
David Oppenheimer Elementary School

~//~

I'm Sorry

I'm sorry I broke the bed
I'm sorry I broke the shed
I'm sorry I smashed the door
I'm sorry I coloured on the floor

I'm sorry I knocked down the trees
I'm sorry I gave the dog fleas
I'm sorry I ate all the food
I'm sorry I had a bad mood

I'm sorry I broke all your planners
I'm sorry I had bad manners
I'm sorry I brought in a rat
I'm sorry for being a *Brat!!!*

Rob (Robbie) Blythe, Jr. (age 10)
Miller Park Community School

~//~

Halloween

Halloween is my favourite day
Ghost and ghouls come out to play
It's spooky and kooky
And every one is snoopy
Dracula and Frankenstein
Come to say hello
There might be more who would know
A devil could be hiding in those
    colourful leaves
Orange, yellow, red and gold
The sky is now dark
There goes a spark
Time for candy it's really dandy
I love Halloween

Megan Robinson (age 10)
Ronald Harvey Elementary School

Untitled

Deep and full of life,
Strong and active,
I beat against the sandy shore
Working to wear away my boundaries.
My face changes, depending on my mood,
From turquoise to emerald to steel.
Twice each day I rush to hug
My closest friend, the land.
I am the ocean!

Savanna Lindley (age 8)
Northern BC Distance Education School

~//~

If I Were a Kite...

If I were a kite my string would unwind,
    off the stick
And off I would fly into the deep blue sky
Since I just started my fun,
    I would feel my brightly coloured body
Twist, twirl, rise, and drop
    making me feel extremely sick
When my owner finally has control
    over me
I would be sailing high up where I could see
Scattering little children watching me
My bow-covered tail swishes around
As if waving to them and saying, "Hello"
While I was up in the air
I would also see fields of large daisies
That look like tiny white dots
When I scanned everything around me
    I could also see
Birds surveying me closely
    before flying away
Oh what is that lovely scent that makes
    me hungry?
Why, it's pink apple blossoms
Down below me from way up here
I can taste those apples that aren't
    even there
I can also taste the air coming from the lake
When the sparkling blue water
    shows me my reflection
I can also hear it splashing around
Mixing in with the sound of the breeze
I would feel so happy being a kite
That is, if I were a kite

Shivani Gounder (age 12)
Talmey Elementary School

18

Little Leaf

Once there was a leaf
As green as summer's grass
But one day this leaf of green
Fell from the branch it once hung from
As this leaf fell so did more
And now this leaf that used
to be so green
Has changed into a golden brown
as the others did
Now this season is fall

Cassie Dawn Pederson (age 10)
Ronald Harvey School

~//~

My Grandma's Kitchen

Stepping lightly on the darkened
burnished floor
Foot after foot I slid closer to that
mysterious smell
My mouth opens watering
The sweet aroma lingering in the air
Apple pie

Rushing relatives
The musty scent of old hay and
wet dogs, drifts through the air
A misted barn cat shyly meanders into
the hallway still unseen

Everyone chats like the hooves
of wildebeest thundering
through the night
Suddenly a young one speaks up,
and puts the idea into our heads for
a game of hide and seek

Dashing behind the cottoned pillows
and the leather coated couch
The hands of a young child touched
the familiar straw-like fabric,
Following an indescribable design

After the game is over all of the
little ones retreated to bed
And the older ones went out
onto the porch,
And talked the night away

Julia Larsen (age 11)
Meadowridge School

A Home

After school you go home
It's a place where you're not alone
You have a family there for you
Think of the things you could be
Now you know where to go when
you're alone
It's the best place. It's home!

Flora Yang (age 9)
Charles Dickens Elementary School

~//~

Leaves

Leaves of the fall
Many different ones
Burgundy of the cherry
Fire red of the maple
Amber of the oak
Prick the ice blue sky
Leaves of fall
Spinning and twirling
Up to the sky
Then plunging back to the ground
Leaves

Collin Tittle (age 10)
Ronald Harvey Elementary School

~//~

Ants

Ants on a log
Ants in the sink
Ants on my arm
And ants in my drink

Ants on a tree
Ants in a mouse house
Ants on the floor
And ants in a grouse house

Ants in the garbage
Ants on the rake
Ants inside anteaters
And ants on the cake

Brook Blain (age 9)
Windermere Elementary School

Gopher Smell

Gophers are everywhere.
Gophers play on our park.
Gophers get killed by a gun.
Gophers smell like cow pie.
Gophers like our school.
The principal wants them out!

Micheal Moyan (age 11)
Elizabeth School

~//~

Real Real Copy

I miss my home in B.C.
I miss my kitten that played with
    my mittens.
I miss my teddy bear that always ate my
    gummy bears.
I miss my friends and my relatives.
I hope to see them all another day.
But now I live in Edmonton, Alberta,
A nice place to be.
I hope one day I meet some friends
And I hope I love it just like B.C.

Sagal Aw-Jama (age 9)
Edmonton Islamic School

~//~

High on the Mountains

High on the mountains lives
    the mountain lion.
His roar is like a rocket to
    mountain climbers
But is like the sound of falling
    raindrops to the people down below.
Deep in the forest lives a jaguar
    in the trees
Quietly but quickly he tiptoes over the
    grass to pounce
On the pig pen of an unsuspecting village.
On the vast prairie lives a coyote
    that howls at the moon
And wakes the sleeping hunter,
Only to walk the path of death.

Alexander Shepard (age 9)
Charles Dickens Elementary School

The Bear

There once was a little bear,
And he had lots of hair.
His first name was Bob,
He liked corn on the cob,
And liked his hamburgers rare.

Rebecca Muller (age 11)
St. Joseph's School

~//~

Free Falling

When I am free falling my
Heart skips, my stomach is gone
    but it still skips.
Especially after a long hike -
the cool plunge, sun to sea, exhilarating!

The ocean calls "Just one more time!
    Jump!" and I do!

The fear of jumping, the urge to go again.

The ocean calls "Just one more time!
    Jump!" and I do.

The thought of thinking back.
What if I had hit a rock?
What if I had drowned?

The ocean calls "Just one more time!
    Jump!" and I do.

It all evaporates in free fall!
Fear and joy become one. Free!

The oceans calls "Just one more time?
    Jump!" and I do.

Proving that I Rosie,
Can and will. Laughing at myself
for being so scared.
Taking a chance.

The ocean calls "Just one more time!
    Jump!" and I do.

The ocean calls "Just one more time!
    Jump!" and I do!

Rosemary Schlagintweit (age 11)
Meadowridge School

Life

The long journey of life can be hard;
You might sometimes even feel hurt
   or scarred.
But really if you ask your heart,
There actually isn't any bad part.
Everything is for a good reason;
Every day, every week, every year,
   every season.

Decisions, decisions
They're always there.
Behind you, in front of you,
They're almost everywhere.

The choice is yours;
No one else can decide.
Life's road may be bumpy.
Don't stop, take the ride!

Marlies Zimmer (age 11)
St. Joseph School

~//~

Deep Into The Woods

Deep into the woods,
'Neath the tallest birch,
Lay a white silken lily,
Upon the soiled earth.
This is in memory,
Of a girl I think brave
No she didn't save,
A single living soul.
Nor climb a mountain,
Or travel the globe.
She just touched the lives,
Of many like me.
She lived with her dog,
As happy as can be.
Yet she had no home,
Just a dog and a tree.
On a hot summer day
When food was scarce,
She passed on with her dog.
What a sad, sad day.
Deep into the woods,
'Neath the tallest birch,
Lay a white silken lily,
Upon the soiled earth.

R.D. Adair (age 11)
Tremblay Elementary School

Your Name

I wrote your name in the sky,
   But the wind blew it away.
I wrote your name in the sand,
   But the waves washed it away.
I wrote your name in my heart,
   And forever it will stay.

Ciarra Meeks (age 12)
Windebank Elementary School

~//~

Ramadan Come Back!

I feel happy because I like Ramadan!
I feel the Gates of Heaven open for me.
I want to go to the sky flying like a bird.
I hear the people reading Qu'ran.

Ramadan do not go away.
Ramadan come back to me some day.
Ramadan, I like you, Ramadan.
Ramadan, Ramadan, I love you, Ramadan.

Mohamed Daab (age 8)
Edmonton Islamic School

~//~

Uneasy Night

Just yesterday our boat slipped quietly
   through unrippled seas.
Dolphins danced in our bow wave as if
   trying to please.

"Scarlett Point: Winds southeast forty
   kilometres rising to sixty
   kilometres overnight.
Pressure nine hundred and ninety-eight
   millibars and falling."

Now wave upon wave crash onto the rocks.
Violent winds show no mercy upon
   stressing docks.
Our boat straining, our dock lines tight...
We wait for an end to this never
   ending night.

Liz Fenje (age 12)
St. Michael's University Middle School

21

The Good Old Football Game

Football is a fantastic and fun game
But force is what you need.
Farther and farther you run with the football
And fake a turn and get there.

Daniel Gauvin (age 11)
Calgary French & International School

~//~

Shell

As the sun reflects on a shell.
As I hear a big, loud bell.
This shell is a home of a crab.
When I see this nice shell I grab.
This shell is so precious to me.
I suddenly see lots of glee.

Kaylee Dribnenky (age 9)
Notre Dame Elementary School

~//~

A Dog's Life

What does my dog do all day
What does he do when I'm gone
Does he run and play and fetch his bone
Or does he read the paper and talk on
    the phone

When I leave the house and say good-bye
Does he dance and jig or does he sit
    and cry
Does he call his friends and invite them over
Or does he play with his squeaky toy
    named Grover

I fill up his bowl with fresh food and water
Does he eat what is there or does he call
    "Spiro's" and make an order

I guess we'll never know just what he
    does when I leave
If I really knew I wouldn't believe
So it doesn't really matter what he does
    when I am gone
As long as he is there when I come home

Elènee Nolin (age 9)
École St. Thomas School

The Goal That Changed it All

They were standing in the centre of the field,
    Fans screaming in the stands.
The ref commands the whistle to blow
        (Players go).
    Players streaming,
    Fans screaming.
Manchester gets a penalty kick.
The Arsenal fans began to get sick.
    Last minute of the game,
    He better have aim.
        It's a goal.
    God bless our soul.
It's the goal that changed it all.

Cameron Handley (age 12)
Neil Middle School

~//~

If I Were a Kite...

If
I were
a kite I would
hear an airplane
zooming above my
square edged head, I
would hear birds, lots of
birds chirping under me. I
would feel the sun shining a
warm light at my back and wind
blowing at my body and making me
fly higher and higher till I fly so high.
I start to fall lower and lower till I hit
the ever so green grass. A little
boy would grab me by my side
and throw me up in the air. Now
I am back in the air, hello
birds, hello airplanes,
hello big tree looking
ever so small, hello
lightning, lightning
oh no, pull me
back. Yes I'm
safe now.
Goodbye
everything
I'm going
home
now.

Dean Liu (age 12)
Talmey School

22

Dolphins in the Deep

Dolphins in the deep,
Seagulls in the high,
And people in the middle
Just casually strolling by.
But the thing that makes us
Look very small is God
In the Heavens
Watching us all.
Now I'm turning out the light.
Go to sleep.
Good night.

Emilie Galambos (age 8)
Pinewood Elementary School

~//~

Candy Store

This is what the term "candy store"
really means.

C - Is for the craving in your mind when
you look in the store window
A - Is for the addiction you get when
you take your first bite
N - Is for the nagging your parents endure
whenever you walk past the candy aisle
D - Is for the desire when you see your
friends got candy in their lunches
Y - Is for the yearning you get when you
want this tender scrumptuous morsel

S - Is for the extremely lucious flavour or
the *extreme* sour flavour of some candies
T - Is for the tantalizing way they put
all the best looking candies
in the display window to mock you
O - Is for the overpowering, seductive
force this food has on you
R - Is for the rush your body gets when
you take that first bite and feel the
taste of Heaven
E - Is for the extravagance that has blessed
your country with this magnificent food

These are the meanings of the letters in
the words "candy store"

Karia Rosenberg (age 12)
St. Michael's University Middle School

Pigs

Do pigs get tired of crawling in the mud?
Do they wish to crawl in the crud?
Why do they eat leftover food?
Do they get in the mood?

Matthew Facchin (age 10)
Miller Park Community School

~//~

The Special Star

In the starlit galaxy there lies a special star
That only the naked eye can see
With the powers of above
This special star is special
Because itself is not made with gases
But with everyone's hopes and dreams
This is the first star you see at night
And wish upon with all your night
I wish I may, I wish I might
Wish upon this star tonight!

Mollie McAllister (age 10)
Pinewood Elementary School

~//~

If

If my mom was a fruit,
She'd be an orange,
Tangy, juicy,
Standing tall on a hot summer's night.

If my mom was a pot of paint,
She'd be a sizzling red,
Hot, shining
Sweet as a strawberry.

If my mom was a drink,
She'd be a glass of water,
Refreshing, relaxing,
Cool and wet.

But she's not a fruit or a
pot of paint or a drink.
She is my mother. A sweet
loving mother to me.

Taryn Vos (age 10)
Windebank Elementary School

I Like Fall

I like fall. I like leaves.
Leaves are fun, fun.
Fun for me.

Felix Hehemann (age 7)
Notre Dame School

~//~

On Halloween Night

Children
Laugh as pumpkins shine
As a moon glows bright
On a dark, spooky Halloween
Evening

Celina Poitras (age 11)
Ronald Harvey Elementary School

~//~

Metamophosis!

It's time to get out.
I hope my wings will sprout.
Life will be different in this other world.
Things happen so fast, it's absurd.
I want to be free!
I want to see
The world that is waiting just for me!
This is metamorphosis!
Do you know what this is?
Will the world be filled with bliss?
The weather is right,
And the sun is so bright,
I think my cocoon may crack tonight!
Things happen so fast,
And yet too slow.
I see the happiness and feel the woe.
What kind of creature will I be?
I want to know, I need to see!
Whatever you happen to be, just like me...
You live in changes,
You go through stages.
So get ready for metamorphosis.
Now you know what it is.

Atiya Jaffar (age 11)
Hjorth Road School

Try to Remember

The death of countless innocents
and thousands of soldiers
For freedom, for freedom.

The hatred and racism of the countries
that start these terrible controversies
With anger, with anger.

To be there and hear the sound
of gunfire in the fields
where the ground is stained with blood.
With fear, with fear.

To see the fields where the crosses lie,
for the men of old who sacrificed their lives
for the freedom that is now shared.
With sadness, with sadness.

Jordan Kurucz (age 12)
Neil Middle School

~//~

Acceptance

You laugh as though you are better
You laugh as though she is worse
You laugh at the way she looks
At the way she holds her purse.

You leave your head up
And force her head down
You say your cruel words
You leave her with a frown.

Another day she cries
Goes without any sleep
It was your fault
You made her weep.

If acceptance is not a goal
Then why are we on this earth
If everyone who is different is ugly
Then why are we given birth?

Is colour really an option
If we look inside what will we find
Are we really any different
Or is it all in our mind?

Rheanna Toy (age 11)
Woodbine Elementary School

My Piano and I

The piano is my enemy
It also is my friend
Sometimes my piano lessons
Never ever end

I love to hear my teacher play
But learning notes is tough
My teacher says I'll play like her
If I practice hard enough

Sometimes I make silly songs
And my teacher says okay
But I'll still have to practice notes
Every single day

Even though piano is tough
And sometimes I get mad
I really can't ever get enough
So piano's not that bad

Alexis Wolfe (age 8)
Aspen Grove Elementary School

~//~

Winter

Winter is when fluffy white flakes of cold
snow begin to fall,
When drinking hot cocoa by a beautiful,
warm fire,
Soaring down the strong, snowy hill on a
wooden sled.
The wonderful Christmas cookies in
the oven,
The loud sounds of the New Year's horns
Angels listening, high in the sky.

Then all of the fun is over.
The sun comes out and melts all the snow.
The sled is put away,
And the hot cocoa is just not the same.
No more fresh smell of the Christmas tree,
Or Mamma's wonderful cookies.

The winter angel cannot hear the sounds
of the New Year's horns.
But we all know that that wonderful
season called winter
Will come again soon.

Sarah Kangas (age 10)
Mother Mary Greene School

Octain

Gary,
the very,
hairy fairy,
likes his toes to be hairy.
He likes to eat one berry,
he is a very funny fairy!
And that's the story of Gary
the hairy fairy.

Heather LePard (age 8)
David Oppenheimer Elementary School

~//~

The Heat Wave

There is a heat wave going through my house
I'm sweating from head to toe
My clothes and shoes are melting
And so is my brain!
I've tried sitting in freezing cold water
And I wished that it would rain
But since none of these things worked,
I'll just have to stand the pain.

Emily Griffis (age 10)
Deep Cove Elementary School

~//~

Not Fair!

I'm sitting here alone.
I turn on the T.V. and guess what I see
Another person died
Another day gone by
This is what I have to say
When bombs are blowing and guns
are shooting
And people are dying and children are scared
What are we supposed to do
When this happens to you
You have no teeth, no hair, no family
No fun to bear or treasury
When food, water, roofs we had
Poor people didn't get mad
No point to swear
Just because it wasn't fair

Meagan Radke (age 12)
John Paul II School

25

Snowflakes

Gently falling from the sky,
Preachers of ice and frost to come.
Elegant patterns engraved
upon their surfaces,
Beautifully carved with God's own knife.
Gracefully floating from the heavens,
White masterpieces of magnificent art,
Snowflakes.

Nicholas Moore (age 11)
Calgary French & International School

~//~

Ramadan

I like praying and fasting
And praying to Allah too.
(Fasting to feel like the poor)
Sad, but I am so excited too.

I like the decorations
Putting them up with my mom
And getting presents too.

Mia Dowaidi (age 7)
Edmonton Islamic School

~//~

Diamante Seasons

Winter
cold, windy
snowing, pouring, blowing
frozen icebergs, cool, shining
cool, breezing, suntanning
bright warm
Summer

Fall
leaves, rain
flowing, falling, braising
trees, seeds, water, flowers
breezing, steaming, sweating
sunny, hot
Spring.

Brianna Senft (age 10)
Windebank Elementary School

Untitled

Witches flying through the sky
Jack-o-lanterns smiling as
the children go by
Trick or treat
for tonight is Halloween night

Melissa van Staalduinen (age 10)
Ronald Harvey Elementary School

~//~

Ode to Autumn

You have such beautiful leaves and
cool breezes.
When your wind comes, the waves
dance around the water.
Your harvest is such a delight
when we share your food with our
friends and family.
What a beautiful season you are!

Bronson Wille (age 8)
South Island Distance Education School

~//~

The Sunset

The sunset in the mountains is beautiful
The soft, evocative light washes
everything in a colour
That has yet to be named
Birds stop their singing, crickets begin
to chirp
Twilight is the time
When I can think serenely
About what the day has brought
And about what path I might
take tomorrow
Soon, the sunset will recede into a
deep darkness
But I will not be afraid, even if the
darkness overwhelms me
I will be surrounded by stars
And the silver moon will show her face
And a bright, warm fire
Will burn like the sunset

Stephani Rondpré (age 10)
Nootka Elementary School

Summer

Blazing sunshine
Cloudless skies
Enormous sandcastles
Slow moving rivers and serene beaches
Steams of watermelon juice
    trickling down my chin
Melted butter dripping off corn-on-the-cob
Hiking, biking, swimming
Sleeping under the star-filled night skies
Fuzzy peaches, sweet cherries
    and juicy wild berries
Wild flowers spread a wondrous blanket
    of colour over the fields
Summer

David B. Mark (age 9)
Distance Education School of
    the Kootenays

~//~

Lovable Dogs

I wish I were a perky, long haired Maltese;
I would arrogantly hop on my salon chair
And let my owner groom me.

I wish I were a handsome, loyal, and
    diligent collie;
I would quickly compose and congregate
All the wandering lambs and sheep.

I wish I were a powerful and
    admirable samoyed;
I would scurry and drill briskly through
    the wet, frosty snow
As I pull a sled.

I wish I were a spoiled and
    pampered poodle;
I would beg and cry greedily for
    more attention.

I wish I were a mighty and clever
    St. Bernard;
I would happily rescue and recover
    buried skiiers.

I love dogs!

Ashley N. Dobson (age 10)
Prairie Elementary School

Bunny

Sunny the bunny had some honey,
He ate it in the summer,
With his friend,
Who was called "Funny".

Daniel Hui (age 8)
David Oppenheimer Elementary School

~//~

I Wish You Could Be Out Here With Me

Looks like diamonds are in the ocean
Reflecting on the sun
It's such a nice view out here
I wish you could be out here with me
I wish I could do this tomorrow again

Well, I guess it's nighttime tonight
And I'll be goin' home
I hope you come tomorrow
And see me at this time
When flowers bloom and summer comes

William Roy Asher Pankhurst (age 6)
South Island Distance Education School

~//~

Friends

Friends help you out when you need
    a hand.
When you fall they help you stand.
They keep your secrets,
And laugh with you too.
They are there all the time
For me and you.

Friends are loyal and kind,
And wherever you go,
They are there right behind you saying,
"Yes" or "No"!

They are loving and caring,
Funny and sweet,
And when things get rough,
They'll help you onto your feet.

Jessica Giles (age 11)
St. Joseph's School

Untitled

Encourage yourself
Do not discourage yourself
Ultimate
Classes
Actions
Totally fun
I like to learn
Opportunity to get a job
Necessary!

April Nesvold (age 11)
William Grayson School

~//~

Teachers Love Me

I am shiny but not always.
Something lives in me, but it's not big.
I travel places but not always.
Some of me are green and some are red,
But I'm not spicy.
I am sold at grocery stores.
I am all around the world.
What am I?

Apple

Kylee Lindner (age 9)
Discovery Elementary School

~//~

Kittens

Kittens are so sweet
They have such tiny feet
I wish I could own one
That would be such a treat
How wonderful that would be
They play so happily
I love their soft fur
They have such a beautiful purr
They love to play with balls of yarn
I hope they won't come to any harm
Imagine if I had a kitten
Then I wouldn't have to look after
    all the mice in the kitchen

Siobhán Barry (age 7)
Glenmore Christian Academy

Black Cats

Do black cats like to get fat?
Do black cats like to wear hats?
Do black cats like to sit on chairs?
Do black cats like to sit on stairs?

Brydon Grace (age 8)
J.W. Inglis School

~//~

My Doll and I

My doll and I go everywhere,
We walk on land or fly in air.

But I would never cut her hair,
And she would never cut it bare.

And when we go for walks I say,
Do not worry what's the way.
And when we went to
    Johnston's Canyon
We saw the store
    called Mansion Canyon

Noelle Rousseau (age 7)
Glenmore Christian Academy

~//~

If I Were a Kite...

If I were a kite...
I would run through a rainbow.
If I were a kite...
I'd listen to the wind telling me stories,
She herself getting infected by pollution
Every moment.
If I were a kite...
I'd smell the air for good after being
Trapped in a closet.
If I were a kite...
I'd feel freedom.
If I were a kite...
I would feel my master pulling my tail
To the ground.
Back to darkness, back to loneliness,
Until the wind has stories again.

Derek Chiu (age 12)
R.C. Talmey Elementary School

Cats

I like cats.
Funny cats,
Cuddly cats,
Playful cats,
Hairy cats,
Furry cats,
Fat cats,
Green-eyed cats,
Sharp-clawed cats of any kind. I like cats.

Justin Tyler Rodman (age 7)
Miller Elementary School

~//~

Best Friends

We are best friends
We always play in dens
We play all day and night
and we never ever fight

My friends are nice
so take my advice
get friends

Courtney Thomas (age 9)
École Joe Clark School

~//~

Horse is Home!

Running fast
Home at last
Mane flies in the air

Look around
Pound the ground
Stop, pause, stare

Green grass grows
Crops in neat rows
Fields where I can run.

Shining bright
Not like the night
Relaxing in the sun

Emilie Sarnecki (age 9)
Jean Vanier Catholic School

Insects

Insects, insects,
Happy as can be.
Insects, insects
Like to crawl on me.

Insects, insects,
Count by two's
And don't forget to tie your
Shoes!!!!!

Dominique Jensen (age 9)
Windermere Elementary School

~//~

Ramadan

I am happy
Because Ramadan is here,
Because I can fast.
I see happy people in the Mosque.
I want to give the poor people money.
I hear people pray.

When Ramadan is gone
I feel so sad.
I hope
That it comes back!

Bilal Chamseddin (age 7)
Edmonton Islamic School

~//~

Peace

Peace is cheerfulness
And cheerfulness is gladness and joy,
    amusement and more.
Peace is a place,
A place that is amusing for you and a friend.
Peace is calm,
For there would be no battles; we could
    all be untroubled.
Peace could make your life natural and calm.
I would use peace in my world by
    helping others.
What would you do with peace?

Jordan (Jordi) Michelle Jones (age 9)
Topham Elementary School

The Dog and the Cat

There was a dog
A lonely dog
He went and sat in the fog
He saw a cat
A fat cat
Chasing a rat
The cat ate the rat
And the dog played with the cat!
And the dog was never lonely again.

Haussein Ataoui (age 9)
Edmonton Islamic School

~//~

Funky Chipmunk

I saw a chipmunk
That had the funk.
It jumped up and down
And hopped in a trunk.
In the trunk it looked around,
And you won't guess what it found:
A pearl, some gold, a jewel,
And a chipmunk-sized swimming pool!

Jeffrey Baldwin (age 8)
David Oppenheimer Elementary School

~//~

The Werewolf

The werewolf prowls tonight
Looking for victims of its bite
Destroying all things in its wake
Hairy snout, long brown hair,
Razor sharp teeth.

Superhuman strength.

Crosses and holy water will not harm it.
Only way to kill it is with a bullet.
Next time the moon is full
And you are out walking,
Beware the werewolf bite.

The werewolf prowls tonight.

Julian Bauto (age 12)
Neill Middle School

Stumped

Here I sit, my mind's gone blank,
My last five poems, they all stank.
I really don't know what to write.
To me this is a major fright.
My mom's beside me, she's no help.
I just sit here and scratch my scalp.

Sierra Castonguay (age 12)
Dallas Elementary School

~//~

Lake of Shining Waters

Surrounded by emerald green trees
In an almost perfect circle.
In the centre,
A lake. A *shining* lake. A lake so
Clear you can see the bottom.
Gold and white sand covers the bottom
Like a carpet. The fish spring back and forth,
Small flashes of lavender and periwinkle.
Suddenly, a shadow appears. The fish
peer upward.
The shadow had on a grey dingy dress and
a shock of red hair.
Skinny limbs and sparkling eyes.
Suddenly,
A ripple spreads through the small lake
And the fish glance at the new addition
To the Lake of Shining Waters.
A sparkling violet stone.
A startled shriek echoes from above.
The shadow's mouth agape.
Another ripple, but nothing for the fish
to look at.
Only the shadow knew what rippled
the lake.
A tear.
The shadow leaves, and life returns
to normal
In the Lake of Shining Waters.
The only souvenir is the small, purple
Amethyst brooch
Dropped in another's carelessness.

*Based on the lie Anne Shirley told Marilla
Cuthbert in "Anne of Green Gables" by
L.M. Montgomery.*

Chelsea Reimer (age 12)
Pacific Christian Elementary School

Freedom

When the eagle flies, oh so high
I just want to cry
For the freedom that we have
And the joy we own.

When the horse runs wild and free
I could shout out with glee.
For the land we have
And the things we do.

When the cheetah hunts his prey
All alone in the day
Wild and free, fast and proud,
I just want to shout out loud.

Why can't we just learn to share?
Our freedom, joy, land and air.
We should now start to share!!
How are they so different from us?

Natasha Kidger (age 10)
Windebank Elementary School

~//~

My Pet Dragon

My pet dragon had a toothache
It started yesterday
I took him to the dentist to see
if he was okay

The dentist tried everything
But nothing ever worked
I took him to a specialist and got
no advice from her

After all this happened I took
my dragon home
I had to skip a day from school
And had to stay at home

The roaring was unstoppable
This had to stop right now
I didn't know what to do when,
where or how
I looked in every health guide to see
what I could find
And to my luck the next day,
pet dragon was just fine!

Shenette Salgadoe (age 10)
St. Paul's Elementary School

Untitled

River rapids roaring,
While the rain is pouring,
Beating on the rocks,
Cooling off the flocks,
The wind is whispering
Through the trees,
Oh so chilling to my knees
Water flowing all around me,
Swift and stinging as a bee.

Molly Johnston (age 11)
Hammond Elementary School

~//~

Wind

Feel the wind on your face,
catch a chill at a race.
Feel the burn with my wrath.
A gust of wind will blow you away.
I will catch you if I may.
Look on the bright side,
I'll dry the rain,
then you can
    go outside and play.

Shawn Yip (age 10)
Miller Park Community School

~//~

Prayer

I will pray all day
I will pray all night
I will be happy I may
See the light so bright
Jesus has saved us, yes He has
He has saved us from sin, which is very bad
We must go to mass
Or the father will be very mad
Some will go to Heaven
Some will go to Hell
Some will be forever enlightened
But please don't worry because all is well
I am telling you this so you may be ready
For the day that will come so we will
    be happy

William Ubial (age 12)
Immaculate Conception School

31

Hot Chocolate

Hot chocolate
Hot and steamy sitting on the table
Picked it up turned on the cable
Had a sip yum yum yum
Do you know what I'm talking about?
Well I sure do! Hot chocolate

Neelam Gill (age 9)
Ronald Harvey School

~//~

Senses of Fall

I love Mother Nature's master.
The colours are so vibrant.
I like crunch under my feet
and the sound of the rake.
I like the way the brisk air cools my face.
I can't resist the pile of leaves.
I dive into the marshmallow brown,
golden yellow, and maple leaf red colours.
Fall completes Mother Nature.

Kael King (age 11)
Aspen Grove School

~//~

Schoolin' a Sonnet

Everyday it's just the same
Going to school is such a pain
Each day is so lame
All I get is migraines.
Teachers say not to talk
And always follow directions
They even say not to walk
Or else we'll get detentions
We have to work all day
Which makes my head really hurt
We don't even have time to play
And my head is just about to burst.
But my mother said,
"If you want to be cool,
Just finish your work
And stay in school!"

Antonio Somera Jr. (age 12)
Immaculate Conception School

Untitled

Roses are red
Violets are blue
You are for me
And I am for you
But what really counts is
The thing inside
The red thing
For if you don't have it you will die
It is shaped like a circle with two bumps
    on the top
With a heart you have feelings
But they are all different
There is a good and a bad
And that's all

Carson Turner (age 8)
St. Patrick's Elementary School

~//~

Dazzling Dreams

A murmur at bedtime
From a kitten asleep,
As it tosses and turns
To roll at my feet.

It smacks and slurps
As if eating a snack,
But clearly this kitty
Is on the wrong track.

My kitten attempts
To lunge at the door,
The silly thing rapidly
Getting quite sore.

This kitten is dreaming
Of chasing a mouse,
As it narrowly dodges
My things in the house.

But now as the morning
Begins to dawn,
I see a small figure
Run through the lawn.

As it passes the house,
I see it's the mouse!
And my cat is not dreaming at all.

Laura Gerein (age 11)
St. Patrick's Elementary School

Family

The cold steel presses
Against my temple,
Sweat glistens on my palms.
My finger trembles as it closes
Over the trigger.
I think to myself
"Why do this?"
But yet why not?
What is the purpose
Of life?
A door closes,
My finger tightens on the trigger.
"Daddy what are you doing?"

Graham Inglis (age 12)
St. Michael's University Middle School

~//~

Goldilocks

The bears went for a walk.
They saw a big hawk.
It went down and down,
And around and around.

While they were walking,
They were talking,
And a girl named Goldilocks
Came with her curly locks.

She went to the house.
No one was there, not even a mouse.
First she looked in the window;
She looked high then low.

She went to the porridge
And then to the storage.
And into the sitting room,
Brought more trouble too soon.

She sat on a chair that was too big.
And then one as little as a fig.
She went up where the Three Bears slept.
And in the bed she crept.

She awoke with a start.
She saw a bear so smart.
And then she ran away.
They said, 'Goldilocks please stay!"

Dwayne John Hofer (age 9)
Spring Creek School

The Crypt

Deep beneath the old church
there lies an old crypt,
Row on row of old coffins
bodies rotting from within.

But inside this old crypt
there lies a creepy tale,
Because years ago a vampire
was killed and stashed there.

They say the vampire had fangs
five inches long
With an appetite much larger than his fangs
beneath the old crypt.

Beneath the old crypt there lies more tales
of rotting men buried in coffins,
in the old crypt.

Bryce Hamelin (age 12)
Neill Middle School

~//~

The Four Seasons

Each and every season
Is special in its way
Mostly for it's weather
That helps us every day.

Cold, dreary winter
Gives us snow and ice
And we get to stay home
Which is very nice.

Warm, fresh new spring
Paints a pretty scene
Of flowers and trees and babies
And birds that chirp and sing.

Hot, lazy summer
Means swimming in the pool
And visiting amusement parks
That are really cool.

Last but not least comes crisp, windy fall
With golden leaves to jump in--
I like them all!

Sally Graham (age 10)
St. Patrick's Elementary School

The Playground

I love to jump. I love to climb.
I love to swing all the time.
The monkey bars, the swings, the slide.
But just be careful
or you will collide.

Beth Lewty (age 8)
James Bay School

~//~

Frost and Snow

Though fields lay golden
Snow was coming soon
Cars were covered by frost
Not a window was open
Everyone was dressed up warm
Not a bit of skin uncovered
While bees and their swarms
Were frozen by frost

Michael Rowell (age 9)
Ronald Harvey School

~//~

Leaves

Blowing leaves,
Crunching leaves,
Falling leaves
And curly leaves

Red leaves
Orange leaves
Brown leaves
And yellow leaves

Wowzers!
Look at the leaves
Some are still
Falling from trees

Fall is here
Let's go and play
In the leaves
For the rest of the day

Amanda Payne (age 10)
Ronald Harvey School

A Cop

A cop works in the city
robbers think they're a pity
their dogs are faster than a kitty
when they catch a crook
they use the big book
in court he has to sit
if he goes to jail he has a fit

Duane Schmidthiesler (age 9)
Notre Dame Elementary School

~//~

It's Not Called Living...

There is every day and night a child
Even when it's not close to mild
She hugs her knees to her chest outside
    the store
She sits ever so quietly huddled by the door
She sits in her only one coat which has
    seen better times
She begs and begs but gets no dimes
Every day she grows weaker and weaker
Longing for that one seeker
To take her far away
But the years pass and so does the day
She's in need of some love and oh
    some food
She asks people for anything but they
    are all so crude
She's a twelve-year-old girl half dead on
    the street
Have no one mercy on her just give her
    a treat
For she knows no love she's never had
    a hug
She's never slept in a bed snug as a bug
She has only slept on the hard, cold sidewalk
She has never read a book or played
    with chalk
She probably doesn't even know how
    to speak
By now she is ever so weak
She has no strength for cries
As slowly she dies
She is now a lump in the night
Sitting by the door holding her knees ever
    so tight

Carolyn Cummins (age 11)
Immaculate Conception School

34

I am

I am...
Good loud music, newborn babies, love
    to dance.
I like shopping and hanging out with
    my friends.
My family, friends, and school are
    important to me.
I like to watch funny movies.
I don't like when my twin brothers try
    to beat me up.
But I can always find a way to win.
I love my mom's homemade cookies and
    my dad's famous milkshakes.
I hate when my hair is all messy when I
    wake up
From an outstanding sleep.
I love to play the piano and have fun
    doing pretty much anything.
This is me!

Ellen MacGregor (age 9)
Brander Gardens Elementary School

~//~

Why

Looking out my window
at the deep dark sky,
My thoughts begin to soar,
Thinking of the word "why"

Why was I created?
Can't tomorrow be the same?
Is the world meant to be separated?
Shall I hang my head in shame?

Answers turning into facts,
Questions to a phrase,
This is how I react,
Ever since I've been lost in this maze

I envy the birds that fly,
So free and elevated,
Maybe I could try,
Without being frustated.

The word "why" is a silly question,
So don't ask me how,
All I know in my devastation,
I can only spend this moment now.

Tia Rambaran (age 12)
British Columbia Christian Academy

Little Sparrow

Brown-speckled sparrow,
Pecking at seeds at lunch time,
Singing cheerfully.

Kurtis Hoekstra (age 10)
Distance Education School of
the Kootenays

~//~

Furious Fall

The leaves so furiously scattering,
    dancing and twisting in the wind.
Like Mother Nature's palette of paint.
All the bronzes, reds,
    yellows, golds, and oranges.
A canvas of colour
    like an artist's easel.
All the sounds of the leaves rustling
    under your feet trying to
    escape to freedom.
Tumbling, turning in all directions.
How fascinating a furious fall
    could be.

Julia MacLeod (age 11)
Aspen Grove School

~//~

My Special Place

My special place
Is a place where I go
Where no one else goes.

My special place
Where squirrels are alive
There lives a friendly beehive.

My special place
With a healthy-growing climbing tree:
This is the best place, I guarantee!

My special place
Is a place for two.
Who's coming? You?

Charlene Koehn (age 10)
Parkcrest Elementary School

Ice Cream!

Ice cream, ice cream
I love it I do
If there was no ice cream
I would sue

When ice cream's around
I eat it all day
Doesn't matter what my
Mom or Dad say.

Samantha Billson (age 9)
St. Patrick's Elementary School

~//~

I am...

I like T.V., comic books, weekends,
Holidays, summer, winter,
    soccer, basketball,
Riding my bike, going on vacation, skiing.
I like building with Lego, my skateboard,
Coming home from school with
    no homework,
Swimming and drawing pictures.
That's me!

Emmett Underhill (age 8)
Brander Gardens Elementary School

~//~

Beauty is Love

A portrait of beauty
Is a landscape of love.
A heart full of soul
Is a face full of feeling.
A lake of pure hope
Is a sky of pure joy.
An island of happiness
Is a mountain of peace,
Because a portrait of beauty
Is a landscape of love.

God kept the sky pure,
And the water clean.
Let's keep it that way!

Hayley Pipher (age 10)
Rose Valley Elementary School

Fear Me

Without muscle,
Without bone,
I am bigger than the trees,
I am feller of the forest.

Without hands,
Without feet.
I tear the seas,
I wreck the ships.

Without blood,
Without flesh.
I am mover of sands and water,
I am destroyer of man.

Without feature,
Without form,
I am terror,
I am storm.

Zachary Taylor (age 12)
Windebank Elementary School

~//~

Preparing for Winter

As winter comes sliding in
Fall gets squeezed out.
Temperatures plunge,
Leaving the ground
Covered in frost.
Plants start to wilt,
As they prepare
For the coming winter.
Bear starts their hibernation
Snuggling together with their newborn cubs.
Animals are finished gathering food
For the long coming winter months.
Geese start their migration
For the long voyage South.
Soon comes the snow
Artistically creating a silky white blanket.
During November the temperature
Keeps slithering down.
April approaches and the mercury
Begins to work its way up.
Shortly winter passes the next season
Into the capable hands of spring.

Vicky Schmidt (age 12)
Hillcrest Community School

Untitled

Isn't it funny when milk comes out
   your nose?
When you find a hilarious photo of
   someone sporting a goofy pose?
April fool's Day is the day of fun,
Yet when twelve o'clock comes, the
   pranksters are done.

Have you ever seen someone performing
   a dance,
Giving the impression of ants in their pants?
Laughter is such a powerful thing;
It's amazing to see how much joy it
   can bring!

If the world consisted of only smiles
   and laughter,
Then everyone could live happily ever after!

Alexis (Allie) Raas (age 11)
Woodbridge Farms School

~//~

Useless Things

A nail without a point,
An elbow without a joint,
A book without words,
A tree without birds.

A rainbow without green,
A crime without a scene,
A fish without gills,
A farm without mills.

A dish without a spoon,
Water without a typhoon,
A chicken without legs,
Breakfast without eggs.

A leopard without spots,
Hair without knots,
A flower without a petal,
A bike without metal.

A kitchen without knives,
Husbands without wives,
A bag without books,
A cupboard without hooks.

Rowan El-Husseini (age 10)
Miller Park Community School

Serpents

Serpents
toxic, venomous
slithering, hissing, moving
fly, breathe out fire, big
flying, flaming, filling
Dragons

David Shin (age 7)
Oppenheimer Elementary School

~//~

The Man With a Hooded Cloak

"Trick or treat," said the ghost.
"Trick," said the man with the hooded cloak.
"I haven't got any treats."
"You will be sorry," said the ghost.
"I think not," said the man
with the hooded cloak.

Later that night the man's house was egged
and down his chimney rolled a head
and whispered,
"Trick or treat."

Ryan Williams (age 12)
Neill Middle School

~//~

Autumn Fun

Red leaves golden leaves sometimes oak
Up to the pond to hear a green frog croak
Leaf piles and leaf piles too many chores
But once you jump in
it doesn't matter any more

Masks and costumes always fun
Look there's a ballerina
with her hair in a bun
Turkey, mashed potatoes, and stuffing
It's all yummy and I'm not bluffing

A snowflake danced in the air,
which gave us all a scare because
No more autumn fun

Simone Mason-Penney (age 9)
Ronald Harvey School

Bear

I was sitting on my chair chewing my hair
Trying to find my purple underwear.
Ohhohh no, there comes a bear
With long pretty hair.
Hey bear do you like honey?
No girl I like money.
Hehehe, that was funny.

Sarah Khabbazi (age 11)
Boundary Community School

~//~

The Mystery Thing

I have spikes, but they don't hurt.
I have a nasty bite, but I have no teeth.
If my claws break they will grow back.
I live in Australia but I am in pet stores
    all over the world.
I am considered a dragon but I don't
    blow fire.
What am I?

Bearded dragon

Connor Martin (age 9)
Discovery Elementary School

~//~

Nature

I asked my sister one night,
"Why is the sun so bright?"
She calmly replied,
"It's rock and fire giving lots of light."

I asked my mother one night,
"Why does a caterpillar go into a cocoon?"
She grinned and replied,
"To change into a beautiful being,
    the butterfly."

I asked myself one night,
"What if I don't understand all of nature?"
My inner self smiled and replied,
"Not everybody has answers to nature."

Henna Dhir (age 11)
St. Patrick Catholic School

Listen

A girl is sitting on the dock
Tracing ripples in the water.
The moon is like a silver coin,
In a deep blue satin sea.

The wind whispers secrets,
The trees tell stories
The sand murmurs mysteries,
The shadows laugh silently,
And the waves call out.

These wondrous things can be heard
Only by those who stop and listen
Listen...
    Listen...
    Listen...
Listen to them speak.

Theresa Doyle (age 12)
St. Patrick's Elementary School

~//~

And No Birds Sing

There's a place deep in the woods
Where people fear to go.
There's a place deep in the woods
Where nothing's friend nor foe.

The trees are bare.
The grass is dead.
You can taste the air
And the taste you dread.

I've been to this place
Where nothing grows.
I've been to this place
Where no water flows.

And in a dark place
Where tears roll down your cheeks
Lack of hope weakens pace
For weeks upon weeks.

But what's worst
Is what the sadness brings.
But what's worst
Is that no birds sing.

Daniela Loggia (age 12)
St. Michael's University Middle School

Drifting to Darkness

Drifting, falling,
tumbling down,
how can I get rid of this everlasting frown

Drifting, falling
coming to a tumble,
I feel my soul is going to crumble

Drifting, tumbling,
worried of falling
I wait but I don't reach
the voice that keeps calling

It's screaming, it's screeching
I can't ignore the great call
I have woken up
I have stopped this everlasting fall

Matthew Saunders (age 12)
St. Cyril School

~//~

In The Abyss

In the abyss,
Creatures live in simplistic bliss.

No light to be found,
Not a spark on the ground.

Creatures ugly by far,
Like chest hair in a jar.
Eyes so gigantic
With a look of being frantic.

Bodies of all shapes and sizes,
Some may think they're halloween
disguises.

Mouths wide open,
No words are spoken.

Teeth like spears,
They could bring you to tears.

And with all this said, and so
much more,
In the abyss you must explore.

Joel Nardelli (age 9)
St. Vincent School

Winter

Grey skies and wet weather,
Raincoats, boots, and a sweater.
Cold days and colder nights,
Four wheel drive and fog lights.

Chilly fingers, frozen toes,
Wet hair and a bright red nose.
I sipped hot milk by the fire side,
As on the outside world I spied.

Georgina Graham (age 12)
St. Michael's University Middle School

~//~

A Friend

A friend is someone who cares about you
makes you laugh
is kind and fun.
A friend is a person who is loving
helping you when you need it
playing with you when you're alone.
A friend is a person that likes you
invites you over to their house
shares their stuff.
A friend is someone who keeps secrets.

Baily Smith (age 9)
St. Joseph School

~//~

Popcorn

I see the bag rising each second
As each boring kernel becomes
A delicious piece of buttery popcorn.
While the bag is rising,
Inside each kernel goes poppity, pop, pop!
When the bag is opened
I smell a burst of buttery flavour,
And when I reach into the bag
To take a handful of popcorn,
I notice that it feels a little smooth
And really bumpy.
When I put the popcorn in my mouth,
I taste a burst of buttery flavour.
Mmm! *I love popcorn!!*

Anthony (Tony) G. Naciuk (age 9)
Brander Gardens Elementary School

In the Creepy, Creaking, Howling, Moaning, Screaming, Haunted Castle

In the creepy castle there are twenty-
six bedrooms.
In the creepy, creaking castle there are
forty ghosts.
In the creepy, creaking, howling castle
there are sleeping monsters,
Sleeping under the twenty-six beds in the
twenty-six rooms.
In the creepy, creaking, howling, moaning
castle there are bats, owls,
And other creepy, creaking, howling,
moaning animals.
In the creepy, creaking, howling, moaning,
screaming castle there lives no one.
Therefore this is a creepy, creaking, howling,
moaning, screaming haunted castle.

Larissa Ianson (age 12)
Pacific Christian Elementary School

~//~

A Time to Remember

Remembrance Day
Heroes and people
who fought and died
in the war

Remembrance Day
People waving poppies
to remember the men and women
who served our country

Remembrance Day
Thousands of people
who died
for our freedom

I thank every Canadian
that fought in the war
to make Canada a free country
so we can do the things
we want to do
A moment of silence
to never forget
what the men and women did
for our freedom and peace

Zakk Coss (age 12)
Neill Middle School

Dangerous Fires

Like a ferocious fast fighter,
Fire attacks everything in its way.
Animals flee from their homes.
It makes breathing very hard.
It will take you down if we don't fight.
It kills lives and people's spirits.
When will this chaos stop?

Ryan Kraushaar (age 10)
Sherwood Park Elementary School

~//~

I am

I am a puzzled girl with the practiced
eye for art
I wonder if my creative nature will take
me far
I hear the sounds of inspiration giving
me the strength to draw and paint
I see the joyful blazing colours of delight,
and the dull dark colours of depression
I want the world to embrace on gracious
harmony and enjoyable freedom
I am a puzzled girl with the elegant
talent of art
I seek life within the unique pictures
and paintings
I feel the artistic drive flowing swiftly
inside my veins
I touch the emotional hearts and souls of
people with my expressive art
I worry that a dark raven will enfold
suffering around us
I cry while the days of misery and pain
shatters our hearts
I am the confused and puzzled girl who
possesses glorious gifts of art
I understand life can hold you down, yet
you can push up and go on
I say the path you take or choose is yours
to decide
I dream of the future and what it holds
for the world and me
I try to raise the sun within people's hearts
with bright happiness and pleasure
I hope for the best for my family and myself
I am the puzzled girl blessed with the
artist's eye

Karen M. Chan (age 12)
Sidaway Elementary School

40

Math

Numbers racing in my head,
Colliding with my brain cells,
Like bumper cars gone wild,
Is there any order?

Equations, decimals, and fractions,
Numbers to confuse,
Do I add, subtract, or multiply?
The question still remains.

Sasha Gray (age 12)
St. Michael's University Middle School

~//~

Betrayal

I feel my heart is pounding,
As you fold my face's pouting.
Once upon a time we're friends
And now we broke up again.

How can I know if I can trust you?
'Cause once you've betrayed me
And made my life so blue.
You threw away my trust
Then left me with your crust.
And came back when you wanted to
'Cause you knew I'd welcome you.

But now you've betrayed me
And left me here to bleed.
My tears of pain and confusion.
I trust you no more 'cause I know you
won't need... me.

Today's a new day;
we're going separate ways.
Then you came back and asked
for my forgiveness you say.
I'll frown and say go away,
stop ruining my wonderful days.

I've already given you your second chance
And I won't give you more to sing
and prance.
I know it's selfish, but you'll bring me
down from bliss
So I can't risk me for a chance,
A chance you've already missed

Jessica Mok (age 12)
Parkcrest Elementary School

Canada

Canada was once lost
but now it's found
and once was empty
and now it's open
to all who wish to come
and once had children
and mothers hoping for
their loved ones
to come home.

Hahlay Buck (age 8)
St. Joseph's School

~//~

Crows of the Sky

The way a crow looked down on me,
The dust of leaves from a birch tree,
Has given my heart a change of mood,
To be upon the bird that I chose.
They wait for me,
Winged shadows of the sky;
In darkened clefts
They speak their mocking cries.
Then flying away altogether
Never looking back, always staying together.

Bhupinder S. Dulku (age 12)
St. Michael's University Middle School

~//~

Wind

My gentle breeze moves clouds
through the sky so graceful
As they change their shapes
they appear so playful
I grow in force from a moderate breeze
And small trees seem to bend at their knees
Are people becoming more frightful?

When I approach near gale
And buildings begin to fail
There is fear of a violent storm
A hurricane must be starting to form
It looks as if people will soon have to bail

Kathryn West (age 10)
Notre Dame Elementary School

Untitled

Players
Free sticks and food
Score goals and get big bucks
Want home team to win Stanley Cup
Canucks

Daniel (Marcus) Kwan (age 9)
Vancouver Christian School

~//~

Snake

Slithering away
Nothing stopping it
Always slimy
Killing his dinner
Eating little mice.

Arron Albano (age 10)
Naramata Elementary School

~//~

My Life!

I have a mom and dad
They love me lots and make me sad
When I'm sad they cheer me up
And give lots of kisses and stuff

When they tuck me in at night
They look at the stars
    and wish me goodnight

In the morning when it's bright
My alarm goes off with a fright
I moan and groan and finally get up
As I hear my mom pour juice into my cup

I hear a yawn; my brother's awake
Our time is at stake;
    we don't want to be late

So we packed our lunches, grabbed our bags
A small kiss our parents each gave
As we flew out the door on our speedy
    little legs.

Nathalie Cuthbert (age 11)
St. Joseph's School

Star

You little star shining so bright up above
I look at you with warm winter love
Oh little star shining so bright
I wish to you with all my might
It's a cold winter but you shine so bright
To keep me warm during the night
Oh little star shimmering with glitter
I love the way you slide and slither
Oh little star into the night
You make me want to
Smile with all delight!!!

Caterina Sorensen (age 10)
Mother Mary Greene School

~//~

I am a Tree

I am a tree standing way up high,
My branches and leaves
    reaching for the sky.
My trunk is embedded in the earth,
And my wide spreading roots
    show off my girth.
I stand tall in the clearing of a glade,
While plants and animals rest in my shade.
My branches reach out
    like long hugging arms,
And embrace the wind to make it flutter
    like soft ringing charms.
With the passage of time
    my leaves turn from green,
To deep reds and browns,
And the rivets along my trunk
    appear as frowns.
My leaves have left and leave me bare,
My branches now thin,
    like long gnarled hair.
The birds in my bough leave their nests
    and begin their flight,
For they know that the goddess of snow
    and rain
Will be arriving overnight,
As the birds fly south
And the animals return to their warm dens
    in fright.
Winter returns and brings forth
    her long dark night.

Colin Sedgwick (age 12)
St. Michael's University Middle School

Marooned

There once was a baboon and goon who
    got on a balloon.
They drifted up in the air, up, up, and away,
    and did not come back by noon.
The mother goon got worried too soon
    and went to look, but she did not know
    they were marooned on the island
    of *Alacazoo!!!*

Daniela Bobadilla (age 10)
Boundary Community School

~//~

Untitled

Standing in the woods below,
Red leaves will scream of the dying flow.
They saw that day was a mistake
But my brother's life they did take.
All was silent in the woods that day,
Yet everywhere was chatter.

Red blood stolen
Watching, screaming

She watched at the horror her eyes
Should have never witnessed.
The fate of death on her fingertips.
So what happened on this death day
Of this child, you ask?

The hunting season had begun
And everyone was out.
Searching for a deer but these men
Got more than they could chew.

Bang! A child was killed,
Mistaken for a feast and for what?
A dear? An elk? For self-satisfaction?

Do you call self-satisfaction
A girl looking into the open eyes
Of her dead brother lying alone in the forest?

Tears flow, the smell of death
This day of agony
Should never have happened but it did.
But it did.

Thomas (Tom) Bridger (age 12)
St. Michael's University Middle School

Puppy

Playing in your bedroom.
Usually in a mess.
Playing with your socks.
Putting you in trouble.
Your best pup.

Alexis Armour (age 11)
Naramata Elementary School

~//~

The Fall Season

Fall sunshine glimmering up above,
Staying high up like a beautiful dove.
Leaves crunching under our feet,
Cool wind, it smells so sweet.
Cars are passing on the street,
All I hear is walking feet.
Bikes and scooters are so in,
In this fall season.
Barbeques grilling, milkshakes filling,
This is the only reason, to have a fall season.

Nicole St. Cyr (age 10)
Mother Mary Greene School

~//~

The End

The sky vanished behind a cloud of gloom,
The dying sun eclipsed by sudden dark,
Nature froze to a halt to again bloom,
Trees crashed down dividing to two,
    the bark.
Volcanoes erupted with displeasure,
Humans disintegrated to thin dust,
Darkness, death, anger, hell all disclosured,
Every item turned into windy gust.
Water overflowed the islands and lands,
Silence ripped through the noise in one
    swift chance,
Down fall rocks in illuminating bands,
The end has come, no time to do a dance.
Gone, it's as though there was never an earth,
Emptiness filled, waiting for a new birth.

Sarah Chang (age 12)
Pinewood Elementary School

Jesus

In the starlit sky
The heavens lie.
In the mist of air
He's right in there.
And in the darkness of the night
He's right by your side.
His name... is Jesus.
And He is open for those who believe!

Britteny Decarie (age 10)
Pinewood Elementary School

~//~

Untitled

Deep in the forest
Way away
A lonesome pine
Came out to play
It waved its leaves
As feathers on a windy day
Its bark shone
In a glowing way
Deep in the forest
Way away

Tiffany Paton (age 7)
Wix-Brown Elementary School

~//~

Eagle Eyes

Soaring through the sky
A beautiful creature
With magnificent chestnut wings
And a blinding white face...
Coming for a landing
His talons outstretched
Ready to grasp the tree branch.

As he sits
On that branch
Of the enormous Gary oak tree...
His bold brave eyes
Wonder over and stare
Straight at me.

Laura Gilmore (age 12)
St. Michael's University Middle School

Witches

Do witches like to fly on brooms?
Do they store the brooms in storage rooms?
What do they put into their brew?
Do they know whose brew is whose?
Do you think they really do smell the brews?

Josalynn (Jossy) Shields (age 8)
J.W. Inglis School

~//~

A Bedtime Hug

It is time to sleep.
You must not cry nor weep.
You look very tired,
For your day has expired.
It is time for bed,
To rest your sleepy head.
Now tuck in nice and snug,
And here's a bedtime hug.

Helena Descoteau (age 8)
Sir James Douglas School

~//~

Sounds

Women, children begging to survive
Moms and dads screaming
Guns blowing
Women and children sobbing
Screams of warriors falling

Everyday I hear those sounds
Playing in my head
I ask them to stop,
But they just won't listen
They taunt me
All those sounds
Of the people who have died
By others' hands

They ask me to set a day of remembrance
For friends that fought and suffered
I did
But they are still gone.

Richard Banh (age 11)
Neill Middle School

44

Unkey the Monkey

Unkey the monkey is lots of fun
He always loves to eat a bun
Yesterday I saw him faint
When he was about to paint
He recycles metal cans
And pans

He eats peas
And plants and climbs trees
He does good stretches
And makes great catches
He gives great hugs
And loves bugs

Noah Shillington (age 9)
St. Vincent School

~//~

Remember

An old man
A war veteran
Standing humble among his squadron
On a cloudy Remembrance Day
Recalling memories from the past

A young man
Out getting the mail
Finding a letter...an enlistment letter
Calling him to fight for his country
Leaving his family with a tear in his eye

An older man
Fighting his heart out on the battlefield
Surrounded by fear and dying
Fallen bodies lying around him
All with a past and a family left to mourn

A young boy
Looking down the lane
At the father he's never seen
Embracing each other
As they both begin to cry

An old man
Remembering the times, easy and hard
Glancing at his grown son in the crowd
And the father smiles...
Despite his sorrow

Jay Johnson (age 12)
Gwynne School

Transparent Beauty

Floating, fluttering, flying in the setting sky.
Crimson orange and black like a delicate
  string of lace.
A see-through glistening silver and orange
  elegant butterfly.

Reed Merrill (age 10)
Sunalta School

~//~

Gold Fever

Gift or curse?
Ordering prospectors
Little winners - lots of losers
Days of carrying thousands of pounds

Fever strikes again and again
Every speck is worth a lot!
  And very hard to find
Vitals stuffed into big bags
Every step hurts the legs
Riches await only the first.

Jordan Kovacs (age 10)
Beaver Lake School

~//~

It's Halloween Night

On Halloween night
We go trick-or-treating.
The witches are out
And zombies are eating.

The warlocks are creepy
And the cats are too.
The witches are cooking in their cauldrons
Eating disgusting stew!

When midnight comes
The ghosts come out.
They scare all the people,
Then you hear them all shout...

Aaahhh!!!

Kelsey Amos (age 12)
Neill Middle School

45

Snake

Slithering through the desert
Napping under rocks
Attacking small creatures
Knowing where to hide
Eating mice and rats

Matthew Gowe (age 10)
Naramata Elementary School

~//~

I Wish My Sister Was Abducted By Aliens

I wish my sister was abducted by aliens
    because then...
She wouldn't be there to yell at me.
She wouldn't be there to bother me.
She couldn't steal my watch.
She couldn't invade my room.
I could wear whatever I wanted.
I wish my sister was abducted by aliens
Because then she could annoy the aliens
    instead of me.

Erica Schell (age 9)
École St. Thomas School

~//~

Ice Cream

Buy me an ice cream
A triple chocolate one
With three thousand and fifty
Little marshmallows that weigh tons
Put a spoonful of grape jelly
And some peanut butter
Half-digested cookie from a belly
And water from the gutter
Garbage from a garbage dump
A piece of fur from a monkey's rump
All these things I really want
So please pretend it's not thirty below
And that Santa's coming *ho ho ho*
So buy me an ice cream
Buy me an ice cream
Please Buy me an ice cream!!

Ian Williams (age 9)
Mother Mary Greene School

The Girl in My School

There's a girl in my school
And she is very cool
She makes all the boys go wild
When she does her best smile

She always does the best she can
She has the best desk; it has a fan
She has the best moves
And she knows the best grooves

She obeys the rules of the class
She never makes Mrs. Bugel break glass
And sometimes she needs a rest
That's when she asks me to be the best

I've never felt like this before
I'll never walk out the door

Alyssa Goodwin (age 8)
École Joe Clark School

~//~

Time

Tick, tick, tick, time flies away
And shall never return
Will there be a chance?

Time becomes memories
Will it be remembered?
What if our clock runs the other way
Will it still come back?

So many knots in time need to be untied
Will time help me?
Counting the marks on my calendar
How many days have passed?

Time created me
Who created time?
What if time changes?
Will I change?

Time is not fair
It's never fair
Why does the fun have to go?
Why does the sadness have to stay?

It all depends on time.

Betty Ma (age 12)
Hjorth Road School

46

Rhyming and Timing

I like to rhyme in certain time
I feel time's up with a sounding chime
I like to rhyme in school
I think it's really cool

I do my rhymes so fast
I'll never be the last
Every time I make a rhyme
I earn a dime

Kevin Jones (age 10)
École Joe Clark School

~//~

Frightened to Cry

I wander the forest as the sun begins to set,
For this is a forest that I've just met.
Sitting down on a log, I stare at the stars;
The moon has not yet come out that far.

I make a face of disgust as I think of
    the moon,
For tonight, full it shall be.
Did I ever tell you that the full moon
    frightens me?

I think of a werewolf, my favourite creature;
I believe in them and their beautifully
    scary features.
But what sickens me is how they transform
For they are in great pain; my heart is torn.

Their hair grows longer,
Their bones grow stronger,
Their figures come down with
    sickening cracks,
The human brain starts to lack.

Through their eyes of amber
And minds of hate
I know the wolf must be late.

Each full moon night in this forest they
    would spend,
Tortured souls without a friend.
They continue to live their lives as a lie,
They're werewolves, they're man, too
    frightened to cry.

Katherine Lozada (age 11)
Immaculate Conception School

Aunt Sadie

She flies up there
Not alone
I sometimes think
What it would have been
If I was there to see her fly
Up into the sky
But, I was not
All I know
Is she will always be
In my heart
And soul
And even though
I have only seen her once or twice
I will still
Remember her
And I know God will treat her right
Because when it's your time to go
God knows what's best for you
Your friends
And your family

Carla Grykuliak (age 12)
Neill Middle School

~//~

The Tree

I once knew a tree
who dropped leaves like tears
when he was glum, he swayed
when he was happy, the bark made a smile
when bored he would shake the branches
when thirsty he would suck up water
when it rained he covered animals
    and was happy
in the summer he was gladly letting birds
stay in his branches
in the winter he would keep
the acorns of the squirrels
when he saw hunters
he tripped them with his roots,
tripped them up by the boots
when he saw the axe
a shudder ran through his branches
when the first axe struck
he felt the pain but was tough
he had done his job for nature
and now his time was over
this was the tree I once knew

Brendan Thomson (age 12)
St. Michael's University Middle School

Winter is Delicious

Reading cozy by the fire,
wrapped in blankets, oh so warm.
Stirring hot chocolate with a candy cane,
watching marshmallows melt.
I'm happily gnawing on some marzipan.
Ice crystals on the window, it's so cold.
Slippers on my feet,
shawl 'round my shoulders.
Anticipating Christmas.
Winter is delicious!

Arista Hanson (age 10)
Distance Education School of
the Kootenays

~//~

Week After Week

I walk down the halls,
No one notices.
I smile at people,
No one looks.
I say excuse me,
No one moves.
I say "Hello,"
No one grins.
I lower my head,
No one cares

Jessica Mugford (age 12)
Neill Middle School

~//~

Somebody Cares!

Though we can't be together,
Somebody cares
If your heart is cheerful and bright
Somebody cares
If you're feeling good
and everything's just right
And somebody hopes
That this message will show
In a warm little heart-to-heart way
And the somebody that cares
Is the man upstairs

Jaimie-Dee Larson (age 12)
St. Francis School

Kitchen

A kitchen is for cooking food.
Everyone knows that.
For when I enter my kitchen
I do just that.
I add a teaspoon of imagination,
To go with my colourful illustration.
Sometimes I write of nature,
Or maybe just friends.
For when I write a poem my
imagination bends.
My paper is a cutting board.
My pen is a mixing spoon.
I can write about anything,
From the city to the moon.
Humour, sadness, anger,
A poem has it all.
Once you start a poem
Your thoughts cannot stall.

Joseph Fieldgate (age 11)
Douglas Park School

~//~

The Warlock

The Warlock is plotting against
innocent souls
He plans on cursing them so they cannot
leave the grave
Where their bodies lie.

The Warlock conjures
Spells to curse you, to hurt you, even to
kill you.
You can't run or hide when the
Warlock arrives.
The Warlock will trap your
unsuspecting soul
Then destroy it.

You can't run or hide when the
Warlock arrives.
If you think you can beat him you're
horribly mistaken.
If you think of a plan he will crush
your mind
With his ultimate power.
You can't run or hide
When the Warlock arrives.

Matthew Kujala (age 12)
Neill Middle School

48

I am...

Fun, loud music, shopping
I love visiting my cousins in Calgary!
I don't like when I have to wake up
so early in the morning to go to school.
I love homemade hot fudge chocolate cake
mmm...*good!!!*
I love to dance! I do jazz and ballet
It is so fun.
My brother and sister are so, so, so, so
annoying and mean.
But I love going to my family cabin.
This is me!

Rebecca McCartney (age 9)
Brander Gardens Elementary School

~//~

Boys and Girls

"What are little girls made of?
What are little girls made of?
Sugar and spice and everything nice.
That's what little girls are made of."

That couldn't be all
That couldn't be all!
They could wear beautiful dresses in fall,
Or run down the hall,
Or hit a hard ball,
Or climb a big wall,
Or take a trip to the mall.

"What are little boys made of?
What are little boys made of?
Frogs and snails and puppy dog tails.
That's what little boys are made of."

There's more
There's more!
They'll slam the door.
They'll splash at the shore.
They'll run in the store.
They'll fall asleep on the floor.
They shoot and score!

These nursery rhymes are cute, but not
quite accurate.
There's more to boys and girls and
that's that.

Valerie Flokstra (age 7)
Home School

Feathers

Soft, light feathers fly
floating high or gliding low
graceful through the air

Sheena Campbell (age 12)
St. Michael's University Middle School

~//~

Rainbow

Puddles cover the ground
The air is made to freeze
The rain is falling down
And leaking through the trees
Falling, freezing, flooding it flows
From the clouds covering the sky
Pouring in puddles wherever it goes
And anything but dry
It's cold and wet and dark
The water falls in drops
And covers the grass in the park
Then suddenly it stops
The sun shines with a glow
I look and see a rainbow

Kirsten Tee (age 12)
Immaculate Conception School

~//~

I Still Remember

I still remember his piercing glare,
Those eyes that haunt my every nightmare.
The figure that makes my stomach lurch,
Every time I walk by
That old, haunted church.

I was transfixed, my head was spinning.
I still remember his evil grinning.
His bony, greenish, grotesque body,
To my human eyes looked gaudy.

I will remember evermore,
The look of terror his face bore.
How I wish I'd never seen his face,
That awkward creature from outer space.

Tom Pearson (age 12)
Sister O'Brien School

Baboon

There was a baboon
That had a balloon
He lives in a lagoon
With a looneytoon

William F. Protopappas (age 10)
Boundary Community School

~//~

Ramadan

I like fasting to celebrate Ramadan.
I like the food after fasting:
The fruit and the cake,
The strawberries and watermelon,
And Greek salad.
To celebrate Eid
I like visiting people
And getting presents.

Jinan Khaled (age 7)
Edmonton Islamic School

~//~

Last Hope

Nothing but snow.
Nothing but white all around.
Cold winds blow.
No signs of life.

But through the cold does a young boy walk.
He walks for hours and many days,
Always crying all alone,
Hoping to find a friend within this
    colourless place.

The snow dies down.
The boy walks onward, never stopping,
    never looking back
Until he sits underneath a tree to rest.
And beside the boy lies a sign of hope.
A flower, a hint of colour remains in its
    dying petals.
The boy walks on, hope restored, knowing
    that spring will come soon.

Jason Bradford (age 12)
Bodwell High School

I Like That Stuff!

People are paid from it
Papers made from it
Trees
I like that stuff

Adults eat it
Children beat it
Food
I like that stuff

Children break it
Adults take it
Responsibility
I like that stuff

People use it
Others abuse it
Medicine
I like that stuff

Christine Scherger (age 11)
Children of St. Martha School

~//~

A Poet's Heart

I drew my heart and labeled it
Renamed the parts to a poet's taste
I started with goodness and thought it fitting
To second it with a humourous valve

My heart has a cavernous humourous valve
Goodness takes its place
Where the pump of flowing-happiness
    is everworking

My sorrow-sifting valve has been put out
    of commission

The ligament of faith has a special power
It shows you who is lying
And who is telling the truth
And it works hard at that

My heart is medium size
Exquisitely placed
A little between big and medium to
    be specific
A medium heart usually belongs to a
    simple man

Serge Pearse (age 11)
South Island Distance Education School

50

Ice Cream

I love ice cream
It's the best
I just can't give it a rest
The delicious taste
It's nothing to waste
Chocolate, strawberry
Vanilla, and raspberry
Butterscotch and toffee
But not coffee
It's good
Just the way it should
'Specially when I eat it with you
I hope you do too!

Christine Houghton (age 10)
Mother Mary Greene School

~//~

I Hear the Lord of the Rings

I hear Gollum fishing
I hear Frodo wishing
I hear the ring taunting
I hear Frodo wanting

I hear drums beating
I hear Gimli eating
I hear Wormtongue lying
I hear Theoden sighing

I hear Merry crying
I hear Pippin dying
I hear the eye seeking
I hear the Nazgul shrieking

I hear dark forces yielding
I hear Gandalf healing
I hear the Balrog growling
I hear cold wind howling

I hear Orcs chanting
I hear Saruman dancing
I hear Ents moaning
I hear armies groaning

I hear fire crackling
I hear thunder cackling
I hear horns sounding
I hear drums pounding

Silas Ginn (age 11)
Children of St. Martha School

Butterfly

Butterfly, butterfly
Transparent wings
Smelling pollen at every flower
Sitting motionless warming in the sun
Delicate as a feather

Nevin Haynes (age 9)
Sunalta School

~//~

Fall

I hear the leaves crunching under my feet
as I walk into the crisp air.
I see the flowers sway back and forth
in the breeze.
I smell the wood fires burning.
I love fall.

Elsbeth (Ellie) Toms (age 10)
Sunalta School

~//~

Growing Up

Every single day
I wish I were sitting by the bay
Life can be so hard
I don't want to be playing the wrong card
The school work makes me crazy
Once the day is done
My brain feels very hazy
As I get older I'm going to need an occupation
Right now I better get a great education
Life can feel like a piece of coal
Dull and dreary
Burning like a fury

When I get older I want to swim like a fish
That is my ultimate wish
When I am about to die
I want to see the clouds in the sky
The smell of fresh air
The taste of a ripe, juicy pear
I hope that I will go up to Heaven
Maybe there will be a Seven-Eleven

David Bennett (age 11)
St. Philip School

Untitled

Dragon
sharp teeth
flies breathes fire roar
scared fright nervous afraid
Big

Jesse Vert (age 7)
Sparling School

~//~

Chewing Gum

Chewing gum makes my
mouth go yum.
It is chewy and gooey,
And wraps around my tongue!
Chewing gum comes in any flavour
you can imagine:
cherry, raspberry, peppermint,
spearmint, juicy fruit as well!

Yum, yum,
please buy me a package of gum!

Christine Thompson (age 10)
Mother Mary Greene School

~//~

Falling Leaves

The leaves are as colourful as a rainbow.
It is time for the delicious treats my
mom bakes.
Oh the delicious pumpkin pies and
rolling brownies.
Fresh corn bread. Oh, the smell.
We go and get out the rusty old rake.
We complain
And go insane,
But we have to,
So we take out our rakes from the shed.
Ready, set, *go!*
We run to the trees and rake the leaves.
Faster, faster
We can taste the treats.

Jeffrey Yu (age 12)
Montgomery Middle School

Gold Rush

Gold glowed in my eyes as I laughed
to myself
Old memories of home filled my head
Long endless songs filled my head as
I panned
Dust burned and watered my eyes

Running for the gold I now claim
Using all my strength to walk the terrain
Soft winds blew my hair every which way
Here I am looking for gold and here I am
to stay

Alexandria Garcia (age 10)
Beaver Lake School

~//~

Useless Things

A pencil without lead
A pillow without a bed
A pen without ink
A chain without a link

A car without wheels
A table without meals
A bottle without water
A dad without a daughter

A dog without a bark
A night without dark
A girl without hair
A fire without flare

A chalkboard without chalk
A boat without a dock
Lights without lighting
Children without fighting

Chips without a crunch
Food without lunch
Halloween without treats
Dogs without meats

A box without a top
Broom without a mop
Scissors without a tip
Mouth without a lip

Rebecca Sarich (age 10)
Children of St. Martha School

Hockey

One day I played hockey on a rink
And somebody tie-dyed my clothes pink
I hit the post
And started to coast

The buzzer rang
And I heard a bang
The game was over
And we started to play Red Rover

R.J. Zorn (age 9)
École Joe Clark School

~//~

Betrayal

A long winding road it may never end
Hatred
Trust you thought was there
but is not anymore
Deep scars
Unanswered questions
Mean secrets that scarred many
in a war or battle.
Dying dreams.
Fighting over what only one started.
The rage in your chest
when their name is spoken.
Too many words
When you try to explain your emotion
you're speechless with anger.
How could they?
Why would they?
What made them do that?
Questions that bring back
horrible memories.
Silence
Talking is not an option.
What words can't explain.
Fingers pointed, people blamed.
Crying
Emotions
When eyes flare and hearts rage.
People flood to churches
praying they will find the right way
Betrayal
Millions suffer from it every day

Stephanie Haynes (age 12)
Gwynne School

Gramatically Incorrect

pece is to hope as hope is to luv...
pece is wat we have with god up a buv
pece is wat meny pepal hope for...
for the diying pepal in the war
some pepal think war is a game
but hoo are we to take sides or blame
pece luv and to end all war...
that is wat I am hoping for

Brenden Fabros (age 12)
Immaculate Conception School

~//~

My Friends

My friends are nice oh so nice.
They are made with lots of spice.
When we are at birthdays we are playful.
And after the birthday we are joyful.

My friends are always by my side
Whenever I go down the slide.
When we go to each others' house
We always play with a fake mouse.

Warren Jackson (age 10)
École Joe Clark School

~//~

Cars

Cars can make you happy.
They take you here and there.
But when they start to fall apart,
You'll want to pull your hair.

They'll take you out for shopping.
They'll take you on a lark.
But when you drive them to downtown,
They'll be a pain to park.

Cars come with different bodies.
And colours in and out.
But if you owned an Enzo,
You'd have the best, no doubt.

Steven Sciore (age 10)
Mother Mary Greene School

Untitled

The moon
Made from basalt
Appearing in the night
Sea of tranquility, crater
Natural

Brittany Godlien (age 11)
William Grayson School

~//~

God is Like Your Best Friend

God is like your best friend
He will listen and see your every bend
You can talk to Him anytime
You can even tell Him about a lime
He won't blow your secret
Or tell your friend Beatrice
Although you may not hear Him
He always has a way of telling you

Jordan Makin (age 12)
St. Francis School

~//~

Ode to Technology

Video games are fun;
They can interest anyone.
Tetris, Mario, Double-0 Seven,
Video games are children's Heaven.

Nintendo Gamecube is the latest;
No one doubts it is the greatest.
The very best graphics in the land,
Nintendo products are always grand.

Bring your Gameboy everywhere,
Small bright-coloured games you share.
Beat the games and get some more,
Look around; there's fun galore!

So there we sit glued to the screen,
Blue, orange, yellow, purple, green.
"Get off there now!" I hear Mom scream.
"Ah gee, Mom, you're just so mean!"

Nick Stoochnoff (age 11)
St. Joseph's School

War is Death

War is death.
You feel sadness as your
Friends beside you fall.

You feel horrible as others,
That you do not know,
Fall at the point of your gun.

Overall you feel fear as mounds of dirt
Pile up around you.
The screams of others
Echo in your ears.

You hope you can see
Your family again.
You hope...and you *pray*.

*In memory of the Canadian soldiers that
died in World War I and II.*

Anthony Loenen (age 12)
Pacific Christian Elementary School

~//~

Drinking and Driving

Sitting in this world all alone
As coldness and shivers
go through my bones
Living in darkness,
with not a person in sight
Wondering to yourself why nothing's right

Then you're walking down the street
And you're looking around
You're seeing cars smash
And people falling to the ground

You hear sirens, and you watch people cry
And you think to yourself
"What would it be like to die?"
Never seeing your old friend's face
Never slowing down, and always in a race

You better think about this
Before it happens to you
And next time you want to drink and drive
Just stop and think of the right thing to do.

Kim Cullen (age 12)
Dr. George Ferguson School

Ramadan Is Here

Fasting like the poor,
Feeling like the poor.
Feeling good, very good.
Like the poor,
Feel the hunger of the poor.
Fasting is the thing.
Don't eat or drink until night.
Feel the happiness and
See the decorations
Of Ramadan
Taste the food of Allah (SWT)
Hear the sounds.
Give the poor some food.
Feel the hunger of the poor.
Feel the power of Ramadan and
Feel the hunger of the poor!

Yasmeen El Hajj (age 7)
Edmonton Islamic School

~//~

Remembrance

Remembrance: Remember us; we fought
    for you.
We sacrificed our lives for you, now you
    remember and respect,
Just because we lie in Flanders Field does
    not mean we are gone forever.

Remembrance: Remember the horror
    and fear
We faced for you,
Remember the sadness and harm we faced
    for you,
Remember the day when our children would
    look outside their window and
    see violence,
That we were fighting for you.

Remembrance: Remember our freedom
    that we lost for you so you could have
    it too,
Remember our family that we lost for
    you so you could have love too,
We fought and died so hopefully one day
    you could have happiness and freedom,
Remember the lives we lost for you.

Robert Marzitelli (age 10)
St. Helen Elementary School

Untitled

Dragons
Evil, wicked
Fire breathing killer
Never try to slay the dragon
Monster

Alexa Pashovitz (age 11)
Pense School

~//~

I Love Popcorn!

Poof, poof, poof!
Sounds like rain on the roof
Looks bumpy, smells yummy
Looks tasty, feels nobbly
One of a kind, you can't beat
    the treat...
    Popcorn!

Rachel Senior (age 8)
Brander Gardens Elementary School

~//~

Autumn

Crisp orange leaves falling,
Towards the moistened ground,
Littered with dry broken leaves,

A bright yellow leaf,
Floating into the long pumpkin patch,
The pumpkins are still dark green
But they are freckled with orange.

The tall, yellow corn,
Swaying in the gentle fall breeze,
Ready to be harvested,
Red juicy apples falling,
Falling to the soft, wet, green grass,

The faint smell of warm pumpkin pie,
In the fresh air,
The turkey in the oven,
Ready to be eaten,
Time to go inside.

Erik Landsvik (age 12)
Neill Middle School

Untitled

Forest,
Forest,
trees, plants,
growing, living, livable
war, stubborn, dying, shrinking,
earthquake, tornado, wet, volcano,
Disaster!

Jeffrey Kim (age 8)
David Oppenheimer Elementary School

~//~

Waterfall

You have a force that demands respect
You are a vision of splendour
High atop a mountainside
With all those jagged rocks by your side
You crash, you boom with such great force
But it's the vision upon which I see
The lush, the tall, the green, green trees
The force and noise are hidden and all I
see is peace

Rebecca Gottfried (age 10)
Notre Dame Elementary School

~//~

Once Upon a Moonlit Night

Once upon a moonlit night,
The owl was screaming, the stars
were bright.
The moonbeams were falling from the sky,
A patch of wind had swept by.

The crickets' chirp filled the air,
The baby bird slept without care.
The grandfather clock ticked and tocked,
Safe because the house was locked.

The little brown mouse scurried by,
The old raccoon gave a sigh.
All was peaceful, all was right,
Once upon a moonlit night.

Morgan Armstrong (age 9)
Silver Star Elementary School

The Balloon

I had a big huge baboon
Who popped my balloon
I got mad at the huge baboon
And ate him with a spoon

Benjamin (Ben) McWilliams (age 10)
Boundary Community School

~//~

Peace

I think peace
Should never cease,
The graceful birds that fly
Should never die,

The deadly battles
Should cease.
The blood, the dead, the guns
I think peace is wonderful

Andrew Froese (age 11)
Hillcrest Community School

~//~

Untitled

There was a sweetheart
His name was Bart
No one liked his name
He always took the blame

If he didn't they would get mad
And that always made him sad
So he changed his looks
And stopped the books

Everyone liked him
Especially Kim
Everything was great
And then came Kate

She was his crush
She made him blush
He changed his look back
And then he had a snack

Ashley Young (age 11)
William Grayson School

56

It's That Time of Year

Snowflakes drift
Quietly to the
Pale white ground
The weather
Is cold
And relentless
But, the spirit
Is friendly
And warm.
Joy rests
In our hearts.
Toys fill
Our stockings.
Either young or old,
Small or tall,
The spirit of Christmas
Lightens everyone's heart.

Neil Hayden (age 12)
Saint Michaels University Middle School

~//~

Ten Little Jets

Ten little jets moving in a line.
One flew away then there were nine.
Nine little jets flying away from a gate.
One crashed then there were eight.

Eight little jets going past Heaven.
One got stuck then there were seven.
Seven little jets in a mix.
One got lost then there were six.

Six little jets by a hive.
One stopped then there were five.
Five little jets moved some more.
One moved too fast then there were four.

Four little jets going over a tree.
One got scared then there were three.
Three little jets had nothing to do.
One got bored then there were two.

Two little jets flying close to the sun.
One melted then there was one.
One little jet left; it's the last one.
It blew up then there were none.

Christopher Thomas (age 10)
Children of St. Martha School

The Giant Bowl of Spaghetti

Today when I was going for a walk,
I saw a giant bowl of spaghetti.
It looked very delicious,
It had cut burger, and red juicy sauce.
It looked so good that I decided to try it.
So I took a spoonful!
It was the best spaghetti I ever tasted!
So I took another bite and another bite,
Until the whole bowl was empty.

Kristofer Salat (age 10)
Mother Mary Greene School

~//~

Saved By the Bell

My fingers are loudly drumming
on my poor worn out desk.
I do not know the answer
of this awful boring test.
I can hear the clock ticking,
every student's anxiety kicking.
Then the clock turns twelve,
and every student for themselves.
I was saved by the bell.

Claire Macdonald (age 11)
Rose Valley Elementary School

~//~

Animal Imagination

Imagine horses burrowed in holes,
Imagine that they took the place of moles.
Imagine dogs sounded like cats,
Imagine that they had wings like bats.
Imagine that snakes didn't slide,
Imagine that they could glide.
Imagine horses couldn't gallop
Imagine that like kangaroos, they pack
    a wallop!
Imagine rats didn't have tails,
Imagine they made a slimy trail.
Imagine this was a different world,
Where little piggies' tails were not curled.
Good thing our world isn't like that!

Troy Giffin (age 9)
Miller Park Community School

Skis

Skis are going down a hill.
On them is a guy named Bill.
On the hill there is a blue and yellow shack,
And a girl hits the shack with a whack.
She gets back up with a sore aching head.
The doctor says you should go to bed.
On her head is a freezing cloth.
In the corner she spots a moth.
In the wall she sees a bend.
And this is the story's end.

Jayden Neumann (age 10)
Notre Dame Elementary School

~//~

Do Not Touch That Wire

Do not touch that wire,
Or it will light on fire,
And it will burn that tire.
The tire is made out of tar,
And it will burn that car.
The car will burn the house,
Killing a poor little mouse.
Then you'll need a dose
Of a medicine that tastes gross.
So do not touch that wire,
Or it will light on fire.

Garrett Thibault (age 9)
Meadowridge School

~//~

Dinosaur

Dinosaur, dinosaur
What do you see
I see a flea on my tummy
Dinosaur, dinosaur
What do you hear
I hear I fly buzzing at me
Dinosaur, dinosaur
What do you smell
I smell burning fire
Dinosaur, dinosaur
What do you feel
I feel a tree falling down on the grass

Osama Darwiche (age 7)
Edmonton Islamic School

Drummers

lying down
I hear drummers drumming
hammering on the roof
and in the gutters
pounding out a natural song
I drowse off...

they've been playing for a while, now
I peer out my window...
so that's what they've been doing
making vicious rivers
and overflowing roads

now they've gone
gone to play for another town
to put them to sleep

Branden Chase (age 12)
Neill Middle School

~//~

Growing Up

What are you supposed to feel,
When you're growing up too fast?
It's hard to feel good
When you're hardly a kid anymore.
Your fun times in life are gone, in the past.

How are you supposed to cope
When you're growing up too fast?
It's hard to fit in
When you're feeling this awkward.
Oh, when will I be a true adult at last?

Are there any exciting aspects
When you're growing up too fast?
It's hard to wait 'til
You're able to drive.
When will I zoom like the wind at long last?

Where in the world will I go from here?
I am growing up at last.
But once childhood is over,
There's no turning back...
I feel like a travelling hiker,
Scaling life's towering mountain.
Oh, I am growing up at last!

Molly Hutchinson (age 11)
St. Philip School

58

A Foggy Day

I got lost in the fog,
tripped on a log,
fell in the dirt
ruined my new shirt.
Two days ago I shared,
I'm scared!

Carmen Smith-Morpurgo (age 11)
Boundary Community School

~//~

Believe in You!

Believe you are valuable
Don't let anyone tell you different because
An original is better than a copy
Understand just in case
Because we are all God's children
Because people are like God
Someone to believe in
Because life is a journey into imagination
Because you never know what you can do
Until you try it...

Janet Wensvoort (age 11)
Veritas School

~//~

The War to End All Wars

It was a sad day,
A day for remembering,
Everyone running
Not wanting brave men taken away,
Soldier on every street corner
Brave,
But nervous, still nervous,
Thoughts running through their heads,
"Will I ever see my family again?
Will I be the best man I can be,
And protect my country?"
Four years of this violence continued,
But the day for remembering came.
Thousands of men, gone,
Thousands of men, injured,
Thousands of men, still alive.

Danica Ferris (age 9)
Lake Bonavista Elementary School

Shark

The very mad shark
is swimming towards the shore,
will gobble you up.

Brent Callow (age 11)
Calgary French & International School

~//~

City of Calgary

Oh, I love the city of Calgary,
Because it's big and beautiful,
With juicy beef and pretty flowers,
And big soaring towers.
There are deserted badlands
That everyone likes,
And lots of chinook winds,
To blow the fresh air in,
It also has marshes, wetlands,
And green rolling hills,
With great rocky mountain views,
And places with rat free.
The city of Calgary is wonderful to be,
Because the wildlife is majestic and free.

Tiffany Wong (age 10)
Mother Mary Greene School

~//~

A Day on the Beach

I saw it fly way up high,
Flying through the bright blue sky.
The other day I saw it dance;
It saw me too with just one glance.

I never did see it land,
While I was standing on the sand.
I watch it soar through the cloud so white;
It really was a beautiful sight.

I yell out "bird!"
I think it heard.
"Good-bye," I said
As I throw out bread.

Patricia Halim (age 12)
St. Michael's University Middle School

59

The Scariest Foggiest Day Ever

It is today a foggy day
and a monster that appeared in May.
The clouds looked like ghosts
and I ran into posts.

Kyle Houston (age 10)
Boundary Community School

~//~

Education

Educational, advanced students
Different, difficult, designs
Unique
Challenging
Amazing
Terrific marks improving each day
Intelligent students
Observing, obstacles
Nervous bodies moving around

Adam Clace (age 11)
William Grayson School

~//~

Untitled

I am - art, music, gardening.
I like it when my cats both curl up on my
bed and purr.
I like playing soccer when it's not too hot
and not too cold -
When it's just right
Honesty, school, and friends are important
to me.
I like it when my Mom takes me to a movie
That I have wanted to see for a long time.
I don't like it when my cat Neville gets lost.
But I got used to him getting lost on the
third time he got lost.
I like going to the river and catching frogs
and crayfish.
The crayfish never pinch me.
Walking in the river valley is fun for
my family!
This is me!

Hayley Calvert (age 9)
Brander Gardens Elementary School

Halloweeeeen!

Halloween, Halloween
My pencilbox is ultramarine
All those scares make me feel unclean
Halloween, Halloween
Halloween, Halloween
Oh, that book is by Tolkien
I can't wait for a jellybean
Halloween, Halloween
Halloween, Halloween
That candy don't taste like no sardine
Even if I'm a preteen,
Without a doubt today will be...
Halloween 2003

Jake Moyer (age 9)
South Island Distance Education School

~//~

Ten Little Monkeys

Ten little monkeys swinging on a vine
One fell off and now there are...
Nine little monkeys went to the state
One stayed home and now there are...

Eight little monkeys floating to Heaven
One fell down and now there are...
Seven little monkeys cried because they
couldn't fix
One went to fix and now there are...

Six little monkeys throwing sticks at a hive
One got stung and now there are...
Five little monkeys pretending to soar
One didn't want to and now there are...

Four little monkeys swinging in a tree
One missed the tree and now there are...
Three little monkeys drinking some dew
One ran away and now there are...

Two little monkeys speeding having fun
One little monkey crashed and now
there is...
One little monkey sitting on a bed
having fun
One fell off and now there are none.

Lane Buck (age 11)
Children of St. Martha School

Untitled

I get stuffed with food but I don't have
   a mouth
I have a hand, but it doesn't move.
You all need me, but not all the time.
I'm in your house, but only in one room.
I'm always cold but I never freeze.
What am I?

Fridge

Kyle Luchsinger (age 9)
Discovery Elementary School

~//~

Why Me?

Do I have the courage to go on,
   day by day?
When I get up in the morning,
   I don't even stop to pray.

Why did God do this to me?
   What did I do wrong?
When I get teased and tortured,
   I don't think I can go on.

People laugh and people stare;
   my friends don't even care.
I don't think I can go on;
   is this who I am?

Someone who gives up,
   someone who wants to die?
So please don't listen to what they say;
   I have feelings that hurt day by day.

But I've decided that I can do this,
   I can go on, I will be strong.
God may have made me different;
   who are they to judge?

I will be a fighter;
   I don't care what they say.
I can, I can, I will!

*This poem is dedicated to all disabled men,
women, and children who carry on life with
challenges; they are our role models.*

Kayla Fedorak (age 11)
St. Cyril School

Untitled

Dew drops
Glowing diamonds
Streaking through clear surfaces
Sparkling in the starry sunrise
Dew drops

Andria Wong (age 9)
Vancouver Christian School

~//~

Thinking

When I sit on the floor, or my bed, or a boar
I think...
I think about my mother
My brother
And all kinds of things
I think about people, places, or things
I think about worlds that have crazy things
Like oogles and boogles
And bloops and things that go oo or boo
I think about what it would be like
To live in that world
Every morning and night

Anna Herman (age 10)
Ashley Park School

~//~

Friends

You spend time with them,
They spend time with you.
Your friendship won't end
Even if you move.
You laugh and play
Not thinking about
How she might leave you someday.

The day she leaves,
You feel it's the end.
You no longer believe,
That nothing can happen.
You miss them
So much.
You'll never see her again.

Marieka Ostermeier (age 11)
Parkland Immanuel Christian School

61

My Sticky Stinky Dog

My dog doesn't like baths
I pushed him into his bath
But he jumped out of the tub
And he ran away
He rolled in the mud
He was sprayed by a skunk
He sure needs a bath now!

LaSheka Morgan (age 9)
St. Wilfrid School

~//~

Untitled

I am...
Art, music, and good books.
I like cats and cute babies.
I like going to school because I can learn
    new things.
I hate spicy food.
I do not enjoy the cold weather.
I like to skate and swim,
And I love to dance and do ballet.
This is me!

Jillene Craig (age 8)
Brander Gardens Elementary School

~//~

Soul of Remembrance Day

In Flanders Field dead bodies lay
That we remember on Remembrance Day.
All that we fought for there's still more...
More death, pain, suffering, and war.

We fought until our time has come.
Some still live while others lay.
In Flanders Field
And we're here to stay.

So my friends this is how it ends.
We fought through day
And we fought through night.
The great story of Flanders Field
Where the heroic bodies of soldiers lay.

Ryan Lasaleta (age 10)
St. Helen Elementary School

My Lover

My lover has this beautiful smile
which I know she has.
I would give up anything like live in a cell,
but I see I chose right
'cause she has the pasazz!
Something about the way she wooes
attracts me like no other lover.
Something about the way she do's
makes me have this incredible fire.
My lover gives me urges in the night
and she's like no other.
She is my strength and my light;
maybe in the future we can have a daughter.
After what I just said, I'd realize,
she was there close to me
staring in my eyes!

Anthony Thor Villagomez (age 12)
Immaculate Conception School

~//~

The Blind Man

Day by day
Living the life of a blind man
Walking in eternal darkness

To never see
Your very own face
To hear the judge
To win the case

To kill the killer
The attempted homicide
Be gone with the man
Who tried to rip out his eyes

The courage to see
With another's eyes
The courage to live
To escape suicide
To never see
And always cry

So you may live
So you may die
Old and shattered
Yet young and blind

Cameron Bellavie (age 12)
St. Cyril School

The Poppy

I watch with thousands
I stand up high
I've seen many people
Come here and cry

I am a poppy
To be worn on this day
So you will remember
The soldiers who passed away

I am the flower that is
Put on a cross
For the people who come here
To mourn their loss

So salute the soldiers
Who passed away
And honour them on Remembrance Day

Chris Murie (age 11)
Langley Fundamental Elementary School

~//~

Nightmare Knocking

It starts to rain outside my door.
I hear the constant drip, drop, drip, drop.
I feel the crack of thunder,
Hear the lightning strike.
Though I cannot see the flash,
I know what's going on.
I sense the wind.
It starts to blow.
I can feel the trees swaying back and forth.
I feel frightened but safe.
The thrill of the storm builds up inside.
I hear the power go out.
There is no more buzz of electricity
Running through my veins.
The rain doesn't stop.
I am trapped inside this nightmare.
I hear voices around me,
But I don't understand a thing.
Is this a dream?
Is this a nightmare?
Is this Heaven?
No it is not, I am different.
I am scared, alone, and very terrified.
I am blind.

Kimberly Kaytor (age 12)
Douglas Park School

I May Grow Tall

I may grow tall, but I might hang down
    a wall.
I help people live, but am often killed
    and disrespected.
I breathe, but I have no mouth.
I come in many shapes, sizes, and colours.
One of my kind is used to build things.
What am I?

A plant

Lee Hux (age 9)
Discovery Elementary School

~//~

Untitled

I will hold
Up the torch of peace in my world
By working
To help the poor in our world.
Peace is...
-Studying history.
-Watching fish jump in the water.
-Going to Laser Planet with my friends.
-Helping my friends with their homework.
-By helping clean up garbage in our local
Environment

Peter Mohanraj (age 10)
Topham Elementary School

~//~

Pianos

A piano has great notes and sounds,
If you want to know them, take a look...
♩♩, ♪, ♩, ♬, ♩, ♪, - and ○
It gives your fingers exercise,
Like working at a gym.
But don't exercise them too hard,
Or else they'll do a spin.
A piano is a kind of instrument,
You'll find one in a store.
A piano sounds so pretty and high
♩♩, ♪, ♩, ♬, ♩, ♪, - and ○

Camille MacBean (age 9)
Ashley Park School

One Day

One day I woke up
And I found a pup
That pup was really cool
He likes to swim in our pool

He really likes to run away
Then he comes back the very next day
This ending is very sad
So don't go crying to your dad

Kade Bleackley (age 10)
École Joe Clark School

~//~

Snow!!!

Sparkly snow from the ground,
    ground, ground.
It's everywhere when I turn around,
    'round, 'round.
Down, down, down went the snow,
It's everywhere you know, know, know.
I see a snowman everywhere, where, where.
There is snow at the fair, fair, fair.
Snow is what we share, share, share.
Everywhere around us.

Shaylene Tynning (age 10)
Ashley Park School

~//~

Taking a Stand

Take your head out of the sand,
    and take a stand!
When people ask you to smoke,
    say, "That's no joke!"
When people ask to give you drinks,
    say, "That stinks!"
When people offer you drugs,
    say no, and think hugs!
Don't let peer pressure get to you,
    or you will feel sad and blue!
So take someone's hand,
    and take a stand!

Rebecca Schmunk (age 11)
Parkside Centennial Elementary School

Watching the Rain

I watch as the rain falls, it hits the ground
Each single drop making a sound
The smell is refreshing
The view is to keep
The scene is amazing
I could fall right asleep

I love when it rains, how the weather changes
The clouds go by slowly from all
    different ranges
The water's a shield around my neighbours
    and me
It runs like a river into the sea

When that rain ends, it's like a new day
You start from the beginning but know
    just what to say

Hannah F. Agar (age 11)
Rose Valley Elementary School

~//~

My Puppy's Tail

I heard barking;
I ran to look.
All I saw was my dog in a husky's mouth.
I was scared,
but I knew he had hope.

When he got away
he was crying.
All I saw were tears dripping down his face.
I was crying, too.
I saw blood on the table,
but thank God he wasn't going to die
because I put my tears in it.

He saw me.
He knew why I was crying,
and crawled up to me.
I knew he was trying his hardest
to make me feel better.

I hugged
and cuddled him.
It was like
a whole new day.

Cody Breuker (age 12)
Neill Middle School

Angels for Guidance

An angel for guidance.
An angel to pray.
An angel to laugh with
And wipe tears away.
Angels for peace and
Angels for love.
Angels sent from the Lord
From Heaven above.
Angels that hope
And care in every way.
An angel to lead us
And show us the way.

Emily Kumpf (age 10)
Jean Vanier Catholic School

~//~

Not Afraid

I hear
the sky rumble
I feel
my voice tremble
but I am not afraid

I see
the rod of lightning flash
I witness
the power go out
but I am not afraid

I hear
the rain pounding on the shackles
I feel
the heat of the candle I am grasping
but I am not afraid

I see
the trees thrashing back and forth
I witness
my dog beginning to cry
but I am not afraid

I love this storm
from the deep bellows of the sky
like the gods are fighting
and I am not afraid

Meghan Francoeur (age 12)
Neill Middle School

The Library

I went to the library and found a book.
I took it off the shelf for a look.
It was a book that was funny.
And in it there was a funny bunny.

But I put it back on the shelf
Then I met a guy named Ralph.
He said he works in a store.
I walked to the store and it started to pour.

I forgot my umbrella
so I went home to get it.
I could not find it so I had a fit.
I found it finally
And thanked my brother kindly.

I called Ralph and said I'd be over soon.
I told him I would be over this afternoon.

Shannon Isaac (age 8)
École Joe Clark School

~//~

Holidays

New Years Day,
Let's make resolutions, celebrate,
and say Hooray!
Valentines Day
At sunset couples celebrate by the bay.
Easter
This is the time of year
when chocolate eggs appear.
Victoria Day
Queen Victoria's birth. Yippee let's play.
Canada Day
Canada's confederation date,
go to festivals, don't be late.
Labour Day
I just want to say, "Honour the people
who are not at play."
Thanksgiving
Time for turkey, to give and be caring.
Remembrance Day
Let's take time to remember those
who took the chance.
Christmas Day
Christmas is fun, but important in a way.

Rhianna Schmunk (age 9)
Parkside Centennial Elementary School

Ramadan

I feel happy when Ramadan is here
Because Ramadan is important to me.
I feel Allah is everywhere.
Everyday I hear birds chirping.
I want to wear a new dress.
What colour will it be?
Can you guess?
Pink, pink, pink!

Faaria Khan (age 7)
Edmonton Islamic School

~//~

Friends

Friends are a gift from our heavenly God
Running, playing they could be your dog
In the rain or shine they will be with you
Ending with some but making some new
Never ending friends even though they
    might die
Depending on them because they are my...
Sweet, awesome, cool, and super friends

Jessica Kuntz (age 11)
Parkland Immanuel Christian School

~//~

Snow

Snow,
The white crystals
Falling down from the sky
Snow,
Whizzing by
The fire lit houses
Snow,
Helping the skiers
Down the slope
Snow,
Freezing the ponds and the lakes
And putting the spell of ice upon them
Snow,
Making way for the best day of all
Christmas

Philip Welch (age 12)
Pacific Christian Elementary School

Untitled

Cheetahs
Kind of big cat
Running fast through grassland
Amazed at their powerful run
Cheetahs

Jaclyn Loewen (age 9)
Vancouver Christian School

~//~

Delighted

Delighted
extremely exciting
hoping, wishing, wondering
expressing a wonderful feeling
disappointed, depressed, compromised
slightly, sadly,
Undelighted

Alex Potié (age 10)
Calgary French & International School

~//~

Frigid North

This is a place
Where Inuit freeze,
But also where they have a dog race.

Up in the North,
Animals with fur coats
Look for a place to find warmth.

Look to the North.
What do you see?
Nothing that looks like its worth.

In the Arctic you're bound,
To see the hills that are not right.
They're rocky and round.

This is a place
Where Inuit freeze,
But also where they have a dog race.

Brent Glowinski (age 11)
Our Lady Queen of Peace School

In the Eye of the Storm

Swaying side to side,
The wind crashes against my branches,
The sound of the ocean beating against
     the rocks.
My roots are breaking; I can feel them snap.
Thunder roars like a lion getting ready
     for battle.
It feels as if a family of them are staring
     down on me.
The rain pummels my trunk,
As water starts to throw itself
At the boats scattered across the shore.
A loud *"bang"* silences the thunder.
A tree has fallen.
The thunder starts again.
The loud band, which people call a storm
     is playing.
Mother Nature is angry.

Lauren Kipp (age 12)
St. Michael's University Middle School

~//~

Bambi

One spring morning
In a hidden forest glade,
A prince fawn was born
As there he lay.

He was very cute.
His name was Bambi
His best friend Thumper,
And also Rambi.

The great prince of the forest said,
"I see a huge big flame,
Cross the river all of you!"
It was the man that he would blame.

The grass grew again.
Bambi married Faline,
Faline had twins
Their names were Chuck and Raline.

Bambi was the great prince of the forest
He was called Good Ol' Buck
Soon Chuck would take over
And like Bambi, bring good luck.

Junia Hofer (age 8)
Spring Creek School

Untitled

They have a big family.
Intrepid and bold, fearless.
Gathering their food.
Exploring the deep forest.
Ready to hunt.

Shyla McInnis (age 11)
William Grayson School

~//~

Dance!

Determination
Always practicing
Never giving up
Can always do it
Everlasting memories

Alexandra (Alex) Bonnett (age 10)
Naramata Elementary School

~//~

Untitled

Trolls are ugly and mean
Roar goes the troll when he's mad
On top of his mind is to eat the goats
Laughing is what he does best
Lying is one of his favourites

Samantha Langford (age 10)
Pense School

~//~

Super Hero

Hero
Courageous, strong
Fighting, flying, catching
Spider-Man, Batman, Joker, Penguin
Robbing, sneaking, smirking
Evil, cruel
Villain

Annelise Louise Simonsen (age 10)
Naramata Elementary School

67

The Wind

The wind is soft and warm,
A beautiful woman with long flowing hair.
The wind is a kitten playing with leaves,
Batting them around.
The wind is a child playing in the sea,
The wind's colourful arms reach everywhere

Shelby Rados (age 12)
Pacific Christian Elementary School

~//~

Peace

Peace is watching the rain fall outside.
Peace is walking along a beach picking
    up garbage
Peace is talking with friends on a
    sunny bench.
Peace is sitting by a stream and watching
    the fish swim by.
Peace is visiting someone in a home.
Let's fill our world with peace!

Gabrielle Starr (age 10)
Topham Elementary School

~//~

Love

Love is for the friendship and care we
    put into being friends.
The times we spent together, the fun
    we had.
Open minded. Ready to search for the
    perfect person to comfort you
In times of sadness.
Very loving, kind, and caring. The person
    who makes you happy.
The person who brings joy to your face.
Entering the world of eternal love.
The end of the search; you've found the
    special person
Who will keep you happy and smiling.
The caring person that makes your heart
    thump on and on.

Kaitlynn Gregory (age 12)
Pacific Christian Elementary School

Dog Dreams

Lazy dogs asleep
Roasting themselves by the fire
Dreaming of dinner

Sam Idler (age 10)
Distance Education School of
the Kootenays

~//~

Untitled

Dark black
Good, nice, and dark
Dark is for sneaky thieves
Makes you feel scared and shiver mad
Cool black

Timothy Cheung (age 9)
Vancouver Christian School

~//~

My Dream

I am running through the fields
And I feel like I've been healed.

All those lovely horses
Are running at full speed.
I see my favourite apple tree,
And settle down to read.

My black Labrador puppy
Chases its ball around the tree.
My kitten bounds towards me,
And settles by my knee.

I can laugh my heart out,
And I sing and dance all day,
And animals surround me,
And they always want to play.

This is what I dream of.
This is what I want.
I might be able to have it one day,
But maybe not today.

Stephanie Cramer (age 9)
Meadowridge School

Gophers!

They like to play around the playground
and make holes in the ground.
They like to mess up your flowers and
pretend they have powers.
They like to stare in your face with their
big round eyes.
Then they walk around in circles to keep
up the pace.

They make little noises that sound like
a mouse
And if cats can see them they like to pounce.
Gophers are everywhere, every place
there is,
So if you can please take them away,
Then I will be able to *play!*

Brittani Cox (age 11)
Elizabeth Community School

~//~

Christmas Wishes

I wish I was a sparkly, glistening
wrapped present;
I would merrily surprise and light up the
heart of a child.
I wish I was a glowing and gleaming
Christmas tree;
I would beautifully shimmer and glitter
to light up the dreary night.

I wish I was a plump, scarlet Santa Claus;
I would cheerfully soar and glide through
the sky on Christmas Eve
Giving presents to all the good children.
I wish I was a swift and intelligent reindeer;
I would promptly hover and dart between
the clouds with Santa behind me.

I wish I was a miniature and helpful elf;
I would eagerly hammer and glue the
gifts for jubilant children.
I wish I was a decorated and rapid sleigh;
I would softly sail and float through the
night air
With Santa on my back

But most of all I wish for peace on Earth.

Dylana Knelsen (age 10)
Prairie Elementary School

I Like to Cook

I like to cook but don't get too close
Or you might get burnt.
I am big and heavy
I come in many colours but I am not
a rainbow
What am I?

Answer *stove*

Jeremy Prior (age 9)
Discovery Elementary School

~//~

Growing Up Is Hard

Growing up can be hard.
It hurts to be left out.
Sometimes you might pout.
You have to feel pain.
You want to have lots of fame.
Growing up is tough,
Especially when you've had enough.
I wish things would go my way.
I feel invisible every day.
I want to be good
Instead of being in the lonely neighbourhood.

Ryker Arsenault (age 11)
St. Philip School

~//~

Anatosaurs, Anatosaurs

Anatosaurs, anatosaurs
What do you see?
I see you laughing at me!
Anatosaurs, anatosaurs
What do you hear?
I hear you screaming in my ear!
Anatosaurs, anatosaurs
What do you smell?
I smell you!
Anatosaurs, anatosaurs
What do you taste?
I taste you!

Saadie Sayah (age 7)
Edmonton Islamic School

Goblins

Are goblins smart?
Do goblins have heart?
Do goblins do weird stuff?
Do goblins play rough?

Tyson Taylor (age 8)
J.W. Inglis School

~//~

When Up Top

When up top the trees look small,
Even though they are so tall,
But when I touch the sky
I get really scared
For the thought of falling down,
But when my mother holds my hand
I am not afraid.
Now when I touch the sky
I feel *alive!*

Stephanie Knill (age 10)
Boundary Community School

~//~

It's a Tough life

It's a tough life in the North Pole,
Underneath the thick layers of snow,
Where it gets so cold,
That mothers have to sew clothes from
    the fur of a doe.
It's a tough life living under a rock,
Where the termites and worms talk and
    talk and talk.
It's a tough life living in a sock,
That had fallen off the dock and been
    picked up by a hawk.
It's a tough life winning a soccer game,
In thunder, lightning, and rain,
Because it would be really hard to aim.
It's a tough life living in jail,
Where you don't get any mail,
Or any meals with ginger ale,
And even if you wail,
You are almost guaranteed to fail!

Mira Motani (age 9)
Meadowridge School

Golden Freckles

It comes each year
Time in as time out
Fall comes with its golden freckles on
    the ground.

The shimmering autumn sun shines down
Upon the stillness.
The golden freckles on the ground.

The old, the new, the peaceful.
The geese fly high into the sky.
The birds get ready for winter.

Under the shimmering autumn sun that
    shines down
Upon the stillness.
The golden freckles on the ground.

Melanie Karen Ashley Galbreath
(age 10)
Ronald Harvey School

~//~

Stallion Magic

Look there, look at that
So beautiful up there
Up there rearing, up there staring
I asked him to come
Though I asked in my mind
The wild stallion acts as if I said it aloud
He is running
He is coming to me

He is white as snow
As soft as silk
But he's a strong stallion
No one can catch him
No one will know
He is my friend
The best of all

Standing in the river
There is magic
Though if I speak the spell will break
He will never leave
We are connected through heart and soul
In spirit we are the same
Sham and I

Katie Knott (age 12)
Wix-Brown Elementary School

Pie

Fe fi fo fum I can smell
some yummy pie
smells so good, smells so fine
I can eat it any time

Asaan Maherali (age 9)
Meadowridge School

~//~

Peace

P - I believe being peaceful is the key to
a better world.
E - I think everybody should be kind and
peaceful to one another.
A - I admit when I do wrong to someone.
C - I am courteous to everyone I meet.
E - I pray for everyone who is in need.

Jamie Hawes (age 11)
St. Helen Elementary School

~//~

Picture Perfect

Blue water clear as the baby blue sky,
Beautiful mountains as far as the eye
can see.
As the wind howls,
Trees move from side to side,
Leaning over the edge letting the wind blow,
Pushing the line between safety and danger,
Silent, so silent you could hear a drop
of water,
Cloudy but clear,
Fresh mountain air, sparkling clear water,
The smell of pine and moss,
Rocks as old as the Earth itself,
The rocks are bigger than Terrace,
White water rushing,
Water splashes upon the rocks,
Birds flying by with a beautiful view,
No need for a camera,
No need for a picture,
For this will stay with you.

Brandy Yagelniski (age 12)
Veritas School

I am Fluffy

I have a tail but it is small.
I have ears but they move side to side.
I have eyes but they are yellow
and they shine in the dark.
I live in the wild.
What am I?

Wild cat

Sydney Elliott (age 9)
Discovery Elementary School

~//~

The Rainforest

The rainforest is a wonderful place.
A magical place.
Where you hear a beautiful sound of
chirps and squawks.
Where army ants march everywhere
you go.
A damp, wet, wonderful place
That makes me feel like
An explorer.

Sooah Lee (age 8)
Meadowridge School

~//~

The War

I am a nurse in World War II.
It's dangerous and tiring too.
Seeing soldiers get hurt and die,
I just want to ask the question "Why?"
Everyday the sky seems darker,
And I'll just have to work a little harder.

On Flanders Field poppies grow
Out of the graves row by row.
Wave their petals as the wind blows.
They are like the fire burning day and night.
They encourage us to win the fight.
Don't fall now, poppies, we're on the way,
To win the battle and to brighten the day!

Jenny Tang (age 12)
École Sperung School

Don't Claw the Curtains!!

Animals...
Friendly and gentle but cautious,
They are scared easily...
Play with them, make them happy
Let them bark, meow, oink, or moo.
Let them greet people to a seat.
But don't... I repeat... don't
Let them claw the curtains!!

Jeffrey (Jeff) Keene (age 10)
Ashley Park School

~//~

The Rising

We are the rising
When we fall we get back up
We're strong enough to keep going
And weak enough to stop
We live off what we can
And survive off each other
Living in this violence and drugs
But pain we've never suffered
Life, of course, is a beautiful thing
Bleeding, dying, tortured, bruised
But we are rising!

Blair T. Atkinson (age 12)
Sister O'Brien School

~//~

Voice of the Fish

We are the fish, who have no voice,
But yet we see and don't rejoice.
You take our home and trash it up,
With all the stuff you don't pick up.
We see the sun and see you run,
From all that you have come and done.
We cannot fight to make this right,
And so we ask that you take task.
When you enjoy the water's shore,
Don't leave your garbage anymore.
Think it through, remove your loot;
This is our home, please don't pollute.

Lorena Griffith (age 10)
Topham Elementary School

Christmas Time

Christmas trees are so bright,
They have lots and lots of light.
They are very pretty on Christmas night.
Outside, snow is falling,
Little children are crawling on
the wet, icy ground.
Hot cocoa is ready for all;
Come inside and you will have a ball.

Tara McLellan (age 10)
Mother Mary Greene School

~//~

Christmas Day

I love Christmas Day, it's easy to say
Santa has some deer
Who see their reflection in an icy mirror
The frozen ground is all around
With the singing, it's a lovely sound
You get a Christmas tree with lots of light
It is oh so bright
You receive so many presents and you are
Very pleasant
Oh, I love Christmas Day!

Marissa Muzzo (age 9)
Mother Mary Greene School

~//~

I'm Sorry

I'm sorry I let the bugs in the bed,
I'm sorry for painting all over your head,
I'm sorry I let the dog eat your pants,
I'm sorry for wrecking your dance.

I'm sorry for breaking your Lego,
I'm sorry for eating your Eggo,
I'm sorry for bringing home a rat,
I'm sorry for letting in the ant.

I'm sorry for taking the last can of pop,
I'm sorry for making you mop,
I'm sorry for always destroying,
I'm sorry for being annoying!

Alex Nicol (age 10)
Miller Park Community School

That's Hockey

You get up early to practice your skating
That's when your parents are
at the rink waiting
When you play hockey
the whistle goes 'tweet'
That's when the puck drops
and hockey sticks meet
You shoot at the goalie
the puck might go in
That's when the crowd cheers
your team's gonna *win!*
Hockey is great!

Alexander (Alex) Heidel (age 9)
École St. Thomas School

~//~

I Hear

I hear the helmets bashing
I hear the shoulder pads crashing
I hear the football players falling
I hear the quarterback calling

I hear the ball being thrown
I hear them all groan
I hear the ball get snapped
I hear their hand bones crack

I hear their cleats dig in
I hear their mouth guards slip in
I hear the ref's whistle blow loud
I hear everyone yell from the crowd

I hear them handing off the ball
I hear the linebackers' "Run" call
I hear the players in pain
I hear as they play the game

I hear the coaches call, "Hit him!"
I hear the players go after him
I hear all their pads go bang
I hear the face masks go bang

I hear them all in the huddle
I hear the linemen call fumble
I hear the crowd roar
I hear the football players go off the
field sore

Sheldon Epp (age 11)
Children of St. Martha School

Soccer

I kick the ball really high.
With a great big sigh.
I kick the ball and I miss the net.
I'm not sure if I was ready yet.

Well I hope my cat
Did not eat my rat.
One to two
I lost my shoe.

Levi Wilson (age 8)
École Joe Clark School

~//~

Love

Love goes the extra mile.
Love is strong and not envious.
Love never gives up.
Love comes from the heart.
Love comforts others.
Love is a strong binding between two
people or more.
Love grows forever.
Love is truthful and whole.
Love never ends!

Amber Oosthuyzen (age 10)
Distance Education School of
the Kootenays

~//~

Change

Ever notice how,
When our purses are looked inside,
Only the loonies and twonies
Are the ones that bring us pride?
I always wonder why that is;
Are the others of no price?
Or are we just too good for them,
To add them up precise?
I don't think it's the laziness,
But it is merely greed,
That we find ourselves overlooking them,
Just like the poor in need.

Alexa Porteous (age 11)
St. Joseph School

Untitled

The voice said to go to my friend's
Because of a special thing.
I started to walk to her house,
And in the end
It was a party for me
Because I gave her my pet mouse.
It was a good party, even if we had tea.

Jeannine Bruneau (age 11)
École St. Thomas School

~//~

The Ocean Blue Butterfly

A butterfly is like the sun
shining over the ocean.
It's colours are majestic.
Irridescent shimmering blue
floating against the sky.
The beauty of the butterfly
sticks in my mind.

Mark McNaughton (age 10)
Sunalta School

~//~

War

War
What is it for?
What does it do
For me and you?

Why guns
And not pens?
Why ammo
And not paper?

People die;
They are forgotten.
Only the poppies remember.

War
What is it for?
What does it do
For me and you?

Michael (Mike) Bridden (age 12)
Wix-Brown Elementary School

One Plus One Equals Two

Did you know that one plus one
equals two?
Apparently I was the only one who knew.
So I was walking along,
Click, clong, click, clong
When this little boy came up to me and said
"Excuse me, do you know what one times
six is?"
And I said
"Hey let's use some sticks."
So I put one stick here and seven over there
But no matter how hard I tried, it
equalled seven.
And I said
"Kevin, I don't really know, but if you
want to know
One plus one equals two."

Danea Jodoin (age 12)
John Paul II School

~//~

God is...

God is peaceful
God is wise
Everyone's special
In His eyes

God is patient
God is kind
If you're looking for Him
You will find...

Joy and happiness
Great faith and honesty
Strength and hopefulness
Just look and you will see

He has a perfect plan for everyone
Coated with lots and lots of love
He guides us down the right path
From His palace up above

So thank Him every day
With an extra special prayer
Tell Him that you love Him
And make sure He knows you care

Shinnea Wilson (age 11)
St. Francis School

Little Mouse

Little mouse in my garage
climbing everything
You scurry up the ladders
to see what's on the shelf.
You find my sister's stuffed turtle
and you play with such delight.
Soon it's time for sleep
and I turn out the light.

Christina Ferrar (age 10)
Sunalta School

~//~

Remembrance Day

On November Eleven, Remembrance Day
at the park,
We remember wars that were lost and won.

With the poppies on our chest,
We remember those laid to rest.

We remember those who died at war,
And I wonder what it was for.

Ryan Scheidt (age 8)
Lavington Elementary School

~//~

Wild Fires

Like a ferocious army of flaming warriors
Fire sweeps over the earth
demolishing every little thing
in its path.
The only thing that can douse the blaze
is the powerful rain
Like a battle of the elements,
fire against water.
Finally, the flames are only a
pile of smoldering earth.
Even though the fire has gone.
It still has left its mark
Destruction!

Rhyse Harnden (age 11)
Sherwood Park Elementary School

My Fighting Fish!

My fighting fish hates red
He puffs out his eyes and gills
when he's mad
It's so cute!
He chomps his food piece by piece
He sleeps having a good time!
He seems sad when we leave
but secretly his wonderland starts again
How my fighting fish hates red!

Andrea Dolling (age 10)
Sunalta School

~//~

Stop Polluting

Stop littering now
before it's too late.
Dude, dude, dude I thought you were cool.
But now I see that you litter in the river.
You're killing the animals and other
nature too.
Yah man this is not a joke.
Now stop it dude, you had your fun.
It's time you act cool.
Now they know who they got to stop,
so be cool, stop littering!

Kaila Joynes (age 9)
Topham Elementary School

~//~

Untitled

I am...
Britney Spears, school, and reading.
I like the summer and basketball.
Biking and playing are important to me.
I like exercising and eating.
I hate lying, cheating, and stealing so I
don't do those things.
I love warm, hot chocolate
with marshmallows.
I like making new friends
And I love the monkey bars.
This is me!

Samantha Paulson (age 9)
Brander Gardens Elementary School

Peace

Polluting the
Environment is
An outrage and
Can be
Even deadly

Nicholas Theodorakis (age 9)
Topham Elementary School

~//~

War

Tragic is the beast of war
Short are its breaths
But for an eternity will its heart beat
Fused to hate and death

What is all the devastation for?
Why must so many perish?
This is why we must remember

For those who walk the empty valleys
And the darkest caves
Leaving only a void
For those who remain

John Bigsby (age 12)
Silver Star Elementary School

~//~

Peace

P - I pray for peace at church, at home,
and before I go to bed.
E - I give encouragement to those who
feel they can't do anything right.
A - I appreciate those who are disabled
for they are all children of God.
C - I create peace by caring for others
and spreading compassion.
E - My goal is to extend peace all over
the world
And to teach everyone about the world
of God and the Eucharist.

Pauline Santiago (age 11)
St. Helen Elementary School

Timmy Tommy

Timmy Tommy is a boy
Timmy Tommy has lots of toys
Timmy Tommy has no friends
Because Timmy Tommy always pretends
To stay home sick every day
Just so he can play
Timmy Tommy stays up late
I bet he'll never have a date
Timmy Tommy's kind of a geek
Sometimes people call him a freak
Timmy Tommy has orange hair
He always says everything's unfair
Sometimes I feel sorry for him
He is really, really bad at gym
Timmy Tommy cannot play pool
I think he should move to a different school

Melissa Smeding (age 11)
Parkland Immanuel Christian School

~//~

Which One?

I wish I were a fierce and bulky polar bear.
I would mercilessly crush and demolish
everything, everywhere!
I wish I were an obnoxious, shrilling
penguin bird.
I would be extremely elegant and graceful
under water,
Even though I would look quite absurd!

I wish I were a diminutive and blueish-
grey arctic tern,
For many moves and stunts I would
encounter and learn!
I wish I were a beautiful and white furred
arctic fox.
I would slyly camouflage and hide behind
many dark rocks!

I wish I were a blubbery and bloated whale.
I would dive and spout and blissfully
splash my tail!
But which one to choose I really
don't know.
I guess I'll be a kid, and just play in
the snow.

Graham Black (age 11)
Prairie Elementary School

The Funky Monkey

I went to a jungle
It was a big tungle
It has a little monkey
That is very funky

It goes tree to tree
And thinks he's free
He lands on a flying lion
Ah, nice cushion, thanks Mr. Lion

The lion keeps on flying
He doesn't know that monkey is crying
The lion goes and looks back
And isn't watching, and crashes into
    a packsack

Maylies Lang (age 11)
J.W. Inglis School

~//~

Pegasus

Gentle hoof beats dance slowly on the
    setting sun,
As feathery wings take flight!
Thy sweet Pegasus hath awoken to the
    sister moon.
A glorious neigh fills the night, as he soars
    over moor and bog.
A sea of light is shone from his
    glistening wings,
As his freedom awakens.
Though thunderclouds roll and
    lightning clashes,
They do not compare to thy swiftness.
He soars and tumbles a chorus of
    flight sending
All night prowlers to shred away.
He bathes in moonlight, and drinks the
    sweet nectar of the gods.
But alas, thy restless beast must disappear
Into the mists of dawn as the dew touches
    the earth.
Farewell thy friend, I shall see thee not again,
Nor hear the gentle hoof beats of rain
    that thy brings
To my ears, or the glorious neighing that
    you bring.
Farewell, dear Pegasus, farewell!

Rebecca Gray (age 11)
Patricia Heights School

Penguins Everywhere

I wish I were a bulky and blubbery
    king penguin.
I would swim swiftly and rapidly in the
    frigid waters.
I wish I were a crowned and regal
    royal penguin.
I would flop and quickly waddle to a friend.

I wish I were a white-flipped penguin
    who would rapidly swim
And float in the Arctic Ocean.
I would devour my prey within seconds.
I wish I were an elegant and reluctant
    gentoo penguin.
I would unforgivably give fish their doom.

I wish I were an attractive and excavating
    rockhopper penguin.
I would relentlessly dig and mine for
    treasures joyfully.
I wish there would be penguins everywhere.

Codi Bergen (age 10)
Prairie Elementary School

~//~

Hockey

Skating down the ice
Going to score a goal
My hands sweating in my gloves
Trying to stay in control
I swerve to the left
And then to the right
Beating everyone in sight
Past the defence
In on goal
I'm just about
To score a goal
But what is this?
The net is bare
No goaltender
In his lair
Then I hear it
My teammates call
Come on Terry, face it we lost
We're going to get yelled at
By our boss

Colin Copes (age 12)
St. Michael's University Middle School

77

My Cat

Cats
Playing, sleeping
Walking, running, stalking
I love my cat
Cute

Hailleigh Evans-Metzger (age 7)
Miller Elementary School

~//~

Peace

You want to be far from war
Where the mind is kind
Where you can embrace the grace
    around you
Where in the night your heart is light
With no worries for a fight
Where the skies are blue and the world
    is new
Where the stars all glow and the breeze
    will blow
Where any fight is out of sight
Where the love will be like a dove up above
Where it's nice and calm... very calm

Heather Hwayoun Lee (age 10)
Topham Elementary School

~//~

Air is a Battlefield

High in the sky you may never die.
Stay brave, bold, and courageous till you
    reach the sky.
The people who were strong enough to
    fiercely ride the clouds
To a new world of mystery and conquest.
They hear words in their minds.
These people lost everything they loved,
    dreamed, and wanted.
In the air the pilots only hear the screech
    of battlecry,
The rumble of engines, and the beat of
    the heart in turmoil.

Rory Percival (age 11)
École Sperling School

Winne-the-Pooh

See the chubby little bear
Searching for honey
With only a shirt to wear
Never feeling crummy

So friendly and kind
Never fighting with friends
Always food on his mind
Chubbiness till the end

Cuddly and sweet
Wonderful to hug
Not tidy or neat
Would hever hug a bug

Can you guess who?
Of course, it's Winnie-the-Pooh

Kristine Mae Espino (age 12)
Immaculate Conception School

~//~

Creations of the World

When I go to sleep at night,
I want to see the stars shining
And the moon high in the sky.
I want to feel Jesus' presence and remember:
This creation is his,
He made it,
He wants us to enjoy it.

When I wake up to a brand new day,
I want to look out my window
And see the sun laying on the horizon.
I want to hear Jesus say:
"This creation is for you,
I made it,
I want you to enjoy it."

When I do my daily activities,
I want to see people happy,
But they're not.
Some are cruel, rude, and violent.
Why can't they just enjoy life?
Then I hear Jesus whisper:
"This world is my creation,
I made everything,
Enjoy life, it is made especially for you."

Catherine Kesteven (age 12)
Branton Junior High School

78

Why We Wear a Poppy

Why wear a scarlet poppy on
    Remembrance Day?
To honour all our soldiers who fought
    their hearts away.
To show that we care for them whether
    they're alive or dead
To show that we appreciate everything
    they did.

Why wear a blood red poppy on
    Remembrance Day?
For they're the international symbol
    which stands out just to say
I care, I care, I really do!
I'm giving all my thanks to you.

Why wear a burgundy poppy on
    Remembrance Day?
Because it symbolizes all the blood
    which fled from soldiers each day.
It shows that we feel some of their grief
    and their joyous screams,
To show that they may have died, but
    beat the enemy.

So we wear a poppy for all of the
    reasons above,
We care and really want to show all of
    our grateful love.
To them, the soldiers, I give my
    greatest thanks,
For giving me my freedom, thanks,
    thanks, thanks.

I give my heart, I'd give life,
To get them to see how I feel.
They fought for us; they risked their
    lives for mine and all of my friends.
They may have lost their lives and thought
    that we wouldn't care,
But we do remember you!

I say this one more time and hope you
    get the point,
I thank the soldiers very much for all my
    freedom tonight.

Lest we forget

Devon Jennings (age 11)
École Sperling School

~//~

Spring

Descend to earth, break the spell, heart
    as pure as gold, this spring
Now evil is gone and good is here, so we
    have nothing to fear,
Spring is all around, and thank goodness
    no snow on the ground!

Lisa Hennig (age 9)
St. Vincent School

~//~

Little Man

Little old man,
Little old man,
Where have you been?
I've gone in the forest.
Now, I can't be seen.

Brooklyn Sass (age 6)
Miller Elementary School

~//~

Remembrance Day

Remember the people who were in
    war. Remember
Everyone who lost their beautiful
    children. Remember
Mothers and fathers who lost their lives.
Everyone will never forget what they
    did for their country.
Many people are thankful for what they
    have done.
Bombs exploded everywhere; blood
    showering in the air.
Remember the people who have to go.
Always know that they are our heroes.
Never hurt people in war if necessary.
Children lost dads and moms during battle.
Everyone respects our beautiful country.

Day after day people die.
Always like our proud country.
Years ago we won our battles.

Jordan Stenhouse (age 11)
École Routhier School

Dirt Bikes

Blasting off the jump
Getting excited in the air
Landing with a thud.

Tyler Sawka (age 10)
Naramata Elementary School

~//~

The Balloon

Long ago,
There was a video
That taped a balloon,
That had a bassoon,
And married a harpoon,
And got a lagoon.
Who got caught in a typhoon,
I guess he liked platoon,
Because he turned himself to half platoon.

What a pity:
He could have turned into a kitty,
A very pretty little kitty,
And lived a great life in the city.

Stephanie Jaehee Lee (age 10)
Boundary Community School

~//~

Spirit of the Game

I come in different sizes.
I was born in Canada but other countries
    use me.
I have blades but I do not slash.
People enjoy me but I can be expensive.
I play in cold, indoors or out.
My brother gets shot but doesn't die.
You can watch me on TV but I'm not the
    famous one.
You can look me up on the computer.
There's books and legends of me.
What am I?

Hockey stick

Rab Bruce-Lockhart (age 9)
Discovery Elementary School

When I Was Young

The rain is God's shower
The sun is a pot of gold
Old is young and young is old
And that's what I was told

Mother Nature lives in Heaven
The moon is God's fingernail
If you litter you'll go to jail
That's the story, that's the tale

You can only get married at thirty
You get a cold, it'll never go
You don't brush your teeth,
    green stuff will show
These sayings are still to grow

Though I heard these things
    when I was young
I still believe them
Well, maybe
Just one

Jaclyn Rekis (age 10)
Rose Valley Elementary School

~//~

Flowers

Have you ever observed how flowers
    are greatly like individuals?
Several attractive, some not so,
Some thin, various thick, some vast and
    some tiny.
Flowers are of all tints, identical to you
    and I
Intensifying and glowing until they die.
But don't agonize; it's not the end,
Just like anyone, flowers are reborn
Fortunately for us, it's Heaven, for
    flowers it's from their roots.
So we're rather immortal.
We equally benefit from peace, poetry,
    and solitude.
Flowers sway in a peaceful wind in a
    poetic fashion.
And in the fields, they rest in solitude-
Until something ruptures the silence.
So with compassion and feeling,
You, I, and flowers are very much alike.

Shae Nakano (age 11)
Heffley Creek Elementary School

Untitled

Kangaroo
little, magical
jump, kick, hop
miss, love, special, hoppy
Joey

Shelby Daignault (age 7)
Sparling School

~//~

Recess

Recess is a world of fun.
Recess is depressing when done.
Recess is a world with no worries
Until the bell rings without any thought
    of the children's sorries.
Recess is a time of happiness
Followed by a buzz that brings sadness.

Oh, no! The bell rung!

Haig Basmadjian (age 11)
Calgary French & International School

~//~

Remember Them

As the stars shine bright one cloudy night,
Soldiers fight to bring us the light.
When victory finally came,
All the soldiers left in shame
For breaking the lives
Of those who died.

In Flanders Field where the poppies grow,
Many soldiers lost their lives long ago.
Countless soldiers fought for us,
But none of them ever made a fuss.
They only had one thing on their minds
    and that was victory.
This is why they have gone down is history.

Let's bow our heads and pray,
So there will never be bloodshed,
And we can have freedom every day.

Chris Pataki (age 11)
École Sperling School

Betty Spaghetti

There once was a cowgirl named Betty
She loved to eat spaghetti
She was wearing a pretty white dress
The spaghetti made quite a mess

Gillian Brownlow (age 10)
Boundary Community School

~//~

Tears

Tears of joy
Tears of sadness
It is up to you
Which tears will help you.
Everybody sheds a tear,
Maybe this year or the next
Tears of guilt
Tears of regrets
These tears are yours
So never forget.

Melanie Baumgartner (age 12)
Berry Creek Community School

~//~

Thinking

I'm just sitting here on my bed
While all sorts of thoughts
    run through my head.
What does the future hold for me?
Will I have kids? One? Two? Three?
I think I know what I want to be.
Flashing lights, a big lit stage,
My CD's will be all the rage!
Singing and dancing and autographs,
Everyone will want my photograph.
Big flashing lights,
Award shows, too!
A manager
And a backstage crew!
But I'm not sure.
I really don't know what I'm going to be.
I know!
Why don't I just be me!!

Olivia Laratta (age 11)
Mother Mary Greene School

81

Vampires

Vampires do you like blood?
Vampires do you bathe in mud?
Do you think it feels good,
when vampires wear a hood?

Lynsay Staal (age 9)
J.W. Inglis School

~//~

Just to Remember

To this day we celebrate,
For our brave soldiers who did so great
Courage and believing is what they had,
To help us make this day so glad.
The nurses from Red Cross were
    helpful too,
Helping the soldiers make their way through.
So take a moment, just to remember,
About the Canadian soldiers
Who fought in November...

Faustina Hsien (age 12)
École Sperling School

~//~

Mother's Day

I like Mother's Day
Because I could give my mother a bouquet
Of flowers,
That are an array
Of blue and grey.
Expressing my emotional powers
And my feelings for my mother.

I want to show her I care
By telling her how rare
And precious she is to me,
Especially when I'm in despair
And I think life isn't fair.
She is very special to me,
Unlike any other.

And at the end I'd like to say,
Happy Mother's Day!

Kuljit Singh Sandhu (age 11)
Khalsa School

I Wish I Were a...

I wish I were a joyous and
    jumbly jackrabbit;
I would freely frolic and flee with the
    glistening sun on my back.
I wish I were an elegant and
    eloquent elephant;
I would constantly swish and sway my
    trunk back and forth.

I wish I were a flamboyant and faithful fox;
I would neatly bound and skip my
    way home.
I wish I were a mischievous and
    miniature monkey;
I would playfully swoop and swing
    through the trees.

I wish I were a precious and playful pig;
I would piggishly wallow and sing in the
    slimy mud.
I wish I were a fluffy, little lamb;
I would joyously skip and bleat on the
    soft meadow.

I wish I were a muscular and mild-
    mannered horse;
I would delightfully graze and chomp on
    yummy grass.
I wish I were a cute, cuddly cat;
I would calmly take long catnaps and lay
    in the warm sun.

I wish I were a brave and beautiful dog;
I would courageously protect and guard
    my puppies.
I wish I were a green and purple budgie;
I would softly sing and dance all day long.

I wish I were a blue, baby beluga whale;
I would silently swim and jump through
    the icy waters.
I wish I were a... well that's a different story.

Shehana (Shawni) Woodland (age 9)
Prairie Elementary School

~//~

My Dress

Yesterday I got a dress;
My brother tried it on and made a big mess.
Once he took it off and lost his boot,
And it landed in the laundry shoot.

The boot was so powerful it turned into
an electric shock,
And that was so powerful
it turned into a sock.

And that sock that once was a boot
That fell down the laundry shoot,
Is now very cute!

Sara Stagg (age 9)
École Joe Clark School

~//~

I Love Sea Creatures

I wish I were a frisky and sturdy dolphin;
I would leap and soar grandly out of the
shimmering water to perform my tricks.
I wish I were a slippery and slimy octopus;
I would swim and explore the ocean floor
And see all the fish that might want lunch.

I wish I were a slow and wise turtle;
I would slowly and carefully swim around
the vast waters in the ocean.
I wish I were an enormous and
interesting whale;
I would glide quickly and silently through
the wonderful waters in the
warm regions.

I wish I were a daring and
mysterious crocodile;
I would patrol my territory and dangerously
slice through the dark and murky waters.
I wish I were a busy and pinchy crab;
I would quickly and slyly play hide and
seek with my enemies.

I wish I were a sticky and bumpy sea star;
I would relax and watch all the fishes and
sea creatures swim above me.
I wish I were a sea creature.

Tana Vermaak (age 10)
Prairie Elementary School

Untitled

Peace is hearing the birds sing
Peace is sitting down with a good book
Peace is looking at clouds in the sky
Peace is helping friends with homework
Peace is keeping our environment clean

Brett Boivin (age 10)
Topham Elementary School

~//~

We Remember

We remember the soldiers,
We remember the fire,
We remember the tanks, and
The cruel barbed wire.

We remember the guns,
We remember physicians,
We remember the wars, and
The ammunition.

Julie Poulsen (age 11)
Langley Fundamental Elementary School

~//~

Angels Up High

Angels up high
Soaring the sky,
Looking for souls
Wondering why -
No bad souls below
Just good.

I sit and watch
While children play
On a summer's day,
Thinking of angels up high
Soaring the sky.

Waiting for me to join
Them some day,
And we will soar the sky
Looking for bad souls
Wondering why...

Chalene Malekoff (age 11)
Aspen Grove School

The Goat of Ramada

Silly little goat
up in a tall cedar tree
running from a bear.

Kody Marks (age 9)
Distance Education School of
the Kootenays

~//~

In Beautiful Flanders Field

Long ago with war in the air
We stood with mighty shields
But lives were lost, and now we lie
In beautiful Flanders Field

Crosses mark our places
Poppies mark the rows
And here in beautiful Flanders Field
We lie where poppies grow

Our souls are now at rest
The larks' voices fill the sky
Our land is now of peace and glory
In Flanders Field we lie

Lindsay Epp (age 10)
Silver Star Elementary School

~//~

War Time

We march two by two to the enemy's camp.
We shuffle among the battle ditches
To find a safe and comfortable position.
Guns start to crackle.
People dodge place to place avoiding the
    high-speed bullets.
Lifeless bodies with bloody wounds fall
    to the mud-soaked ground.
Surrender is called.
Famished hawks and ravens circle
    the graves.
The crosses stand weak yet tall.
Poppies delicately float among the land.
War is over.

Anthony Hicks (age 11)
Hillcrest Community School

Flowers

The sweet sensational smell...
It can only mean one thing: it's spring!
Flowers pop up like popcorn, with
    different colours of the rainbow.
Violet, pink, and purpley-blue.
Colours of love, of joy, in every petal.
Red, orange, yellow, green.
Pretty colours you must have seen.
Tulips, daisies, buttercups.
You must know what I mean!
Petals growing look like they're growing
    in the still wind.
Flowers have powers to inspire!

Ella Laure Hipolito (age 10)
St. Paul's Elementary School

~//~

Spooky

The monster was there.
He wanted some cheese.
Then I looked back:
Huge hairy beast.

I had a dog.
He wanted a kiss.
When my cat heard about it
He gave a hiss.

I went to sleep.
I had a good dream.
All of a sudden
I heard someone scream.

One, two, three, four, five, six.
Oh, I forget seven.
I tripped and fell.
Just then I went to Heaven.

Ghosts, goblins, and gulls
Have come to to my party,
And some of them
Like Smarties.

I have lots of food.
I called it a feast.
I heard something so I turned around,
And saw a gigantic beast.

Tina Jones (age 9)
Lavington Elementary School

Fish For Supper

Stinky, smelly, soggy fish,
for supper that night I did not get my wish.
As I look down at my plate,
I pondered the severity of my fate.

Should I feed it to my dog Pete
or pick up my fork and begin to eat?
Upon my face grew a frown,
because I knew I would never keep it down!

Dylan Ford (age 11)
Calgary French & International School

~//~

Golden Gates of Glory

He loves you and everyone.
At night He runs his coarse fingers
    through your hair.
He's the night's moon and the morning sun.
He'll always be there.

He watches over you.
He whisks your problems away.
He watches over everything else, too.
He tries to successfully complete your day.

Although you cannot feel it, He clutches
    your hand tight.
He owns a huge lot.
He hears your prayers at night.

Maybe someday you will meet Him.
Maybe some will not...
He tries not to keep the lights so dim,
He even tries to make sure you're not a
    snobby snot.

But when you do go and meet Him,
He will meet you at the Golden Gates
    of Glory.
And will hand you a goblet of happiness
    filled to the brim.
He will then tell, you're in Heaven's story.

You have to stay forever...
For now you're one of Heaven's angels...
You have to stay forever...

Hillary J. Duke (age 12)
Neill Middle School

Autumn

Sunsets come and go
Lovely flowers fill gardens
Tumbling in leaves

Brandon Maglio (age 9)
St. Joseph School

~//~

Rain

Rain I think of you
That your raindrops look like crystals
And stars in the sky.
With anger you thunder
Down to the ground,
And you frighten children
With your strength.
With joy you fall gently to the world,
And wash us all very clean and healthy.
Rain, that's how I think of you.

Allegra Scrugham (age 10)
Miller Park Community School

~//~

Untitled

I went to go and mop.
There I saw a cop.
He said I wasn't doing it right.
And that I have to use a light.

I said, "Fine!"
And then I braided twine.
The cop said it had to be green.
And then I ate a bean.

The bean was yummy.
It went right to my tummy.
I went to get a clover.
And then a friend came over.

Then I had lots of luck.
And we had roast duck.
I went to go and bend.
And I'm sorry to say this is the end.

Veronica Montgomery (age 11)
William Grayson School

Snow Is So Wonderful!

Snow, a wonderful thing
The most wonderful thing in the world.

Its softness is softer than
A pillow, softer than a feather.
The most wonderful thing in the world.

If only snow wouldn't melt,
If it could always stay
All year round
The world would be the best.
My life would be perfect!
The most wonderful thing in the world.

And you can always make angels
And snowmen
If there was no snow
The world would be dreadful!

So remember snow is a wonderful thing
The most wonderful thing in the world!

Erin Medforth (age 9)
Ashley Park School

~//~

Remembrance Day

We remember this wonderful day
When their mothers and fathers
bow their heads and pray

Some soldiers march with gun in hand
With others fly over the land
They all tried their very best
When others forever lay to rest.

So today we are praying happily
And others are crying sorrowfully.
Today we have a field of red and green;
To me it's a beautiful scene.

From this day it's been lots of years past
And we remember that
Some men and women did not last.
The Germans took over the land
But we are thankful that God has our
lives in His hands.

Leanne VanderVeen (age 10)
Parkland Immanuel Christian School

Snow Angel

Snow angel, snow angel
How I wonder how comfy you are?
Lying in the snow over there.
Who made you I wonder
Was it me?
Snow angel, snow angel
How did you get so beautiful?
With your astonishing gown
And your oh-so pretty wings.
Snow angel, snow angel
Whoever would wreck you?
Not me and that's for sure!

Ashley Sauder (age 9)
Ashley Park School

~//~

Remember Us

Remember us
We came out of our nation
We headed for their station
We lent a helping hand
We supported those who lost their land
We met our foes with open arms
We fought them over rivers and farms
We blew the blows that matter most
We never would desert our post
We didn't run when we were scared
We held our ground because we cared
We gave our lives and fought for peace
We thought the war would never cease
We lived our life on fields of death
We often felt we'd breathed our last breath
We kept on going, on we ploughed
We walked underneath the cannons, so
    very loud
We heard our wives and daughters weep
We waded through mud that was knee-deep
We played our cards and won the hand
We beat the foe back to their land
We turned our thoughts and minds to home
We never thought again to roam
We've enforced the peace till now and
    always will
We remember everyone who was lost
We remember the war and what it cost
Remember us

Meghan Ross (age 12)
Silver Star Elementary School

Untitled

Gold rush fever stuck us, the prospectors
On we went to the Cariboo to start our
    hunt for gold
Long hard journeys took up our days
    until we got to the Cariboo
Death caused by the shimmering thing
    called gold - fur filled the air

Rocker boxes surrounded the river sides
    and streams
Us prospectors got more amounts of gold
    from the rocker boxes than in the
    gold pan
Sluice boxes took over the rocker box
    and gold pan in no time flat -
Finally I got my share of gold
Home sweet home, it's good to be back.

Adam Schwann (age 10)
Beaver Lake School

~//~

We Ask For Forgiveness

Now we lay in Flanders Field,
Without a sword or a shield.
But we have our weapons and our strength,
So we pray to the Lord for some health,
And for all we had killed.

The Lord had answered and said:
"No more war or you shall be punished
For you have done wrong
    and shall be finished."
So we go home,
With proudness, and sorrow.

We donate all we have,
Until there's nothing left.
And say to the Lord:
"We have learned there is no meaning,
So our sins we will be cleaning."

So we enter
Your world of peace.
Forever we will live side by side,
Knowing we will be right this time.
And we say once more:
"War, it has no meaning."

Anna Monica Koualczuk-Siy (age 11)
St. Helen Elementary School

Black Cats

Does a black cat like to hide in a hat?
Would a black cat rather be fat?
Do black cats like to sit on bats?
Would black cats rather sit on rats?

Boyd LeWarne (age 8)
J.W. Inglis School

~//~

Skyscraper

I stand so high
Way up in the sky
As tall as I can
With my head up high
But when I look down
I put on a frown
I wish I was never up here
Oh no I don't
I really don't like this
Not one bit
My only advice to give is
Don't look down!

Taylor Phillips (age 11)
Boundary Community School

~//~

Dinosaurs

Dinosaur, dinosaur
What do you see?
I see a bee.
Dinosaur, dinosaur
What do you feel?
I feel mud under my legs.
Dinosaur, dinosaur
What do you smell?
I smell a fish.
Dinosaur, dinosaur
What do you taste?
I taste leaves.
Dinosaur, dinosaur
What do you hear?
I hear water.

Mustafa Shakoor Jamal (age 7)
Edmonton Islamic School

The Injured Insects

The itsy bitsy spider lay near
the water-hose
Then came the ant and broke the
spider's nose
Up rose the spider and ate the ant's toes
And that is the story that everybody knows

Essie Zahoui (age 11)
Edmonton Islamic School

~//~

Summer

Two people in the forest picking blueberries.
A bear comes along.
Just sitting there on a pile of leaves.
Not too happy because the girl was picking
his nose!!
The beautiful trees and berry bushes gleam
With the warm summer light.
Disturbed by screams and running people!!

Tanielle Reardon (age 10)
J.W. Inglis School

~//~

We Remember

On November eleventh at eleven o'clock
We will stop what we're doing; we will
not talk.
We will bow our heads and we will pray.
For on this day is Remembrance Day.

We remember those who gave their lives.
They fought for freedom; they left
their wives.
They may have had a daughter or maybe
a son.
And their kids will remember what their
parents had done.

They must have had courage.
They must have been brave.
For the love of their country
That those soldiers gave.

Brooke Palahicky (age 11)
Veritas School

Mitchell

I play outside
With everything
Every day,
Then I go inside
And play
With everything
Every day.
I like to play.

Mitchell Dales (age 6)
Miller Elementary School

~//~

Sleeping Beauty

To a king was born
Seven fairies on the way
She was born in the early morn

Her name was Beauty
She is so cute
Always on duty

Seven fairy grandmothers sitting at the table
Along came the eighth one
Angry she was

The angry witch said she will cast a spell
The fairy grandmothers secretly hid
the spell
They hid her until her sixteenth birthday

She toured the tower
When she got to the top
Into the big room she went

There she saw a woman spinning
"May I try?"
Beauty did ask

Sharply she pricked her finger and fell
fast asleep
She slept for one hundred years
Then a prince came

He kissed her and she awoke
Soon they married
And lived happily ever after

Clarissa Elizabeth Hofer (age 8)
Spring Creek School

Just Imagine

Close your eyes and listen to the sound;
It's rising above from beneath the ground.
It's imagination, beating and drumming,
Singing, ringing, and continuously humming.
Think of a world with darkness or fear,
Just imagine and you will be here.
Where you are in charge and you rule all,
Where you'll feel stong and no longer small.
Wish upon a shooting star, falling from
the sky;
You'll end up in a wonderful place, where
you can even fly.
In a land where everyone is jumping
with glee,
Your imagination is the place to be.

So just imagine!

Kirsten Meadus (age 11)
École St. Thomas School

~//~

Without

A wallet without money,
A clown that's not funny,
A book without words,
Feathers without birds.

A cactus without spikes,
Bikers without bikes,
A monkey without a tail,
A storm without hail.

A cow without a moo,
Counting without two,
A lawyer without a suit,
A hiker without boots.

A lion without a mane,
A board without a game,
A couch without a seat,
A heart without a beat.

A nose without a sneeze,
A hive without bees,
A mountain without trees,
Winter without freeze.

Adryn Galambos (age 11)
Children of St. Martha School

I Hope They Like Me

I'm locked in a room,
Where everyone's born in Canada,
But I was born in Korea...
I hope they like me.

I'm locked in a room,
Where everyone has blonde hair,
But I have black hair...
I hope they still like me.

I'm locked in a room,
Where everyone speaks English,
But I speak Korean...
I hope they still like me.

I finally got out of the room;
I hope they like me.

Karol Yoo (age 12)
Wix-Brown Elementary School

~//~

Outcast

Those people who watch as time goes by,
Those creatures who see midnight pass,
Those lone stars in the dark sky,
Outcasts.

An unpopular person,
An unimportant detail,
A pitiful tiny insect,
Outcasts.

Some are proud, but alone,
Some are hidden, but alone,
You cannot avoid the lifelessness,
But can only know the inner self
counts most.

You may feel sorry,
You may feel pity,
You might even feel both,
Or you might feel thankful.

How can I prove all this?
How do I know about these outcasts?
As you might have guessed,
I am one of them.

Joey P. Laguio (age 10)
St. Paul's Elementary School

Untitled

Fairies
Magical wands
Helping, flying, granting
Fairy dust used to put to sleep
Magic

Linnea Ulrich (age 11)
Pense School

~//~

When You Don't Eat Your Veggies

When you don't eat your veggies,
Something horrible will happen.
The goblins and ghouls will come,
And give you your whappin'.
They'll give you your whappin',
As well as some wedgies,
And all this will happen,
When you don't eat your veggies.

Dennis McNair (age 11)
Calgary French & International School

~//~

Remembrance Day

Remember all the great soldiers
Everywhere who fought for our freedom.
Mothers and fathers losing their children
Everyday in the terrible war.
Many fearful pilots flying high and low
Bringing peace to our enormous country.
Running around the immense fields killing.
All of them trying to finish the
    dreadful war.
Nobody came back without injuries.
Canadians, Americans, Australians, the
    French, and
Even the English went to the horrible war.

Doing wonderful things for
All the people in the world,
Young soldiers sacrified their lives.

Patrick Gaudet (age 11)
École Routhier School

Thanksgiving

I like fall.
I go to the mall
I ate pie in the sky.
The fairy
ate my berry.
I needed to do laundry
instead of my family.
I like Thanksiving.
I am giving.
Keith is only four;
he ate a junky core.
There's a word "lame";
it has a funny name.

Mikaela Kemper (age 8)
Lavington Elementary School

~//~

Useless Things

Paper without words
Wings without birds
Babies without toys
Girls without boys

Roof without walls
A cold without 'Halls'
Bandage without blood
Rain without mud

A magician without tricks
Fire without sticks
A ball without air
A fish without a bear

Water without boats
Mountains without goats
A dog without a vet
A kid without a pet

Tractors without farms
Cows without barns
Friends without phones
People without bones

A hammer without a nail
Mailman without mail
Houses without doors
Bedrooms without floors

Nathan Carlson (age 11)
Children of St. Martha School

When I Lay in the Field

I dream about something far away
In the grassy field, there I lay
I feel the soft grass brushing my face
In my heart, I know that this is a
secret place
I can hear the winds calling my name
There is a voice inside me deep within
The sound of a fire will crackle and snap
It makes me feel warm and like I'm in
my father's lap
I look beyond the very green hillside
Where it makes me feel all fuzzy inside
Beyond the mountains and
Under the sun
Where I lay is calm and fun!

Megan Gee (age 11)
Master's Academy

~//~

If I Lived in the Past, Present, and Future

If I lived since the beginning of time,
Then I could see God the All Mighty
Create the world in six days.
On the seventh day I would
Sleep in the grass
And swim in the ocean,
With the little, long, and big fish.
Then I would have lived in the past.
If I lived in the present,
I would see people running in terror,
Their lives decreasing,
Never seeing life again.
I couldn't sleep in the grass,
Or swim in the ocean with the dolphins,
God wanting to stop sins.
Then I would have lived in the present.
If I lived since the end of time,
Then I could see fairy tales come to life,
The war, the end of man.
To live in the future would be like a sin.
Then I would wish to be in the past,
To swim with the fish and the dolphins,
To breathe clean, fresh air,
Not polluted and deadly,
*Only then will I have lived in the past,
present, and future.*

Victoria Webb (age 10)
Patricia Heights School

I Like That Stuff

Kids lay in it
People play in it
Snow
I like that stuff

I need them
Most people read them
Books
I like that stuff

Everyone dies from it
Animals lie in it
Time
I like that stuff

Dentists hate it
Kids can't wait for it
Halloween
I like that stuff

Jonathan Vos (age 11)
Children of St. Martha School

~//~

A Pirate Tale

I see a pirate ship setting out to sea,
In front of a sunset beautiful as can be.
As I looked closer, could it be?
I was looking straight at a pirate,
And he was looking back at me.
It looked like he had a claw for a hand,
Stepping out on some yellow sand.
My eyes much be deceiving me,
He's stepping on one of three islands
that were never there before!
But I thought pirates aren't real;
Looking at one now, that's a great deal.
People say that pirates are fantasy,
Also that one imaginary island of three.
I walked down to the shore,
When my sight just got very poor!
The pirate drifted away,
But before he did,
With a wave of his hand, he waved goodbye,
Then grew wings, and started to fly.
I said goodbye, and goodbye he did.
I never saw him again,
Nor the pirate ship.

Robert De Luca (age 9)
Meadowridge School

Untitled

Fairies are small
A fairy can fly
I wonder what it is like in Fairy Land
Really small as they fly away
Inspired fairies that can help people
Enchanted fairies can be good
Sparkly little fairies fly to Never
Never Land

Kyla McMartin (age 10)
Pense School

~//~

Sssnake

When sssnakes slither acrossss
They hisss snakey tunessss
Hiss, hiss I will not missss
When I am hunting
I am concentrating
I'm assss fasssst assss you can run
I'm sssssneaky
I'm sssso cool
Now it's the end ssso
Good bye!

Hisssss

David St. Gelais (age 9)
St. Wilfrid School

~//~

Wild

Have you been in the wild
With all the trees and plants
Have you been in the wild
Where deer only prance
Have you been in the wild
With the growling grizzly bear
Have you been in the wild
With a cute little hare
I have been in the wild
With only the star's twinkling light
I have been in the wild
What a beautiful sight.

Nicholas Bigiolli (age 10)
Miller Park Community School

It Wasn't Like This Yesterday

In the fall the pumpkins grow, oh they
do row by row.
The time is ticking, keep the flow.
Watch out for the winter breeze. Uh oh,
here comes the snow!
When I am wrapped in a blanket I feel
very snug,
Especially when I get a hot chocolate
filled mug.
Now bundle up, it's getting cold. Mom's
fall rules are still very bold.
Snow is coming down with the fun,
So spend your time wisely. Fall is
almost done.
Now I can see that fall isn't what it's
cracked up to be,
But what this fall has in store,
I'm not sure I know anymore.

Tyrel Stokes (age 10)
Brett Sorestad (age 10)
John Paul II School

~//~

Halloween

Halloween is my favourite time,
'Cause I always have the Halloween chime.
When Halloween costumes are around,
You get in with the spooky sound,
And I especially love
When the fireworks rain from above.
The twinkling stars in the sky,
When I look up it makes me sigh.
The moon's reflection across the water,
In my heart it makes me softer.
The wind so chilly,
As it blows through the trees,
It's more like a Dracula's breeze.
Halloween pumpkins with evil faces,
It's one of the many Halloween cases.
A werewolf's howl across the night
Sends many of us hiding from the sight.
A mummy's mourn through the streets
Makes lots of us jump our seats.
Frankenstein's deadly tauntings
Makes it feel just like hauntings.
Monsters wail from the distance.
Halloween is my favourite time,
'Cause I always have the Halloween chime.

Elanna Eagle (age 10)
Grief Point Elementary School

The Beauty

The beauty once told me that you plant
    bulbs in the spring.
Her voice is as soft as a chiming bell's ring.
The beauty then told me the day after that,
To come for tea and have a serious chat.
I came the next day and walked into her lair,
Saying "If only, if only she wouldn't despair
Over the life that has been taken from
    her family so shared."
The beauty and I talked for a while
And then finally she started to smile!
The smile that then had come onto her face
Was filled with no mourning, but style
    and grace!
The style and grace that has come
    once before,
But then the accident and it became no more.
The beauty I will love all through my life
Just had to end all her pain with that knife.

Chelsea Bomford (age 12)
George Bonner Middle School

~//~

Sports

I wish I were the amazing and awesome
    Paul Kariya;
I would rapidly score and check the
    other team.
I wish I were the two-time winning MVP
    Kurt Warner;
I would pass and perform beautifully on
    the field.

I wish I were the great home run hitter
    Sammy Sosa;
I would hit and smack those balls for
    mostly the whole day.
I wish I were the superb slam-dunking
    Michael Jordan;
I would awesomely dribble and dunk to
    win the game.

I wish I were the high-flying, back-flipping
    Shaun White;
I would fly and soar amazing and
    land perfectly.
I love sports!

Levi Flokstra (age 10)
Prairie Elementary School

Great Big Whale

The great big whale
Has a great big tail.
He likes his tail
Because his tail likes him.

Enya Revoy (age 6)
Miller Elementary School

~//~

Spring-Time

In spring the birds come back to mate,
And there are many worms for fishing bait.
The daffodils glow like evening stars,
But the magic isn't spoiled by passing cars.
Calves are born in fields full of clover,
Their mothers' tongues licking them over,
    and over.
Flowers awaken from their long
    winter's sleep,
While farmers shave the wool from
    their sheep.
Butterflies fly 'round, and 'round,
And fresh grass sprouts from the rain-
    soaked ground.

Anita Shen (age 10)
Aubrey Elementary School

~//~

My Trip to Rome

Once I went to Rome
I wish I was back home
I was walking and met a snake
He said he already ate
I was relieved to hear such
But I didn't want to see much
For he had some of his lunch
That he did not get to munch
He carried with him a rat
He said he lived in a hat
I ran back to my dad
He said I was very bad
I said I want to go home
He said now we live in Rome

Amy Wagner (age 11)
J.W. Inglis School

Untitled

Hockey
centre ice
skating checking fast
good happy special tired
Toronto

Trent Kowal (age 7)
Sparling School

~//~

Hockey Night

It's hockey night tonight!
The flash of the red light,
The crowd goes wild.
Sticks chatter,
People cheer
At the sound of the puck in the air.
Swoosh
Against the hard cold net.

Matty Hagman (age 10)
Ashley Park School

~//~

Bitter Beauty

Throughout the golden, glistening field,
Jack Frost sprinkles and scatters mounds
     of silver frost.
Off toward the unsuspecting and
     innocent town,
There the clever, talented painter
     will remain.

Up and about varnishing the clear, clean
     windows with some colour,
In the morning it will be a thrill to children.

Instead of pausing to look at his frosty,
     white masterpiece,
Jack Frost must flee and start to think
     where he might proceed
To next make the land a winter.

Jack Frost is the king of bitter beauty.

Christina Harper (age 10)
Prairie Elementary School

My Dog

One day I bought a dog
He likes to play in fog
He once was crazy and chased a cat
But that ugly old cat really got him back

He eats a lot
From a pot
He used to bark and growl
And now all he does is howl

One day he really bit me
And it felt like someone hit me
But that's not all
He made a fall

One day he sat
And that was that
And once he wrecked my toy
That time he was a bad boy

That's the end of the story today
I hope I get one more good day

Josée Fortin (age 8)
École Joe Clark School

~//~

The Mad Monkey

There's a mad monkey in my house
He even took my little pet mouse
He ran onto the street
And found some rotten meat
He jumped over an old man
Who had mistaken him for a tin can
He jumped on a purple van
Then the can moved and went *kablam!*
He ran to the grocery store
And some French people said, "Alore!"
He stole some bananas and went away
Then the store man yelled, "You'll pay!'
He ran up a tree
And was stung by a bee
He caught sight of me
And started to flee
I caught him by the tail
And he started to flail
We sent him to jail
And he started to wail

Cameron McDonald (age 10)
Mother Mary Greene School

Halloween

It's Halloween night, what a scary sight.
It's thundering and lightning
Ghosts and goblins, black cats too
Jaws are open ready to chew
Here comes the witch, stirring her brew
There are lots of things to do
Lots of candy, scares galore!!!
Then I get my candy onto the floor
My mouth is ready wanting more
What a delicious sight
What do you do for Halloween night?

Chayse Dell (age 9)
Juniper Ridge Elementary School

~//~

Awakening

Lightning strikes, dawn breaks,
Wars are made for lives to take.
The pain by war loved ones feel inside,
Is something that they must abide by.

Why must the flag carried so proud,
With a brave voice yet not expectantly loud,
Hoisted every battle swung to and fro,
Fall to the moistened grounds below?

Death is the answer as well as the clue,
What does death mean to all of you?
Is it a laugh, a joke, a housewife's old tale?
Or is it a word that sounds more like a wail?

A scream screamed by someone who cared,
Or a yell yelled by someone who dared,
To release it all in one liberating breath,
To fade all away, including a death.

After a war, we all must unite,
And counter-attack the results of a fight.
Waiting for time to plug off the sting,
Since time the great healer can heal anything.

To accelerate the healing
we must all come together.
We must smooth out that
which was never weathered.
We much reach into our feelings deep,
And wake that which was never asleep.

Andy Chau (age 11)
École Sperling School

Peace

Peace is watching the water pass in a
quiet place alone.
Peace is reading a book by the fireplace
while it is raining outside.

Peace is helping a friend with his or
her homework.
Peace is helping others celebrate life.

Peace is not leaving garbage in the ocean.

Courtney Markin (age 9)
Topham Elementary School

~//~

Untitled

Dinosaur, dinosaur what do you see?
I see a bee looking at me.
Dinosaur, dinosaur what do you see?
I see a stegosaurus looking at me.
Dinosaur, dinosaur what do you see?
I see a flea looking at me.
Dinosaur, dinosaur what do you see?
I see a T-Rex looking at me.
Dinosaur, dinosaur what do you see?
I see a dinosaur looking at me.

Taariq Kudoos (age 7)
Edmonton Islamic School

~//~

The Plant

The plant grew up high. So high it grew.
It touched the clouds. It reached the sky.
It grew up tall. It would not fall.
I thought to myself, "I will climb it,
I shall, I shall."
Too bad for me I fell, I fell.
I was mad at that plant. That stupid thing.
I was glad to cut it down, I think.
It crushed my house, it smashed my car.
Now I live outside by a bar
And that's the story of the plant.
"How I hate that stupid thing," I chant,
I chant.

Samantha Glaves (age 10)
R.L. Angus Elementary School

Skateboarding and Killing Animals

Sliding rails and taking bails
Snapping boards and buying boards
Grinding boxes and killing foxes
Riding vert and getting hurt
Entering comps then getting stomped
Dropping stairs and killing bears
Going to Copperside and Taylor falls
  when he rides

Jacob Lambert (age 12)
Veritas School

~//~

Dinosaur

Dinosaur, dinosaur what do you see?
I see you looking at me.
Dinosaur, dinosaur what do you hear?
I hear you talking to me.
Dinosaur, dinosaur what do you smell?
I smell your shoe.
Dinosaur, dinosaur what do you taste?
I taste leaves from your tree.
Dinosaur, dinosaur what do you feel?
I feel your hand.

Zakiya Kudoos (age 8)
Edmonton Islamic School

~//~

Cougar

Thrashing the poor deer
Shrieking through the woods
Plummeting through the air

Cracked the tree branch
Smacked the hawk
Napped in the grass

Swatting at the bee
Raging at the bear
Crawling to his victim

Pounced at the fox
Snapped his leg
Cornered by hunters

Taylor Sander (age 9)
Enchant School

Sky

Fog
Thick, white
Creeping, wrapping, disguising
Whispering through the darkness
Calming, inviting, frolicking
Joyful, bright
Light

Antoine Boyer (age 11)
Calgary French & International School

~//~

Peace

Peace is the calm after the storm.
Peace is the sound of new babies born.
Peace is something we're all looking for.
Peace can only come by ending wars.
An open mind, an open heart opens many
  doors to peace.

Chelsea Nielsen (age 11)
Langley Fundamental Elementary School

~//~

Dogs

Jumping onto a bursting cat
Barking at a badger
Running after his prey
Sneaking toward a deer
Sleeping in the sunshine
Having fun in the river bank
Killing mice
Drinking water
Eating dog food
Digging a hole
Chasing after a squirrel
Leaping onto a hollow log
Playing with another dog
Taking a nap
Putting a bone in a hole
Coming after me
Finishing his supper
Fetching a ball
Getting playful

Peter Ketler (age 9)
Enchant School

Spring Days

Warm sunny spring days
flowers blooming all around
big busy bees buzzing

Annette Harvey (age 11)
Calgary French & International School

~//~

Cats

I really love my pet,
A cat whom you've never met.
I'll tell you about her.
Sit still, do not stir.
She catches mice.
She's done it twice.
She has whiskers long.
She likes to hop along.
She likes yarns and strings.
She likes to do all these things.

Helena Friesen (age 9)
Enchant School

~//~

From Life to Death

When you wake up in the morning
Do you ever wonder
What happens when you're six feet under
Down way down
Underground almost forever
Never to see another glimpse of light
Having a concrete stone right there
   above you
Do you ever wonder what life is before
   it's life
Or what death is after it's death
Taking the breath of life away
Only to feel the cold wet ground
No sight no sound
There will be nothing around except for
   the squirmy worms
No more life, no more hugs or kisses
Just cold squirmy bugs and small creatures
That's it; there is no more...

Shane O'Connor (age 11)
St. Patrick Catholic School

Summer

cool bubbling creek
games and sports
birds sing
picking strawberries, raspberries, cherries
happy, fun

Stefanie Mindek (age 10)
Distance Education School of
the Kootenays

~//~

Baseball

Balls sailing in the air.
All three bases full.
Strike one!
Everyone yelling.
Batter up!
A foul ball.
Last try.
Looks like a home run to me!

Kyle Unruh (age 8)
Enchant School

~//~

Remembrance Day

Remember the strong soldiers who fought
Every chance by losing their lives for
Members of our country and freedom.
Even those who died while suffering against
Mighty gun shots and losing friends
   and family.
But that's why today we live in freedom.
Remembrance Day is to thank those
   who fought
Angrily to give us freedom and justice.
Nobody can feel the pain that the
Caring families have to go through.
Even the thought of the pain hurts us.

Day after day someone dies in the war.
Although we think about them on
   Remembrance Day,
Yet we couldn't thank them enough.

Krystin Aubin (age 11)
École Routhier School

Knight

Kills people
Needs a helmet on his head
Is riding on a horse
Gives protection to the peasants
Has a lance for jousting
They can fight in battle
Squire until dubbed

Henry Peters (age 8)
Enchant School

~//~

Homework

My dog chewed my homework.
He kicked it with a zoom,
Across the floor and into my bedroom.
Homework is yucky; it looks like black.
I never want homework in my backpack.
I bet my teachers don't agree.
Instead, they will load me up with more.
I wonder. If I give my teacher a nice
  red apple,
Would she not give me any homework?
P.S. that is what you call a bribe.

Samantha Skidmore (age 8)
Enchant School

~//~

Bully

Bully is an awful word
That we have all heard
Some bullies punch
Some steal your lunch

A bully's just a coward inside
Who will push you off a giant slide
But if you just walk away
The bully won't hurt you today

So if a bully's picking on you
You should know what to do
Even if you forget
Someday that bully will be full of regret

Sarah Blackwood (age 10)
Aurora Elementary School

Friendship

Mountains that point high in the sky and
  echo through the valley saying
Friendship, a special gift that should be
  treasured for always.

The valley's golden grass sways in the
  breeze of the wind saying
Friendship, a golden ship that sails forever.

The waterfall whispers a gentle melody
  that softly says a friendship
Like a secret people between two people
  who are the best of friends.

Charlotte Molloy (age 10)
Jean Vanier Catholic School

~//~

Useless Things

A bank without money
A clown without funny
A book without words
A nest without birds

A guy without a girl
A snail without a swirl
People without Earth
A sea without a turf

A skateboarder without feet
A band without beat
Police without robbers
Bingo without daubers

A forest without trees
A lock without keys
A ping without a pong
A singer without a song

A puzzle without pieces
An agent without leases
A girl without hair
A hunter without a bear

A rink without ice
A game without dice
A hat without a head
A pillow without a bed

Katey Schmidt (age 10)
Children of St. Martha School

Homework

Homework is due.
I think I have the flu.
Homework stew.
Homework goo.

Homework is dumb.
It gives me a red thumb.
Homework stew.
Homework goo.

Homework from school
I'd rather battle in a duel.
Homework stew.
Homework goo.

Homework is drool.
I think it's not cool!
Homework stew.
Homework goo.

Curtis Dorchak (age 8)
Enchant School

~//~

My Favourite Team

My favourite team has a theme
Because if I missed a game I would have
a dream
In my dream I would scream
'Cause I missed a game and my name
Would be in the nightmare hall of fame in
the rain.
Then I went insane.
My favourite team has a great aim at
the game
And all the other teams are lame.
My favourite team is the Calgary Flames.
Sometimes they are lame 'cause they
wear a horse's mane.
Then they go insane on the train.
Then one named Gus went on a bus.
Then Gus gets undressed.
Everything's a mess
On the bus that is heading west.
All the people freaked
In their sleep.
The boss fired Gus
Then hired a new person; he was worse.

Joey Scrimshaw (age 8)
École Joe Clark School

Loneliness

Loneliess is blue like the still silent sky.
It flows through my head like a dry river.
It makes me feel like the flower in the middle
Of the field with only dirt around it.
It makes me want to disappear
And never feel like this again.

Maria Sokolov (age 10)
Sunalta School

~//~

Horses

Whining at the other horses
Trotting in the field
Galloping into a pen
Neighing at the people
Feeling frisky in the cold air
Eating the hay
Jumping over a fence
Kicking the gate

Brianne Reynolds (age 8)
Enchant School

~//~

The Rose

A single red rose lays dead and limp
under the small child's lifeless hand
Its beauty fading fast yet its significance
calmly setting into the girl's still heart

She bears no smile, her eyes gently closed
hair laid around her like a precious gift
No angels come offering her soul a home
instead tears of loved ones fall upon
her cheek

Running down to give the rose one
last breath
The tears cried to keep her
memory flowering
She is dead. Still is her heart and soul
as she continues to forever sleep

Selina Boan (age 12)
George Bonner Middle School

The Horse

Trotting through the meadow,
Jumping in the tall, green grass,
Flying dust in the air,
Galloping as fast as he can,
Trying to win the race.

Sarah Skidmore (age 9)
Enchant School

~//~

Swimming

Playing in the water,
I wish the day was hotter.
Friends that chase in tag,
As we zig and zag.
I will start to do belly flops,
And I will never stop.
My friends will go diving for rings,
And they will just want to sing.
We will do ten laps.
Just in a snap.
I have a smiling face,
As we walk to my place.

Tiffany Howg (age 8)
Enchant School

~//~

People

People here,
People there,
People, people everywhere.

Some are short,
And some are tall,
Some are large,
Some are small.

Some are old,
And not so bold,
Some are young,
And have lots of fun.

I like to meet them, everyone!

Donovan Chambers (age 9)
École St. Thomas School

Untitled

Glimmering gold in my hands.
Oh so great and shiny
Looking up at me from the palm of
   my hand.
Daring me to spend it.

Racing to find some more, it slipped out
   of my hands
And fell into the creek bed.
Under all that water I still could still see its
   shiny brightness.
So precious - I would love to have it - I
   was ashamed I'd dropped it.
How come I dropped the gold? I needed
   it so badly.

Alex Flatman (age 10)
Ian Espin (age 10)
Beaver Lake School

~//~

Classmates

Eva is a fast runner.
She is very good at poems
And she is very, very small
Eva is my friend.

Tiffany is a very kind girl.
She is super duper in math
And has great, great ideas.
Tiffany is my friend.

Christina is very neat.
She is a good printer
And always, always has a smile.
Christina is my friend.

Sam has three names.
She is very nice to others
And never, never gives up.
Sam is my friend.

Jordan is quite smart.
He is very cool
And always, always reaches his goals
Jordan is my friend.

These are some of my friends.

Verne Virostek (age 8)
Enchant School

The "Bold" Eagle

Here I am, sitting high in the sky,
Waiting for a fish to go by.
Man, I want a big fat fish,
For it is my favourite dish.

The sunlight makes my talons flash;
I am ready for that final dash.
A flash of silver, scaly skin;
I have just spotted my dinner's fin.

Oh to chase that salmon down the stream
Like I do in my favourite dream.
But for now my knees grow weak and I
    begin to frown;
I have a bit of an issue with looking down.

Duncan Clarke (age 12)
St. Michael's University Middle School

~//~

Happiness

Yesterday seems like today,
The war has started, fathers,
Brothers, husbands, and sons,
Everybody went to the war.
I remember as I stood
In the doorway thinking about you.
I wish that one of you would come.
But nobody did come to me.
I felt so bad about it.
We all prayed our souls to sleep.
One night when it was silent,
Somebody started
Breathing in my ear,
And started saying something but
    didn't finish.
When I awoke I remember the teardrops
Falling from his face.
And I couldn't believe my eyes.
Tears started rolling down my cheeks.
The first thing that I said was,
"You're alive."
He was quiet for a moment,
Then started crying,
And said something,
But I couldn't understand him
And couldn't end it.

Cindy Zacharias (age 12)
Menno Simons School

The Sad Day

Gazing up into the sky,
Sarah slowly said "Good-bye,"
As she slowly walked away,
Thinking about her sad day.

Sarah ran into her room
Thinking of flying on a broom.
So she quickly sailed away,
Forgot about her sad day.

Tayler Malm (age 9)
Enchant School

~//~

Halloween

Red is my favourite colour
    but I like green.
My birthday is special,
    but I love Halloween.

On Halloween night
I went to the skateboard park
But it was
    very very pitch dark.

Kyle Borman (age 9)
Lavington School

~//~

Ponies

Jumping over the pole
Racing in the hole
Laying beside a pail
Eating a piece of bale

Going so very slow
Running after snow
Sneaking in a forest
Hiding for a rest

Hurdling a bird bath
Riding through the path
Pulling a red wagon
Shuffling through fields of sun

Frank Klassen (age 10)
Enchant School

The Bat and the Cat

The spooky little bat sat
on a black cat.
The black cat screamed.
The spooky little bat shot a beam.
Now the cat is a ghost
that likes to eat toast.

Daryn Lau (age 10)
Boundary Community School

~//~

The Arms of Death

Such a word as death
Means so much to a person's heart and soul
It could be such a mess
You hear the news
And feel pain
Hope they go on
To a better place
And hope you can see them
One more time
Death

Zachary (Zac) Peters (age 12)
Wix-Brown Elementary School

~//~

Dance

On Thursday I go to dance
I have to wear my special pants
We dance to some music that is fast
And I always have a blast
I think my dance is really cool
And I wish there was a pool
My teacher Manuelle explains what to do
Sometimes it is hard 'cause everything
is new
Manuelle is a dude
When I have some food
Manuelle is cool
Even though he acts like a fool
One day I fell on the floor
And I fell right through the floor
After dance I went right home
I brushed my hair with a comb

Jaycie Slade (age 8)
École Joe Clark School

Winter

Weather is colder
Leaves fall from cold winter trees
Christmas is coming

Dominic A. Underhay (age 12)
Winchester Hill Community School

~//~

A Moment in Time

He was an eager young man who worked
extremely hard
To buy a sparkly new Lancer.
He worked long hours
For this very car.

Finally at sixteen he was able to buy
his dream,
A car of his own and the freedom that
came with it.
No more rules or adult supervision,
It was his very own.

One fateful day, he called up his buddies,
Who were always there now that he had
a car,
To go for a ride down east of the city.
His buddies said, "Step on it, see how
fast she can go."

It was just a moment in time when he made
his decision.
No hesitation, no consideration as the
pedal hit the floor.
He lost control and went hard into the ditch.
The car started flipping and a new life began.

From that fateful day, everything
became harder.
The injuries to his head made the once
easy school a nightmare.
High school graduation as well as his
dreams faded.

His buddies were gone.
His life took new direction,
Spiralling downward.
Now there were rules and adult supervision,
Everything the car was to guard against.

Jack Wesche (age 12)
F.E. Osborne School

A Foggy Day

I went for a walk
On a foggy foggy day
And I thought that I had gone the
    wrong way.
I saw a pond
And took out my wand
And I turned into a frog.
I hopped and hopped away.
I got lost in the fog and I tripped on a log.
I fell in the pond.
That stupid old wand.
Now what will I do?
I heard a cow go moooo.

Adara L. Stelter (age 10)
Boundary Community School

~//~

I Hear War

I hear the people fighting.
I hear the threats in writing.
I hear victims dying.
I hear the people crying.

I hear countries invading.
I hear bad guys trading.
I hear us trying to help.
I hear poor children yelp.

I hear General's orders.
I hear people flee the borders.
I hear the wars go on.
I hear soldiers long gone.

I hear the larks still singing.
I hear machine guns ringing.
I hear widows weeping.
I hear nobody sleeping.

I hear the mobs attacking.
I hear buildings cracking.
I hear citizens yelling.
I hear planes propelling.

I hear starving kids.
I hear killer weapon bids.
I hear the bombs drop.
I hear me yelling, *"Stop!"*

Nicole Stewart (age 11)
Children of St. Martha School

Halloween

Teachers beware
Or you'll get a scare
From our Halloween treats
If you dare.

Matt Unruh (age 9)
Enchant School

~//~

Artist

There was an artist
Whose name was Blartist.

He cannot decorate.
His paintings disintegrate.

To one he said, "Good-bye"
But I do not know why.

Trent Mathieu (age 9)
Enchant School

~//~

Phantom

Thundering swiftly throughout the land,
Glides a black figure across the hot sand.
Gaining speed at every stride,
His nostrils flared, and eyes opened wide.
He runs from fear and doesn't turn back,
Then tosses his head in rid of his tack.

He canters now free across the range,
And all his ways then start to change.
His mane of fire, and coat of night,
Shimmer across the blazing light.
But days come to end and nights sail away,
As he runs endlessly astray.

Silver-grey his coat has turned,
And all is forgotten which he once learned.
Phantom is the name of which he's
    now known,
For only that is what he has shown.
With a heart of fire, and spirit of flame,
None could prove that he was once tame.

Jacquelynn Lupick (age 11)
Kelowna Christian School

Untitled

Yesterday we have some snow
Now school is really slow
Now I saw a cat
Now I'm afraid of a bat

Now I am wearing a hat
What do you think of that?

Spencer Meszaros (age 9)
École Joe Clark School

~//~

Snow is Something

Snow is something for all of us.
Snow makes you care about other people,
Because it is so fun to play with,
And to play with other people too.

Snow makes you feel good about yourself
And who you are,
Because it only comes once a year,
But when it is gone you want it back.
Snow is just special to me.

David A. Woelk (age 10)
Ashley Park School

~//~

Carolers

Their songs are joyful in the spirit
Spreading smile at doorways
Cold all night
But they go on
Colourful lights give them joy
Solos, duets, quartets, and more
They are family and friends who
come together
Not knowing who is jolly, grumpy,
or whatever
After all that cheerful cold
Hot chocolate and cookies
A nice warm fire
Then as their pillows grab them
They dream about the next night!

Nicole Godwin (age 11)
St. Michael's University Middle School

Contests

Contests are a special thing,
Even if you have to sing.
There may even be some prizes,
In many different shapes and sizes.
Even if you're big or small,
You can try to win it all.
There might be some challenges,
Or even some advantages.
Contests are just like a test,
So remember, do your *best!*

Jen Lee (age 12)
Hjorth Road Elementary School

~//~

Could There Be Peace?

Maybe, somewhere far away there is peace.
Wouldn't it be strange if we knew what
peace was?

Or,
Maybe peace is just a dream.
Maybe peace is not possible.
Seeing is believing,
And has anyone ever seen:
Peaceful people,
Peaceful communities,
Peaceful cities?

So peace is probably not possible,
Just a vision, dancing on the horizon,
And settling with the sun.

Some dream,
Someone special dreamt in a
peaceful nightmare.
How our world could be a better place.
Maybe.

But we will never live in peace,
because peace and man
can't share the same sentence,
So...

Maybe, far away there is peace.
But, here on Earth it will always be,
A puzzling image floating with the mist
on a sunny day.

Chelsea Langlois (age 12)
St. Michael's University Middle School

104

The Solar System Song

Mercury is the first planet, closest to
the Sun.
It circles that great star, but spin it has none.
Venus, the second planet, in clouds is
always covered,
So she was always mysterious until the
Magellan spacecraft hovered.

Earth is our planet; it really is our home.
That's the reason why it is included in
this poem!
Mars, the red planet, named for the Roman
God of War,
It has great canyons, polar icecap, and
desert floor.

Jupiter, the giant planet is largest in
our group.
It hurtles 'round the Sun in a great and
arching loop.
Saturn is the great gas giant best known
for its rings;
Turns out these halos are composed of
ice and pebbly things.

Uranus, oh Uranus, how bright and blue
you shine,
A gaseous ball, flying through space with
moons greater than nine.
Neptune, the last gas giant, also
coloured blue,
Has dark spots spied by Voyager probe
where storms are thought to brew.

We finally come to Pluto, the last
planetary bit.
She speeds through space with Charon, a
moon half as big as it.
That's the end of the story, this solar
system song,
But maybe we will learn more about
Planet X before too very long.

Alyssa Joy Friedman (age 11)
Our Lady of Good Counsel School

~//~

Untitled

Summer
Hot, sunny
Running, jumping, playing
Green grass, orange leaves
Falling, floating, crunching
Mostly cloudy
Fall

Josh Warn (age 11)
William Grayson School

~//~

Lynx

Scratching at mice
Biting at a snake
Chasing an antelope
Pouncing on a jack rabbit
Hiding from a poacher
Eating raw meat
Licking his thick fur
Hunting alone for meat

David Jacobson (age 9)
Enchant School

~//~

We Remember

The soldiers that fought in the war,
They were brave and so strong.
They fought for our piece of land,
And fought for so long.

The families waited while they cried,
Wishing that the soldiers will arrive,
And hoping that they hadn't died.
But the soldiers kept fighting day by day,
And knew that they had to pay.

So we remember the soldiers that died,
But we will never forget them and put
them aside.
The soldiers will always be in our hearts,
And we know that they gave us peace,
And they did their part.

Robert L. Couzens (age 11)
St. Helen's Elementary School

Milking

At early dawn,
The sleepy rooster crows,
Signaling the start of a new day.

The farmer goes to milk the cows,
Quietly, rhythmically collecting
Their warm, creamy milk,
While they happily low.
The sweet scent of hay
Mingles with the stinky
Smell of manure.

Then the young farmer lifts
His cumbersome milk pails
And goes for breakfast.

Rosemary McAllister (age 9)
South Island Distance Education School

~//~

Child

Oh, to be young again!
To be able to nestle in my mother's arms
To be able to order from the kids' menu
To play Barbie dolls and not care who sees
To be a carefree, innocent child

To be a flamboyant toddler
Who doesn't know the pains
    of embarassment
Who doesn't know the pressure of peers
Who doesn't know the struggle to fit in
Who is learning right from wrong

I was once this cheerful child
But, alas those days are slipping away
I am now a youthful preteen
Struggling to climb the mountain of life
Having to deal with the hardships of change

My childhood is flashing by
I am trapped by responsibility
I want to get rid of my worries forever
Sometimes life is like turning a corner
You never know what you will find
I must accept the challenge and move on
Why can't I be young again?

Beverley MacSpurren (age 11)
St. Philip School

I Made a Mistake

I went to Ghana to get a skirt
I made a mistake and got a shirt
I went to my closet to get my hat
I made a mistake and got a mat

I went to school to get a pen
I made a mistake and got a hen
I went to Japan to get a bag
I made a mistake and got a flag

I went to a store to get a fish
I made a mistake and got a dish
I went to a mall to get a hose
I made a mistake and got a nose

Jennifer Amoako (age 12)
Children of St. Martha School

~//~

The Talking Sea

The sea calls me,
Does it call you?
Into darker waters,
It churns and spins with foams of snow.
Like a waterfall's bottom,
I am called to the bottom.

The sea calls me,
Oh yes it does.
Voices sing and call.
I am like a child under a spell,
Helpless, weak, a "no hope" kind of feeling.

I feel the water,
I long for the water.
No! I must stay on the ground,
But I long for the sea, and I go,
Because it longs for me.

I have begun to swim
In the darker waters.
I sing to the sea,
I am lonely.

I am singing to you,
Come to the sea.
What is *your* decision?
Will you join me?

Aleasha Forbes (age 12)
Immaculata Regional High School

Books

Books have pages.
Books have stages.
Books have coloured pages too.
Books with puzzles you can do.

Books have rhymes.
Books have lines.
Books have people you can see.
Books have people that are he.

Books have words.
Books have birds.
Now books can bend.
And books can end.

Troy Reimer (age 8)
École Joe Clark School

~//~

I Wish I Were an Animal

I wish I were a friendly, welcoming dog.
I would furiously lick and jump on
  welcomed guests.
I wish I were a purring, fluffy cat.
I would actively creep and spy on
  my owners.

I wish I were a tiny and clean mouse.
I would silently creep and dash into a hole.
I wish I were a tall and slender horse.
I would gracefully neigh and trot around
  the field.

I wish I were a clever, clean monkey.
I would swiftly swing and glide from
  tree to tree.
I wish I were a bulky and
  enormous elephant.
I would powerfully swim and drink in
  the water.

I wish I were a tall and skinny giraffe.
I would quietly eat and drink in the field.
I wish I were a sluggish, green turtle.
I would slowly waddle and swim
  everywhere I go.

I wish I were an animal!

Kristy R. Douglas (age 11)
Prairie Elementary School

Dreams

It's sometimes hard to tell reality
From fantasy when you dream.

Sometimes it's disappointing,
When you finally realize,
It's only a dream.

Everything can be impossible
But when you really think about it,
Nothing's impossible
When you dream.

Sometimes it's scary,
If it's a nightmare,
But it turns out
It's only a dream.

Cassie Marno (age 12)
Wix-Brown Elementary School

~//~

God's Perfect Creation

Among the glassy and shimmering oceans,
  glides a black and white whale
Waiting to whisk a soaring fish.
Beyond the twirling and twinkling lakes
  lies a shining glittering otter
Ready to show off.

By the oceans, fall prepares a seal to set
  a net
Across the sparkling and charming oceans
  to catch fish.
Beneath the stirring oceans lies a starfish
Taking a nice and pleasant sunbath.

Above the water a crab has a dainty and
  relaxing day
On an agreeable tepid rock.
In a soggy and grimy pond, a frog burps
  as loud as he can
To get a girlfriend.

Across the fields of water, the dolphin
  jumps happily across
The beautiful and gloomy sunset.
The water creatures are God's
  perfect creations.

Naomi Kim (age 10)
Prairie Elementary School

Peace

P - I prevent fights from happening
    by compromising.
E - I enjoy the friendship when I make peace.
A - I appreciate the peace we have in Canada
    because we can live freely.
C - I care for the people who are suffering
    from bombings.
E - I have everlasting love for the
    whole world.

Vanessa Herdman (age 11)
St. Helen Elementary School

~//~

Can I Have

Can I have a truck Dad
Can I have a boat
Can I play in the muck Dad
Can I have a goat

Can I have a train Dad
Can I have a swing set
Can I dance in the rain Dad
Can I have a pet

Emily Edmundson (age 11)
Juniper Ridge Elementary School

~//~

You're Too Slow!

I really got to go
You're moving too slow
I'd rather bike
Than take a hike
Time is ticking by
It was too slow
Now it's too fast
I'd rather hike
Than take a bike
Time is flying by
Now it's just right
It's not too fast and it's not too slow
I'd rather meet a Viking
Than go biking, or hiking
Time isn't too fast or too slow!

Aidan Parker (age 9)
Meadowridge School

Me

My eyes are blue,
but there is more about *me!*
My brother says I'm
creative, fun loving, and friendly.

I like biking, scootering, soccer too.
I like to fish when the sky is blue.
I love nature;
vegetables in the garden are quite neat.
But I'm a real
carnivore; I'd rather eat red meat!

I really like science,
reading and writing,
and cram in as much art as I can.
My teacher said
this makes me a
"Renaissance Man."

Blake LeBlanc (age 9)
Sunalta School

~//~

Dream to Dance

Dream a dream I love to dance,
In the morning, afternoon, evening.
I can twirl, spin, and prance.
Dancing truly keeps me moving.

Bending, stretching, I can do it,
Keeps my dancing onward going.
I can dance lots or just a bit.
I will never find dancing boring.

I like ballet, tap, and hip hop.
My feet keep in time to the beat.
Please don't let the music stop.
Dancing really is my treat.

Dancing dancing all around,
I can dance all over town.
Here and there, homeward bound,
Dancing princess with a crown.

Recital time, it's time to dance.
People watch me up on stage.
Clapping, cheering I'm in a trance.
I can dance at any age.

Ariana Joseph (age 10)
Swanavon School

Halloween

On Halloween you see a witch
and a big fat black cat
When you see a wizard
you'll see a cranky weird green hat

Witches, goblins, and ghosts
are what I like the best
When we're trick or treating
we see the orange and green bird's nest.

On Halloween maybe we'll scare
the goblins and ghosts
to see them run
with their candy and light posts

Michael (Mike) T. Kent (age 9)
Lavington Elementary School

~//~

Magic Forest

I came upon a forest one day
On my birthday, the last day of May
I decided to go in, to see what I could find
But what I saw was not what I had in mind

I heard bees buzzing, collecting nectar
And birds cleaning, ruffling their feathers
I saw and heard the soft ripples of waves
And something (a bear?) entering its cave

I took a boat across the shimmering lake
Thinking for a moment, I could smell
my birthday cake
I came out, running by a gingerbread house
Which was currently being eaten by a
rather large mouse

Then I saw a very tiny cottage made out
of wood
And seven dwarfs with seven hoods
But I ignored it all, for my house was a
few yards ahead
Expecting family, friends, and more to greet
me, as they had said

I finally reached the door of my home
When I realized I was all alone...
"Surprise!!!"

Jaime Kwok (age 12)
Aubrey Elementary School

I Can Hear

I can hear the golfer as he gets ready
to shoot
I can hear the other golfers collecting golf
balls just like they were loot
I can hear the guy yell 'darn' as his ball
falls in the sand trap
I can hear golf balls ricochet off the trees
collecting sap

I can hear the honk of the big fat goose
I can hear him walking on the loose
I can hear my ball skimming across the water
I can hear the scream from the otter

I can hear the flapping of the flag in the hole
I can hear myself yell 'darn' because I hit
the pole
I can hear the humming of the little golf cart
I hear walking is good for the heart

Zebbadiah (Zebb) Carpenter-Reurink
(age 11)
Children of St. Martha School

~//~

Useful Inventions

Unbiquitous inventor constructed a
Sonar instrument to detect
Enemy ship.
Factories designed printers that passed
Ultra cool information in a blink of an eye.
Local cats help dig holes for wells and ponds.

I think the telephone is a
Neat invention so now we can
communicate with
Very important people.
Especially, the microwave helps kids when
No parents are in the house.
Two of my favourites are the radio and the
Interesting television that helps us
communicate with people
On the other side of the world.
Now that's all the useful inventions but
there are
So many more inventions, not
enough room.

Caryn Coulombe (age 11)
École Routhier School

Autumn

I smell leaves
I hear the wind
I taste apples
I see coloured leaves
I touch the grass

Emily MacKay (age 6)
St. Joseph School

~//~

Earthquake Rumble

Earthquakes rumble all around
Most of the time it's very loud
Deep underground there are lots of plates
That shift and roll to make the earthquake
Lots of homes would be destroyed
Most of the people are very annoyed
Because of all the times they occur
We wish for answers, even better a cure

Eric Lochmueller (age 11)
Lake Bonavista Elementary School

~//~

Sometimes I Wonder

Sometimes, I wonder if someone was born
    with a horn,
That exactly match one of a unicorn.
If there is a vast golden valley that is under
    a dark lonely alley.
If there is thunder that plundered
    many ships,
While the waves curled up to your lips.
If there was a stallion that was
    being attacked,
By a vicious battalion.
If there was a king who had a ring that
    packed an awful sting,
That would force you to sing.
If there was a monstrous dragon,
That loved to scorch passing wagons.
If there is water that can slaughter
A cute little sea otter.
Sometimes, I wonder.

Reilly Poku (age 11)
Aubrey Elementary School

Remembrance Day

Remember the people who died for us.
Everyone who fought in the wars.
Members of families cried
Every time they died.
Many didn't come home.
Because they never gave up
Remember their courage.
Always think of your freedom.
Never stop fighting for freedom.
Caring for us as they did
Each of them were good people.

Day after day their families missed them.
All the time we enjoy together is because
    of the peace they provided.
Year after year we will remember.

Carter Schindel (age 9)
Lavington Elementary School

~//~

Princess

Princess my cat
She is the colour of snow
She has a cute fluffy tail
I hear her purr when she sleeps
Her eyes are the colour of the crystal
    blue ocean
She likes to climb the trees up high
She is terrified when the water hits her
    furry coat
She thinks her treats are candy
She likes to chase the bushy tailed squirrels
She likes to play with my soft
    stuffed animals
She loves to scratch the wooden walls
She loves to sprint after the buzzing bees
She likes to hide in shrubby bushes
Oh she is adorable and loveable
She loves to eat my dad's big greasy steak
She doesn't like to be left alone
She likes to dig for bugs in the dirty dirt
She is terrified of the loud vacuum cleaner
She loves to be petted by family and friends
Princess is the most friendly and playful
    cat in the world

And that's my cat Princess

Luca Lavorato (age 10)
Aubrey Elementary School

Snow

Nice fluffy snow
soft as a trampoline
as sparkly as silver
as fluffy as sugar
so much fun to toboggan on

Josh Siemens (age 9)
Ashley Park School

~//~

Friends

Friends are happy, joyful, and glad
When we are not together we are sad
When we are at birthdays we jump for joy
Then we play with all the toys

We will be friends until we die
Until then we will eat apple pie
My friends are *great*

Kirstin Vercleyen (age 10)
École Joe Clark School

~//~

Was a Soldier

Was a soldier, who fought in the war
Came out one day, right out of the door.
To save my country,
Also my family
Was scared, but a job had to be done.
I can hear my wife yelling, "Goodbye hun."

I had arrived in Flanders Field, where
soldiers have been killed.
I fought until I got tired, then heard a voice
saying one more killed.
I tried looking over to see who it was but,
Three minutes later I got shot.

Looked up at the sky being so high,
Then I knew I was going to die.
My body will still be here,
But my soul will be up there,
Was a soldier and always will be.

Angela King (age 11)
St. Helen's Elementary School

Buddy

I like my fish.
I feed him.
I watch him swim.
His name is Buddy,
And he loves me.

Shawna Yelland (age 6)
Miller Elementary School

~//~

Cats and Dogs

Cats are cool.
Dogs are too.
The only gross part,
You have to clean up their doo-doo.
You have to feed them everyday,
And train them so they don't run away.
If you want a pet you should research
on the internet.
Or research by book,
But whatever you do,
Do not judge by looks!

Nikola Marlin-Conrad (age 9)
Aubrey Elementary School

~//~

Pablo Picasso

Picasso was famous for all the paintings
he created
Although all of his fame was always belated
By the age of fifteen he was amazing at art
As he got older a girl soon won his heart

Picasso was painting pictures with a lot
of blue
This was something he started to do
The public was thinking this was a disgrace
His father was ashamed and hid his face

He started to paint using all new designs
This was a technique criss-crossing lines
This painting was used with dark colours
and beige
And poor old Picasso died of old age

Cassie Mucciarone (age 11)
Children of St. Martha School

111

Untitled

Castle is a stronghold and a fort.
A king and queen live in a castle.
Stronghold and a drawbridge is in a castle.
Tournaments are outside of a castle.
Let's make a castle big and made of stone.
Eat feasts after collecting the harvest.

Jesse James Smith McLean (age 10)
Pense School

~//~

About Vikings

The Vikings first attacked Lindisfarne,
Lindisfarne and the monks who lived there.
Monks who lived there thought they
    were devils.
Devils were not what the Vikings were.
Vikings were cruel savages,
Savages who believed in a different
    god, Odin.
Odin the war god who had only one eye.

Naomi Muller (age 9)
St. Josephs School

~//~

Me!

I swim like a frog
My sister thinks I sound like a dog
Then I had a friend over
She said you have a lot of clover

I'll play a song
That's very long
I'll stay up late
And have a midnight break

I dance
To romance
I listen to my sister tunes
On some dunes

My pants
Go glance

Keara Holmes (age 9)
École Joe Clark School

Untitled

Hockey
rough, tough,
passing, shooting, checking,
teams, divisions-levels, dances,
spinning, jumping, practicing,
graceful, beautiful,
Figure skating

Ashley Rossi (age 10)
R.L. Angus Elementary School

~//~

Stories of War

A young girl comes to me everyday.
She looks at me in the most peculiar way.
She tells me of the wars and its ways,
And how her parents fought until the
    end of their days.
She always looks at me so sad,
And she always wishes she had her dad.
Nobody bothers the girl for many a day,
For if they do she just turns away.
The little girl just died last year.
She died with much courage but plenty
    of fear.
She died at the age of ninety-nine,
And her life was far from fine.
I will always remember
That sad day in November,
And that sad moment when she
    said goodbye.
The day that she died was a very
    strange day,
And many people were looking her way,
For the day that she died was
    November eleventh,
And the people that she lost she met again
    in Heaven.
The little girl whom I once loved is now
    gone forever
But now she has a granddaughter and to
    her I am passed on
To teach her the meanings and thoughts of
    November eleventh, Remembrance Day,
For I am a teddy bear sent to listen
And to teach and for that reason and that
    reason only
Do I wear a poppy on Remembrance Day.

Alysha van Akker (age 11)
George Bonner Middle School

112

Five Minutes to the Bell

I really can tell
It's five minutes to the bell!
I'm waiting,
I'm aching for it to ring!!!
I'm sweating,
My mind is whirling!!!
With one minute left I find I must go
You know go...
To the *bathroom!!!*
Ring!!!
Yes I can go!
"Wait Bobby!", the teacher says, "I'd like
   you to stay for an hour or so."
Oh no!

Ryan M. Sekulic (age 10)
Mitford Middle School

~//~

Wild and Free

There you were,
So wild and free...
Now I see what's meant to be.

Not stuck in a stall,
No not at all...
You were made free...
That was meant to be.

Now look at you, no longer free,
But yearning to be.
You lift your head,
To see the others,
Running free.

I open the door
And lead you
Through the fields
Into the wilderness...

I see a herd running by
And take your halter off
And slap you goodbye...

There you go...
Galloping with the herd...
Soon your hoofbeats were all I heard.
So wild and free...

Kylee Philcox (age 10)
Pinantan Elementary School

Peace Is...

growing a tree
reading by a stream
riding bikes with a friend
not hurting people
not polluting

Robert Duncan (age 10)
Topham Elementary School

~//~

The End

How I hated the parts
The end
Where you have to leave
Where you have to go
How I hated the parts
The end
When summer ends
When morning ends
When life ends
When friendship ends
How I hated the part
The end
What can I do
To stop the end?

Jana Dao (age 9)
St. Wilfrid School

~//~

Lots of People Use Me!

I run a lot but don't have legs.
Mostly boys love me but girls do too.
I'm round but I'm fun.
I can't talk, hear, or smell but I can move.
I love what I am but could be better.
I'm used on a field but I never stay still.
I get kicked but it doesn't hurt.
I'm black and white but I'm not a zebra.
I score goals but not on my own.
I am used to play with but I'm not a piano.
What am I?

Soccer ball

Jasmine Cossey (age 9)
Discovery Elementary School

113

Popcorn

Crunch, crunch, crunch.
People eating popcorn.
Tastes buttery, greasy,
Almost always mouth watering.
Crunch, snap, butter fingers.
Rough, jagged popcorn in my tummy.
Marvelous, lumpy, greasy too.
I love popcorn.
Do you?

Lena Wood (age 9)
Brander Gardens Elementary School

~//~

The Moonlight Mare

As I patted the soft and fragile fur of
my mare,
I looked up up into the sky.
In the *moonlight*
I saw a beautiful black *mare.*

As the misty black clouds
Slowly covered up my wonderful vision,
I looked at my mare
And saw it was the beautiful black *mare*
In my wonderful vision.

David Chin (age 9)
Meadowridge School

~//~

A Sparkling Dream!

As I walk into a land, I open up my hand.
To my surprise a sparkle, lit up by hope
and startle.
I look up and see a star, blazin' in its lark.
It's lonely but I know, I own a piece of
its glow!
But then a sudden chatter, a rain of
noisy clatter.
I see a scene with sudden gleam, clouds
in a world of beam.
But then I awake, and to my own mistake,
It was all a dream!

Emma Coyston (age 11)
Lake Bonavista Elementary School

Dinosaur

Dinosaur, dinosaur
What do you see?
I see a pretty butterfly looking at me.
Dinosaur, dinosaur
What do you hear?
I hear a ghost whistling in my ear.
Dinosaur, dinosaur
What do you smell?
I smell a diaper on my tail.
Dinosaur, dinosaur
What do you taste?
I taste ice cream on top of my head.
Dinosaur, dinosaur
What do you feel?
I feel a kid on my back.

Melek Bayraktar (age 7)
Edmonton Islamic School

~//~

I Hear the Computer

I hear the computer humming
I hear the message box coming
I hear the characters griping
I hear the keyboard typing

I hear the monitor fading
I hear the computer test grading
I hear the printer printing
I hear the object tinting

I hear the virus working
I hear the mouse pad jerking
I hear the scanner scanning
I hear the monitor panning

I hear the buttons beeping
I hear the enemies creeping
I hear the game disk that is cracking
I hear the knowledge that I'm lacking

I hear the time limit ticking
I hear the switches clicking
I hear the memory leaking
I hear the wood desk creaking

I hear the expert gamer playing
I hear the animated horse neighing

Brendan Cowan (age 11)
Children of St. Martha School

114

Halloween

G is for ghost that scared himself white
A is for a goblin that got a fever by mistake
B is for boogieman that's been asleep forever
M is for mummies eating macaroni
S is for spider that spied on us
And a snake that snored a lot
V is for vampire that has a good
    singing voice

Peter Nguyen (age 9)
St. Wilfrid School

~//~

My Invisible Dog

My invisible dog is a fool.
I think my invisible dog is cool.
My invisible dog is furry.
My invisible dog is in a hurry.
My invisible dog plays in a pool.
My invisible dog plays with Dad's tools.
She swims inside a pool.
I'll say it again - my invisible dog is cool.

Madison Ellsworth (age 7)
École Joe Clark School

~//~

Spring

The warm sun wakes me up with a great
    kiss on my cheek.
Fresh flowers smell heavenly and
    taste sweet,
Sweet from the soft rain last night that
    left dewdrops
On the slightly rough leaves of a wildrose.
The fresh morning air fills your lungs with
    a desire to live.
The sky is a clear blue.
The grass lush and fresh
As far as the eye can see.
A fuzzy black and yellow bumblebee
    buzzes towards a gigantic flower.
It sucks the delicious fruit nectar from
    its soul within.

Monique Green (age 11)
École Branton Junior High School

Untitled

I like sitting at my table
Reading my delicious fable.
The book is so big.
It's perfect for a dig.
If you want a chair
Look over there.
If you want a stool
You have to be a fool.
When I went for a ride
I had a little slide.

Oliver Hunter (age 7)
École Joe Clark School

~//~

Cheese

I like cheese the kind that's blue
It's sticky, slimy, and tastes like glue.
I've liked cheese ever since I was four.
And now that I'm ten I eat even more.
I buy so much cheese,
That it's up to my knees.
I also like cheddar;
It's much better.
I don't know why I love cheese;
I think it may be a deadly disease.

Matthew Torriero (age 10)
Mother Mary Greene School

~//~

My School

I think my school is very cool.
I wish there was a pool.
Yesterday I wore a hat.
The next day I saw a cat.

Yesterday I sat on a log.
The next day I saw a dog.
Yesterday I went to dance.
I had to wear my special pants.

Yesterday I rode my bike.
I know it is a red trike.

Chantel Robertson (age 8)
École Joe Clark School

115

Butterfly

It is as free as the wind that blows all around,
It is as quiet as a winter morning.
Gentle and soft, it caresses the air.
It soars like rushing water going down a
smooth but fast river.
It is as beautiful as a dream garden.
This is what I hope my life will be.

Ashley Hawes (age 12)
St. Michael's University Middle School

~//~

My Heart

My heart is sometimes sad
And sometimes angry
When I'm laughed at
By other people
By my friends
That is mean
They are mean
And I am sad
And angry

Robert Stone (age 9)
St. Wilfrid School

~//~

A Nightmare From the Prairie

Anshaswifalone, a strong prairie wind
is coming
I do not run away from the bitter dust
I let the callous Southland dirt shoot at
my neck and the dust spit at my face
I cannot see, the grit smothers my eyes
The mighty gusts shoot thistles at my
blistered legs
The tiny specs of earth make my bone-dry
hands bleed
My teeth are filled with the desert sands
and I cannot hear for my ears are
Deafened by the screaming winds
My head throbs
My heart pounds
I cannot escape

Emily Kirbyson (age 12)
Newell Christian School

My Dream of No Cares

I dreamt I could fly
Like an eagle in the sky
With the wind through my hair
Without a single care

I flew over mountains
And drank from gold fountains
And slept at night
Under stars shining bright

I flew for hours and hours
And saw beautiful meadows of flowers
Until I felt a pain in my head
And woke up under my bed

Theresa (Tess) Borwein (age 10)
Aubrey Elementary School

~//~

Songs of Thanks

Thank you, for my ears that hear...
The voices of my family,
The leaves, rustling in the wind.
The sounds of the birds chirping,
And the rain, drumming on the roof.

Thank you, for my eyes that see...
The swaying stalks of golden wheat,
A blazing sunset, the bright green grass,
And all the fall coloured leaves.

Thank you, for my nose that smells...
Chicken in the oven,
Pumpkin pies baking.
The sweet aroma of chocolate,
And the whiffs of a smoky fire.

Thank you, for my mouth that tastes,
Juicy turkey soft and fresh,
Stuffing, spongy and brown.
Mashed potatoes squishy and soft,
Crunchy carrots, wet and hard.

Thank you, for my hands that feel...
A hockey stick,
My little brother's warm hand.
A smooth apple,
And the powdery snow.

Jordan Doerksen (age 11)
Hillcrest Community School

116

Dragons

Creepy, scary
Throwing, blowing, huffing
Keepers of the best princesses.

Austin David Hoffman (age 10)
Pense School

~//~

Seventy-Two-A Avenue, Delta

I beam with delight - we are here - finally!
Running up to the memory-filled house,
   my heart skips a thousand beats.
Twitching finger meets the house's
   sturdy door.
A ruffled "bang, bang" of my knuckles
   fills the air.

Silence, waiting, then the door opens.
A wrinkled, finally-you're-here smile beams,
Warm arms wrap around me like a
   wool blanket,
Inviting me into their home.

My nose twitches at the faint smell
   of mothballs.
I look around, and, like a flick of a switch,
   memories erupt in my head.
Memorable family gatherings fill my head
   and make me feel happy.

I find myself sitting on the tattered
   couch, listening,
Letting myself be dazed by her
   comforting words.

Time flies, until it is time to say farewell.
I give her a loving forever-lasting hug that
   seems to cheer me up.
Getting into the car, a chill in the air,
Driving away, gazing back, never looking
   away until she's
Going, going, gone...

For months I hold tight the memories,
Never daring to let go for fear of losing them,
Until they slip away
But I will recover them again
When I go back to my favourite place
At Grandma's house.

Georgina Price (age 10)
Meadowridge School

Autumn

I smell wood
I hear rustling leaves
I taste apples
I see falling leaves
I touch trees

Andrew Tranfo (age 7)
St. Joseph school

~//~

For Sale

One brother for sale
One brother for sale
One crying and whining brother for sale
I am really not kidding
And I'm very willing
Just start the bidding...
I don't see the money
On the table!

Patrick Steele (age 8)
St. Wilfrid School

~//~

The Emperor of Bitter Beauty!

Within the frigid and blustery cold weather,
Jack Frost paints his frosty and
   creative designs.
With his invisible and helpful paint easel,
He creates in the quiet and still of the cold
   and bitter night.

Into the quiet and slumbering towns
   he soars,
Ready to decorate and beautify
   every window.
In the stillness he covers every frozen and
   transparent window
With magnificent and gorgeous patterns.

During his flight he swoops by carefully
   and silently,
In order not to disturb a single soul.
Jack Frost is the emperor of bitter beauty!

Kayla Abbott (age 10)
Prairie Elementary School

117

Fear

Fear is black,
like a dark, starless night sky.

It enters my room,
like a wailing ghost,
floating around limply.

It makes me feel
alone and scared,
like a graveyard dark at night.

Hannah Teminsky (age 10)
Sunalta School

~//~

Jim Henson

In college Jim Henson made his
own puppets
About a year later he created the Muppets
The Muppet Show went really big
"Oh no, here comes the flying pig"

He also created Sesame Street
This show is now covered in peat
Before he died he had a wife
A strange disease took his life

Liam Prost (age 11)
Children of St. Martha School

~//~

The Worst Birthday

I had a birthday party and ordered
some fries
But when the delivery man came he gave
me some pies
When he came back I gave him a whack!
I ordered some ham
But when he came back he gave me
some jam
I went to a restaurant with my friend Leesie
But the food was too greasy
So that was my birthday
I did not have fun
Thank goodness it is done!

Melina Geremia (age 10)
Mother Mary Greene School

Indee

This story is pretty sad for me
My cat named Indee is dying
His black legs aren't working
They way they used to
I am sad that he is dying
I don't know why I am telling you this
I guess I'm just so sad
And no one knows how I feel

Darby Gropp (age 12)
Wix-Brown Elementary School

~//~

If I Were a Kite

If I were a kite
I would fly in the cool wind looking
for excitement
And adventure.

If I were a kite
I would hear the birds singing like
flute players
Up in the clouds above me

If I were a kite
I would swoosh and twirl all around
Like a butterfly
In the nice and cool breezy wind.

If I were a kite I would have bright colours
Like a rainbow formed after a rain shower.

If I were a kite
I would hear the roar of an airplane
above me
Like a lion.

If I were a kite
I would get stuck in a tree
And I would cry
Like a baby who has lost its mom

If I were a kite
I would fly into the solar system
Exploring all planets
Looking for Martians
I can't wait for my next adventure
Tomorrow.

Navron Stephens (age 11)
R.C. Talmey Elementary School

Nobody

When the teacher says
Who was talking
Everybody says nobody
The teacher wondered why
She knew she heard something
But the teacher carried on
And so did I
The teacher asked who was talking again
They all said nobody
That's my new name
So when the teacher says who was that
Everybody would say nobody
My new name
Nobody
And I'm proud of it

Jenessa Kostynuik (age 9)
St. Wilfrid School

~//~

Keep My Feelings Down

I want to burst out my tears, but I know
    that I won't
My feelings are hidden at the deepest
    inside me
I'm choking with tears
Want to pour them out but I know that
    I can't
Discipline and perseverance I may have
But love and happiness I don't
My feet are shaking on this world's surface
But I know that I can't do it
I'll go on as the world keeps spinning
But you'll never find my tears falling
'Cause if this world is harsh
I know I have to be tough
Even the people that I care the most
They certainly won't realize my tears
Because they've been hidden deep in me
I keep thinking about life and death
Then don't realize the differences
    between them
Wondering how I was created
Should I turn my heart into concrete?
Hatred makes people get stronger
But it will turn me into a glacier
All that I want to do now
Is... keep my feelings down

My Duyen Tran (age 12)
Hjorth Road Elementary School

Buddy

I have a pet.
It is a fish.
Its name is Buddy.
I keep him safe.
My fish is nice.

Jenna Oucharek (age 7)
Miller Elementary School

~//~

Wildfires

A peaceful day, a quiet night.
A flash of lightning
and suddenly...
There is a fire.
Fire dancing through the trees,
like a thousand enemies.
People fighting all day long,
never getting rest,
Fighting fire in all directions,
north, south, east, and west.
Fires keeping you at bay,
you finally have to
run away.
Fires burning everywhere,
nowhere's safe from the fire's stare.

Natalie Carr (age 10)
Sherwood Park Elementary School

~//~

Winter

I gazed longingly up at the shining blue sky.
The roses glittered as the wind stroked
    the delicate fresh petals.
Just then all there was were stems sitting
    uncomfortably in the ground.
The scarlet blue pansies soundlessly
    died away.
The dirty old water froze into white
    cold snow.
The smell of burnt wood drifted in the air.
I will always remember that cold winter
    night out in the snow.

Michael Chin (age 9)
Meadowridge School

Untiled

Delightful
Obviously cute
Looks adorable
Paramount
Humble
Is lovely
Neat and tidy
Smart, curious animals

Jessica Rusitch (age 11)
William Grayson School

~//~

Softy

You can buy me in the store and take
   me home.
I am soft and fluffy.
You can use me to make things that are soft.
Most grandmas use me.
I am not a cotton ball.
I am long, skinny but I am not spaghetti.
I can be colourful but I am not a rainbow.
What am I?

Yarn

Taylor Jackson (age 9)
Discovery Elementary School

~//~

Everyday

Everyday I wonder why isn't that me.
Everyday I wonder why I'm picked last.
Everyday I wonder why her hair's perfect.
Everyday I wonder if they're looking
   at me.
Everyday I wonder why oh why they
   laugh at me.
But not today...
Today I'm a rock too solid for that.
Today I'm not afraid.
Today I'll laugh with them.
Today I'll be whom I'm suppose to be
And that person is me.

Kandra Kaczkielo (age 11)
St. Patrick's Elementary School

The Willow Trees

Guarding the forests
Like tall ancient statues they stand
They see all; they know all
Their rings of knowledge grow ever on

Alone in the dark
They whisper words long forgotten
And gossip news of friend and foe
Though silently they watch
When passers glance their way

They offer peace and quiet
And shade from all worry
While singing a sweet lullaby
That tells of all who come and go
Between the willow trees

Allegra Wolansky (age 11)
Silver Star Elementary School

~//~

The Wish

A wish is like an open door
Be careful what you wish for
It's up to you what lies behind
What I wish will be mine?

From cheese to bread and in between
I can't believe what I've just seen
For what I wished is not there
For what I see is very rare

It's not a puppy like I wished
For what I see is a witch
She's green and ugly with a wart on
   her nose
And what is with those ugly clothes

All black and tattered with a little bit
   of grey
Oh! She's having a bad hair day
I wished again and I saw
A puppy with a broken paw

I fixed her up and took her home
And showed my mom the broken bone
When she said we could keep her
We lived happily ever after

Nikki Funk (age 10)
École Joe Clark School

120

I Made a Mistake

I went to my car to take a trip;
I made a mistake and took a slip.
I went to the ocean to get a shell;
I made a mistake and said "Oh well!'

I went camping to make a fire;
I made a mistake and burnt Dad's tire.
I went to London to see the Queen;
I made a mistake and caused a scene.

I went to Hollywood to see a star;
I made a mistake and saw Dar.
I went to China to see a panda bear;
I made a mistake and cut his hair.

I went to Egypt to see the Nile;
I made a mistake and walked a mile.
I went to my car to go to Rome;
I made a mistake and went back home!

Kali A. Deck (age 11)
Children of St. Martha School

~//~

Laughing

Laughing, laughing, laughing in bed.
Giggling at my birthday.
Laughing at dawn and night
Even when my dad gives me a fright.

Laughing, laughing, laughing at Christmas.
Giggling at a marriage ceremony.
Laughing, laughing, when I'm ten, and
    when I'm fifteen,
Laughing when I graduate.

Laughing, laughing, laughing when I'm old.
Giggling until I smell like mould.
Laughing when I draw.
Laughing when my mom's hair looks
    like spaghetti.

Laughing, laughing, laughing when I'm fed.
Giggling when I walk.
Laughing when I run
Laughing when I play play play!!
The only time I'll stop is when I'm sent
    to bed!

Dakota Ray-Andreola (age 9)
Miller Park Elementary School

A Hockey Champion

A hockey player
Takes the puck,
Skates very fast,
Shoots on the net,
And... he scores!

Lucas Litzenberger (age 6)
Miller Elementary School

~//~

Wind

The wind blows
And no one knows
What great secrets it leaves behind.
I hear the breeze whistling through the leaves
Looking for its way everyday.
So you see what a great mind the wind has
That no one can find.

Saeed Zahoui (age 8)
Edmonton Islamic School

~//~

I Wish on a Falling Star

I wish on a falling star
Far beyond my reach.
I will someday reach that star.
One day I will reach it
And I will see what it is made of.
I would really like to know
What it is made of.
I wish on a falling star
Far beyond my reach.
Something good will
Happen to me someday.
I wish on a falling star
Far beyond my reach.
I wish something good would
Happen in my life one day.
Oh, if something good
Happened in my life one day,
I would be happy.

Dedicated to Dad, Wendy & Mom, George)

Cassie Leonard (age 8)
View Royal Elementary School

Cool Cats

Cats with hats.
Cats with bats.
Cats eat rats.
Cute cats.

Tiffany Crandlemire (age 7)
Miller Elementary School

~//~

My Mom

My mom is like a dove;
She is always full of love.
My mom is very kind.
She has a thoughtful mind!

Atazia Hadjirousev (age 8)
Mitford Middle School

~//~

Why?

I look up in the sky
And ask God why
He had to die.
I tell Him it's unfair,
That they were such a pair,
Tyler and Aaron.
He was always carin'.
Tyler was nineteen,
No more to be seen.
They were just having fun,
He was young,
Why nineteen?
Just too young to leave,
I truly miss him in every way.
I wish he could come back and stay.
But now he can soar;
He's walked through that white door,
That night.
He has seen that shiny light.
His name was Tyler Andrew Vanderhoek
And oh, how I miss his loving look.

*In loving memory of Tyler, dearly missed
and always loved.*

Brittany O'Rourke (age 12)
Windebank Elementary School

The Winning Goal

I ran and ran with the ball at my feet,
Dodging the other players.
I ran and dared not pass,
For I knew it would be stolen.
My head was spinning,
As I ran down the field.
Faster and faster I went.
Then all of a sudden the ball slipped away.
Two seconds left on the timer.
"Roll ball," I yelled,
With one second left.
Then past the goal line it went.
"Bzzzz," went the time buzzer
And then and there,
I was lifted into the air.
I had scored the winning goal in soccer!

Heather Davidson (age 10)
R.L. Angus Elementary School

~//~

I Hear the Ocean

I hear the people swimming
I hear the sun dimming
I hear the people splashing
I hear the water crashing

I hear the people dunking
I hear the rocks plunking
I hear the people diving
I hear the birds arriving

I hear the sand crunching
I hear my brother munching
I hear the boat sinking
I hear the man drinking

I hear the kites flying
I hear the fish frying
I hear the tall man floating
I hear the toy boat floating

I hear the people washing
I hear the young kids sloshing
I hear the people wading
I hear the people shading

I hear the water swishing
I hear the sand squishing

Chesney Wiggers (age 11)
Children of St. Martha School

You Need Me

I show a big distance but I am very small.
I have symbols but I don't play in a band.
If you lose me I can't help you
But if you find me I can.
The world is on me but I am not the universe.
I come in many colours but I am not
    a rainbow.
There are many names on me but they
    are not people's names.
I am sometimes hard to read but
    people can.
What am I? A map.

Renée Kennedy (age 9)
Discovery Elementary School

~//~

Remembrance Day

One day I was called to war;
That was the day that my family tore.
I was young and brave.
As I packed my things,
I thought of all the lives I would save.

I remember my mom screaming for me to
    come back,
As I walked along that cold narrow path.
As I walked away, I thought of childhood,
Remembering my Mom's stories about
    the first time I stood.

They took me to a retreat,
Asked if I cared for something to eat.
I was too scared to take a bite,
Because to me, war is just a painful fright.

Next day was the first time I held a gun;
As a kid I dreamt it would be fun.
My feet, my arms... all shaking,
Bones feel as if they were breaking.

The terror I felt was deep inside,
Tears I shed were tears of pride.
First day, I was shot, and held my side,
My days are numbered, as I begin to die.

Now I live, above the sky,
Having to watch my mom, always cry.

Amanda Webber (age 12)
Veritas School

Cat

Animal
Furry, frisky
Springing, purring, clawing
Sleeping in a chair
Cat.

Shea Bennett (age 10)
Naramata Elementary School

~//~

The Cat

There once was a cat,
    that sat on a mat.
When he caught a rat,
the family would give him a pat.
He lived in a house,
and when he caught a mouse,
    he'd gobble it down,
    while going downtown.
If drums were in a room,
    he'd make them go boom.
Then he'd sit hoping that soon
    it would be noon.
Then he'd go catch another rat,
and once again sit on his mat.

Jessica Wilson (age 11)
J.W. Inglis School

~//~

I am Sometimes Fun

I am a fun pastime but I lay flat.
I am part of a board game.
I lot of people play me on a rainy day
But you can also play me on a sunny day.
I have many squares but I am also a square.
A special kind of person moves on me
But I am not a floor.
It's an old game but it's still fun.
There is a king and a queen but they do
    not rule the land.
What am I?

I'm a chess board

Thomas Roy (age 9)
Discovery Elementary School

Not All It Seems

Life is but a small journey in eternity,
An insignificant speck in the big picture.
Life is not always smooth sailing,
Nor is it easy.
Much can go wrong;
Much can go right.
The longer my life is,
The harder it is.
Then why do I want to live forever?

Death is the start of something new
    and fresh,
The end of something old and worn out.
It's a transition,
Another start.
Death is an opportunity to redeem myself,
And to change my shortcomings.
Death is inevitable,
So why do I continue to fear what is bound
    to happen?

Hussein Allidina (age 12)
McKernan Junior High School

~//~

Up In the Sky

Up in the sky,
Beyond where birds fly,
There is a place,
Way up in space.

Where animals run free,
Not climb up a tree.
Where humans are few
to none, it's true.

Where plants are big,
Like a bush, or a fig.
But we've never found it,
Where such beauty has lit.

It's hidden away.
We'll find it someday.

Up in the sky,
Beyond where birds fly,
There is a place,
Way up in space.

Maria V. Rosvick (age 11)
Our Lady Queen of Peace School

The Ocean

Deep, dark, and silent.
Fish fluttering past,
jellyfish bobbing
up and down,
up and down again.

Shells of wonderous colours
glistening from the light
above the water.
Hermit crabs chittering
across the plant-covered rocks.

Oh! I just don't want to
swim around the docks,
I want to be under the water
with everything
so beautiful
around me.

Zoey Poulsen (age 11)
Neill Middle School

~//~

I am

I am an intelligent girl who loves horses
I wonder if horses were ever able to fly
I hear them trotting through the fields
I see them running until they soar in the air
I want a stallion of my own
I am an intelligent girl who loves horses

I pretend that I am soaring with them
    across the fields
I feel the soft fur when I stroke the horse
I touch the air that's flowing by me
I worry when a colt is ill
I cry when a horse has to get put down
I am an intelligent girl who loves horses

I understand when horses have to be
    put down
I say horses are extremely intelligent
I dream of a ranch with many
    outrageous horses
I try to help whenever I can
I hope that one day I can own a ranch of
    my own
I am Anastazia Matak-Markovic

Anastazia Matak-Markovic (age 10)
Aubrey Elementary School

Crusade

C - Chivalry was thought of.
R - Richard the Lionheart was a
famous general.
U - Used weapons were trebuchet
and mangone.
S - Some more weapons were battering
ram and the ballista.
A - And knights fought to rid their sins.
D - Dead knights, no one cared.
E - Everyone fought bravely.

Courtney Hoffman (age 11)
Pense School

~//~

War

I saw the soldiers
March down the streets,
I saw them fight
Within my reach.
I feared our soldiers
Would all die,
Throughout the night
I heard their cry.

They will remember.

I smelled the smoke
So thick and black,
I felt the sweat
Drip down my back.
I felt as though
I couldn't walk,
Like I was stuck
Beneath a rock.

I will remember.

The dawn has come
And all is calm,
The soldiers left
And we have won.
From this day on
We all should pray,
And thank our God
For this glorious day.

We will remember.

Amelia Suter (age 12)
Distance Education School District #27

Christmas Wishes

I wish I were an emerald and bulky
Christmas present;
I would make a child jump happily
with surprise.
I wish I were a scarlet red Santa Claus;
I would squirm and squeeze hopelessly
down the chimney.

I wish I were lots of glittery and shiny
Christmas ornaments;
I would gleam and shine warmly through
the night.
I wish I were a fat and bulky turkey;
I would be demolished and devoured rapidly.

I wish I were a cool and fat snowman;
I would meet Jack Frost and be really happy.
Those are all my Christmas wishes.

Russell Olson (age 10)
Prairie Elementary School

~//~

To and Fro

To and fro I'll never know,
Where I am and where I'll go.
These words I speak of are crystal clear.
The words in the air are spoken dear.

Where do I go from to and fro?
The life I had has now been forgotten
And my life has now been broken.
The pain and sorrow
Are lifted high by the painted sparrow.

I haven't gone too far from the hills of the
forgotten souls;
But soon enough I'll return from the land
of to and fro.
The air is crisp, the land is soft;
These forgotten souls have fought enough!

It is time I leave from the land of war.
I have lived a life that will never be as before.
I pass this on from me to you
So that the forgotten souls live on so true.
This is the story of the forgotten souls of
to and fro.

Lindsay C. Rankin (age 12)
Rosslyn School

Family

Family is about loving
Your family helps you through tough times
Family is about holding your hands
And telling you how much they care
    about their lives
That's what a family is about!

Verily Hill (age 11)
G.H. Primeau School

~//~

Our Space

Terabitha is a wonderful place;
All of us had the most wonderful race.
We love to play there all day;
It's a new adventure as we play.
It may put a smile on your face,
When you dream about that space.
You may bring a friend or two;
We even might make a yummy stew.
Now that our friendship is finally true,
That's what we really wanted to do.

Chelsey Garand (age 11)
École St. Thomas School

~//~

Birds

In the morning I see you fly in the high sky.
I can hear you chirping like a flute in
    the sky.
So beautiful and calm I see you fly.
I love birds especially in the morning.
I hear you sing your lovely song.
One day I will find my own.
Lovely birds I hear you, I feel you,
    and sometimes
I can be with you.
Sometimes I worry you won't come back
But then I see the joy of that
I see you come back then, I wonder when
    you'll be leaving now
Well all I can say is bye, bye for now
And I'll see you in town.

Nicoletta Mainella (age 10)
Aubrey Elementary School

Animals

There is a monkey in my drawer,
There is a gecko on my door.
There is a lizard on my chair;
Where is that werewolf with long hair?
I Don't Care!
Get them all out of here!
They're drinking my beer,
They're coming in the rear.
Someone is looking in the mirror.
What! That looks like me!
I look like a monkey,
A bird, an elephant herd.
A dog and his dish, a fish.
A hairy canary.
A dog, a hog,
A pig, a rabbit, a hamster.
I guess that's me!

Haley Joel (age 11)
St. Helen Elementary School

~//~

She is Who Walks Alone

She has eternity stored within her
Her heart is harder than stone
She has no feelings or emotions
She is who walks alone

She listens to the angry screams
And laughs at the heartfelt moans
Of people long dead and past
She is who walks alone

She pushes against the wind
But remains upon her throne
Battered but still living
She is who walks alone

She is never lonely
And casts chills to the bone
Alert and ever wary
She is who walks alone

She is cruel but wonderful
Her heart remains her own
Through windswept barrens and icy deserts
She is who walks alone

Casey Spearin (age 10)
Silver Star Elementary School

Useless Things

A book without a reader,
A ruler without a metre.
A dog without a tail,
A boat without a sail.

A school without a teacher,
A baseball game without bleachers.
Music without a CD player,
A ship without a sailor.

A beach without sand,
Fingers without hands.
A mouth without biting,
A map without writing.

A nose without a smell,
A bike without a bell.
A pen without ink,
A skunk without stink.

Sivan So (age 10)
Miller Park Elementary School

~//~

To My Unborn Child

When you are a baby it will be hard to walk
And you will also learn to talk
You will chew and chew and grow new teeth
But... through these troubling times I know
    you will succeed

When you are a kid you will meet
    new friends
You will try new things
And have new dreams and goals
But... through these troubling times I know
    you will succeed

When you are almost a teen you will mature
You will be faced with bullies
You might be made fun of
But... through these troubling times I know
    you will succeed

I can't tell you anything more
You have to learn on your own
*But... through these troubling times I know
    you will succeed!!!*

Sean Grant (age 12)
Immaculate Conception School

Wildfires

Fire is like a wound...
scaring all in its path.
It's fast...
flaming flashes,
are fierce and frightening.
It burns hopes,
dreams, and history
As smoky demons
choke the air.

Keah Ellis (age 10)
Sherwood Park Elementary School

~//~

The Game

There is a game that is fun to play,
But all the rules you must obey.
The game is called football across the sea,
But is known as soccer to me.
You kick a ball to score a goal,
And hope and pray you don't hit the pole.
It is not just a win that makes it great,
It is the spirit you have as you participate.
So play the game and have some fun,
And get good exercise as you run.

Gilchrist Griffith (age 12)
Home School

~//~

God is There

When you do something bad and you
    think no one will will forgive you,
God does!
When the sun goes down and you think
    the light is gone,
He is the light and hope of our lives!
When it seems the whole world is
    against you,
He is on your side!
Every minute of every hour of every day
God and the angels are with you.
They help you and care for you every
    moment of your life.

Stephanie Harris (age 11)
St. Patrick Catholic School

Snow Falls

One day it snowed.
I went outside
To play in the snow.
I made a snowman.
Then I went sliding.
I really like the snow.
It makes me happy.

Sarah Kushniruk (age 6)
Miller Elementary School

~//~

Untitled

Witches are mean
In water I melt
Touching kids on the back with long
    creepy fingernails
Cat as black as the dark sky
Hates little kids
Enchanted all night long
Soars through the dark sky

Kaitlin Fleury (age 10)
Pense School

~//~

Bike

Because I couldn't stop my bike
I had a little fit I like.
When I rode my bike to school
I had a little duel.

Once I rode my bike to the pool
And I had a little drool upon my stool.
I once rode too fast
And got a cast.

When I rode my bike to France
I made a little dance.
When I rode my bike in November
I said this is a month to remember.

Once I rode down a hill;
I had a little spill of a gill.

Jayden Kristian (age 8)
École Joe Clark School

Homework

Homework oh homework
You are always in my way
Especially when it's time to play

Homework oh homework
You make my brain swell
Over and over, I hear the school bell

Homework oh homework
I wish you were gone
I hear my friends calling, "Game on -
        game on!"

Homework oh homework
I know I need to do
My future depends on you

Nickolas Brletic (age 10)
Aubrey Elementary School

~//~

No Escape

From the horrid memories of having
    seen death,
There is no escape.
From the hatred that surrounds
    the battlefield,
There is no escape.

From the stench of blood and decay in the
    roughly dug trenches,
There is no escape.
From the many diseases that ravage
    people's lives,
There is no escape.

From having no one come back home after
    the war is over,
There is no escape.

By getting along with others,
By taking a stand against injustice and evil,
By stopping further fighting before it's
    too late,
By working together to make the world a
    better place,

That is an escape from war.

Luca Fogale (age 12)
École Sperling School

To Love and Remember

Beneath the poppies
Our soldiers sleep
Resting now
They shall not weep

Shooting guns
Sharpening bayonets
Before they're off
Soldiers bow their heads

So we all take the time
On November eleventh
To love and remember
Those who went to the heavens

For those we lost
We must all pray
Giving their lives away
On what we now call Remembrance Day

Katherine Ivy Wareham (age 12)
École Sperling School

~//~

Why We Wear a Poppy

Within our hearts, within our minds
We wear a poppy to symbolize
That the soldiers gave freedom for you
    and I.
Deep in our hearts, we thank the guys.

We honour the soldiers who fought for us
By wearing a poppy on Remembrance Day.
With their love and trust
They bravely gave their lives away.

Poppies grow in Flanders Field around
    the soldiers' graves.
It hurts so much to think about this day.
Although wear a poppy to remember the
    soldiers' brave.
For a moment of silence we pray.

We will always remember the soldiers in
    our minds.
So wear a poppy as red as it can be.
Sweet memories for the brave ones behind,
For love, peace, and freedom for you and I.

Kimberly Lee (age 12)
École Sperling School

What is Small and Black?

I am fast but have no legs.
I fly through the air but have no wings.
I can hurt you but I have no weapons.
I make a loud sound, but I have no mouth.
You can use me once and no more.
I am black but when used I am invisible.
What am I?

A bullet

Taran Fairwell (age 9)
Discovery Elementary School

~//~

My Mother

My mother gave me a brother,
    So I am thankful.
When my brother got a blister,
    She gave me a sister.
"Mother, may I have another brother,
    Please!"
Now I have a mother,
Two brothers, and a sister.
But wait, I'm missing one.
My mother gave me a father
And a loving family!

Ameliea Sawatzky (age 9)
École Joe Clark School

~//~

The Eagle

Swooping towards its prey from the sky.
Leaping off the tree as it takes flight,
Keen eyes sweeping the horizon.
For the prey there is no escape;
Life is one meal after another.
A flash of black and white,
A streaking bullet flies across the sky,
Watching over its territory,
Skimming across the water.
Very few are left,
Respected by most,
Hated by few.

Elliott Wheeler (age 12)
St. Michael's University Middle School

Dolphins

Sweet sounds
Come from the ocean
I know they come from dolphins
Everybody has to know
About these helping mammals
I wonder if I could
Turn into a dolphin
And see the wonderful colours
The fish and the coral reefs
If only I could be a dolphin

Olivia Htoon (age 9)
St. Wilfrid School

~//~

My Little Brother - The Brat

My little brother is such a brat
He likes to hit me with a bat
He sat on my shoes
Which went very flat
I told you my brother
Is such a brat
He cut my hair in the night
It was such a fright
And that is the story
Of my brother the brat

Leandra Ashton (age 9)
St. Wilfrid School

~//~

My Dream and My Wish

I dream that my work
Is safe and fun
For all people, work in Vietnam
During the war
Night time bombs
Into my mother's home
Killed my mom's dad
My grandpa
My mom and I never saw
My mom's dad again
My heart cries
In my dream

Tony Tran (age 9)
St. Wilfrid School

Bad Hair Day

I woke up one morning
To my dad loudly snoring.
Hurray! Hurray!
It was picture day!
As I looked in the mirror,
I gasped with fear!
My hair was poofy!
It looked all goofy!
I feared that day to go to school.
For the kids would think I was a fool!
As the class all laughed,
To the bathroom I dashed.
Then I sneakily came out
To hear laughter, no doubt.
When pictures were over,
I thanked my four-leaf clover.
That long day was finally done!
And guess what? I had *fun!*

Reeghan Gripich (age 11)
Swanavon School

~//~

The Alien's Curse

In the war
Of Twenty-Three Fifty-Four
The aliens tried to destroy the land
But the navy came, guns in hand
They wiped out the creatures
But an alien yelled and cursed
"This planet and all who live in it
Shall be consumed by a great black pit"
Then he ran into his ship
And flew off to planet Xerxeszip
The alien's curse was put aside
And the navy departed with pride
Five years came with great happiness
They also came with grief and sadness
Then one boy looked up and yelled
"It's big and black; it's the end of the world"
The people looked up at it
And screamed, "It's the great, black pit"
They yelled, they screamed
They shrieked, they cursed
Just like clouds the black pit came
Causing everyone very great pain
That's how planet Earth was killed
It's also how the alien's curse was fulfilled

Craig D. Ferguson (age 10)
Parkland Immanuel Christian School

130

Two Kids

I am popular
I am teased
I am rich
I am poor

I get A's in school
I get F's in school
I have a wealthy family
I am an orphan

I am an only child
I come from a family of six
I get what I want
I maybe get what I need

I am teacher's pet
I am nothing to teachers
I am white
I am black

Meagan Whyte (age 12)
Veritas School

~//~

Good Advice

Here's some good advice:
Don't take cheese from mice.
Their tiny teeth hurt,
They'll chew through your shirt,
Don't take cheese from mice.

Here's something not so funny:
Don't give a bear any honey.
It's really a mess,
I have to confess,
Don't give a bear any honey.

Here's something bold:
Never lick a toad.
They're slimy and warty,
Just like Uncle Marty,
Never lick a toad.

Never's something not to cover:
Never talk back to mother.
She'll spank you silly,
I'm serious, really!
Never talk back to mother.

Jaclyn Paches (age 12)
H.A. Kostash School

Fall

The leaves are a beautiful colour brown,
A shower pours cooly down.
The air is crisp and cool,
Once again I'll go to school.
Then comes Thanksgiving Day,
When summer toys are put away.
Winter will come and a smile will grow
   from ear to ear,
That fall will come again next year.

Tracy Martens (age 10)
Hillcrest Community School

~//~

My Dark Angel

My dark angel
Lives in my heart
Making me sad
Ripping my feelings apart
Making me want to live in a shell
Making me feel dead as well
I never want to meet him
I never want to see him
I hope I never will
If I do I'll tell him
I'm running my life at free will

Crystal Sipila (age 10)
Miller Park School

~//~

Hungry

The ocean beckons
Whispering the untold words of past
Screaming confusion and pain
Reaching with its long cold fingers
to pull down innocent flesh
The ocean is hungry
It has not killed in a while; it will take
one of us soon
Armed with fog and hate, it will kill
Sometime it appears calm, but it is evil calm
The ocean will forever yearn
The ocean beckons

Jennifer (Jenny) Jackson (age 11)
George Bonner School

Viper

Do you think vipers are fast?
Do you think vipers have a blast?
Do you think they come in last?
Do you think they can fish and cast?

Austin Richardson (age 9)
J.W. Inglis School

~//~

I Go to School

I go to school
'Cause I can talk to my friends.
Play sports with my friends.
Have a sleepover with my friends.
I work with my friends.
And even study with them.
Mom says my education is the most
important for my future.
The most important thing to me,
Are my friends.

Jeremy Peeke (age 12)
Margaret McClumb School

~//~

I Will Remember

I will remember...

What all the soldiers did years ago
In the war.
Like how they fought in World War I and II.
Living, healthy, young men and women
dying for peace.

Remembering the war with a poppy is
not always
Enough, even though most of us do.
Most brave and loved soldiers left us
during the war.
Explain to me why so
Many people die in unnecessary wars?
Because, we all want our freedom.
Everybody wants peace.
Remembrance Day will live on forever.

Joèl Aubin (age 11)
École Routhier School

My Cat

There is no school;
We went to the pool.
When we got home,
The cat made a mess.
It ripped my dress.
My mom sewed it.
She fixed the rip.
I'm glad.

Caragana Ennis (age 6)
Miller Elementary School

~//~

What is the World Coming To?

What is the world coming to?
I thought about it and so should you.
Children are going to bed hungry at night.
Everything now is always a fight.

Men are mistreating women just to
feel strong.
Gangs are killing, doing wrong just to belong.
Teenage mothers are raising children alone.
People are suffering in a painful moan.

Wars are being fought, when we thought
we were free.
Pollution is fouling the air, people cutting
down trees.
Parents are fighting with their own
children there.
Peaceful behaviour is getting more rare.

Racism! Sexism! Discrimination! It's
happening more!
Children taken from parents, right out
their door!
Murdering! Kidnapping! Abuse! It happens
each day!
Parents scared to let children go out
and play!

There are many more problems in the
world today.
We shouldn't put up with it! It'll look like
it's okay.
What is this world coming to?
I've thought about it, and so should you!

Kathryn Greenshields (age 12)
Margaret McClumb School

132

War

I can hear the guns across the ocean.
I can feel the sadness all around.
I can feel the hearts tremble.
Look, another soldier going down.

Am I all alone in this hateful world?
Is everyone afraid like me?
Is everyone around me gone?
I can't wait until we're free.

Everyone wants to be somewhere other
    than here.
We hope the war is over soon.
But it's not up to me.
I hope our men see the enemy hiding in
    that sand dune.

Am I all alone in this world?
Or are we being cared for?
Sometimes it's hard to know
Exactly what's in store.

Daniel Bailey (age 11)
Margaret McClumb School

~//~

I am the One...

I am the one who likes to play
Not at night but during the day
I am the one who likes sports
Especially when I'm wearing my
    lucky shorts

I am the one who likes to shop
Shop, shop until I drop
I am the one who ran to the door
When my mother asked me to do the chores

I am the one who loves money
Even more than runny honey
I am the one who likes to sleep
Most of the time I'm counting sheep

I am the one who likes to cook
From pork and beans to a twenty
    pound chinook
I am the one who wrote this poem
Sitting at my kitchen table at home

Melissa Garcia (age 11)
Rose Valley Elementary School

Peace

Peace is playing with your friends
Peace is sitting on a rock by the river
Peace is not killing animals
Peace is helping others
Peace is love
Let's all be peacekeepers

Danny Grange (age 10)
Topham Elementary School

~//~

Fireflies

Flying balls of light
keeping fields bright at night
from where comes your power?
Are you charged by the hour?

Gas, electric, wood or coal,
nature's energy for all to behold.

Stewart McIver (age 10)
Windermere Elementary School

~//~

Memories

I remember the times
We laughed and cried
The times we smiled
When we went down the slide

I remember the memories
We used to share
The times you said
You'll always be there

I remember the time
When I needed a lift
My, my friend
Had a perfect gift

I remember the night
I stayed up and cried
All because
My best friend died

Natasha Billy (age 12)
Neill Middle School

I am

When I get to school, I put on a fake smile,
Thinking that it might last awhile,
But there's only one person who knows
   the truth
The smile, the fake personality.
I need to go into reality.
I ask myself, "Who am I,
What am I doing here?"
I'm just a little girl in a big world.

Alexandra (Ali) Pastega (age 11)
Aubrey Elementary School

~//~

Halloween

Halloween is the best time of the year.
When it comes I want to cheer.
Witches, dragons, fairies too,
Devils, candy, and a ghost in a shoe.
When you walk past it will jump out and
   say, *"Boo!"*
Trick or treating is the most fun,
Getting candy from everyone.
In your costume on the street,
Wear good shoes so you don't freeze
   your feet!

Hailey Richardson (age 11)
Aspen Grove School

~//~

Answers to Life

Where will we find all the answers to life?
Would we find it in a book or in a dark
   night sky?
Would the smartest man know or will he
   just wonder?
Will we ever know or will we just
   keep wondering?
Would we find it in our dreams or in our
   bedroom closets?
Is it all around us or is it in a deep dark hole?
Where will we find all the answers to life?
No one will never know until we find out...

Christine Lieu (age 10)
Admiral Seymour Elementary School

Best Friends Till the End

You and I were the best of friends;
We were like paper and glue.
We knew our friendship would never end,
Because it was always you and me, me
   and you.

All that changed on that day,
Somewhere in November,
You got mad at me, and looked the
   other way.
The good times, you refused to remember.
I was your best friend, I still am,
But it will never be the same,
All because of that ugly day,
The day the heavens rained.

Karen Cheng (age 11)
Admiral Seymour Elementary School

~//~

I Hear Soccer

I hear the soccer ball bouncing
I hear the referee announcing
I hear a player's foot snapping
I hear the whole crowd clapping

I hear the other team scoring
I hear my coach roaring
I hear a player trying
I hear another one crying

I hear the soccer clock ticking
I hear someone kicking
I hear the scoreboard change
I hear the other player's range

I hear my friends cheering
I hear a girl lost her earring
I hear the players falling
I hear the crowd calling

I hear stomping on the ground
I hear the players going around
I hear the other goalie smacking
I hear my team attacking

I hear all the games all done
I hear going home is really fun

Brittany Weasel Head (age 11)
Children of St. Martha School

134

I Like That Stuff

Boys ride on it,
Girls glide on it,
Skateboards,
I like that stuff.

Girls glide on it,
Boys stride on it,
Ice,
I like that stuff.

Boys grew on it,
Girls chew on it,
Gum,
I like that stuff.

Trees grow on it,
Leaves blow on it,
Ground,
I like that stuff.

Grayson Mutter (age 11)
Children of St. Martha School

~//~

Computer Lovin'

There's something I love, that's amazing,
    it's true.
It's undoubtedly helpful and creative too.
It helps me with homework if I ever need,
It collects information with excellent speed.
It can play music, pleasant to the ear,
It comes up with rhymes, from nursery
    to good cheer.
It can pay bills to keep the house warm,
It shows ways to cook with no fire alarm.
It has dozens of buttons. Wrong ones I
    push not!
For if I do... it crackles. The wires get hot!
It can catch a virus and crash down for
    the night,
And once it gets better, it's up for a fight.
Now I believe it is time to tell..
Who do I love so very well?
If you guessed a computer, sadly
    you're wrong.
The way off you are, is very long.
The one I love is none other -
Than my own flesh and blood - It's
    my mother!

Matthew Dalen (age 11)
Swanavon School

Untitled

One day I hit a ball real high
So it went up to the sky.
One day I went to dance;
I fell on the floor and split my pants.

Kendra Freeman (age 8)
École Joe Clark School

~//~

Basketball

Basketball is really cool;
I play so good I'm not a fool.
I take the ball and make a shot
And now I play really hot.

I can dribble down the court;
The court to me seems very short.
It's the coolest sport to me;
You don't even have to pay a fee.

Katie Waring (age 9)
École Joe Clark School

~//~

I Wanted to Know

I love my mom and dad
with all my heart.
In the summer they were acting strange
but in a good way.
They seemed happy,
spending lots of time together.
I thought it was a dream come true.

One day
mom came to me sadly.
"Your dad is moving out."
I was confused.
I didn't know what to think or do.
It was all blurry to me.

I'd always wanted to know
the secrets adults talk about.
Now that I know,
I wish I didn't.

Julie Pletti (age 12)
Neill Middle School

Autumn

I watch leaves falling
Squirrels are eating acorns
Sunsets are glowing

Dana Knapik (age 9)
St. Joseph School

~//~

Bugs

On the table was a mug.
In the mug was a bug.
The little bug gave me a hug.

Ben Boese (age 8)
Enchant School

~//~

Untitled

Stars at night
Show lovely and bright
With a beautiful light
Some people love the sight
From a very great height

Alan Tran (age 10)
Admiral Seymour Elementary School

~//~

Untitled

Apples are ready to eat

Crazy summer day
All of us are at the river
Not everyone has a canoe
Off the log, alligators are watching
Eating everything they see

Dangerous lightning might hit the canoe
Alligators will hide from the white lightning
You should be here

Brendan Nguyen (age 9)
Admiral Seymour Elementary School

If I Had a Million Dollars

If I had a million dollars there would be
   no wars
Because I'd buy them all away.
I know I can't do that but I'd buy
   them anyway.
If I had a million dollars I'd buy lots and
   lots of hats.
If I had a million dollars I'd buy a cottage
By a lake with lots and lots of land
There would be cows and horses, but
   definitely *no* cockroaches.
There's lots of things I'd buy if I had a
   million dollars.

Shanoa Enns (age 11)
Pinantan Elementary School

~//~

A Flower Garden

Sunny, bright, golden flower garden inside
   a secret door.
Red, yellow, blue, pink, purple flowers
   that bloom in the sunlight.
Golden sunrays break through an ivy roof.
A soft blue sky high above the flower garden.
Bright, white clouds in a soft blue sky.
The bright yellow sun beaming down on
   the ground.
The bright white clouds moving gently in
   the soft blue sky.
Everything is calm, bright, cheerful.
Little white bunnies hopping, playing.
Cheerful little blue birds chirping happily.
Beautiful wild grass grows among the
   bright flowers.
The day ends; the fireflies come out to
   light up the garden.
A big bright moon shines through the
   ivy roof.
The bunnies and birds sleep in dark brown
   dirt in small holes.
Dark grey clouds now come out.
The beautiful wild grass lays with nothing
   in it.
Laying quietly, growing.
The bright moon beams making the
   flowers glow.
Dew sits shining in the grass and flowers.

Cheri Sweeney (age 10)
William Grayson School

Remembrance Day

Remember the soldiers who fought for
Everyone in our country.
Miles away from home, in a battle field
Encouraged soldiers lose their lives.
More families are in sadness.
By the end of the war, only few
    are survivors.
Remember the loss of the soldiers
And celebrate their memories.
Never forget this day we
Celebrate the heroes and other soldiers.
Everyone deserves peace.

Daring soldiers are fighting for what's right
And today and always for peace.
Yes, our hearts are with all those who
    fight for peace.

Curtis Houde (age 11)
École Routhier School

~//~

My Old Friend

There was an old lady
She would walk down the street
Every so often
Whenever she did I would walk
By her side

She couldn't speak
Couldn't hear
But she touched my life in so many ways
She would show me things I would have
    never known without her
She was like my grandma I never had
I told her my secrets, I told her
My feelings

She would read my lips
One day she didn't walk by
I walked around to see if she was there
She wasn't
I asked her neighbour
"I'm sorry," she said, "she died last night"
I cried and cried
I went to her grave to say goodbye
I put down flowers
She had taken my secrets to the grave

Rachel Wiens (age 12)
Wix-Brown Elementary School

Skateboard

Do skateboards imagine their grip tape
    is skin?
Do skateboard wheels like to spin?
Are skateboard decks very nice?
Do skateboards have to pay the price?

Kayle Kessler (age 8)
J.W. Inglis School

~//~

Fall

Fall is the season I like the best.
The beautiful colours are laid to rest.

The sunset is shining like never before,
The birds are singing; you won't ignore.
Every morning the sun up above,
Fills my heart with joy and love.

Fall is the season I like the best.
The beautiful colours fall carries west.

Soraya Enriquez (age 10)
Mother Mary Greene School

~//~

Where is it

Where is a place for me?
Is it here with my friends and family?
Or is it somewhere where I can
Live in peace and harmony
Or maybe in a place where I will be happy
    forever and ever?
Or maybe there is no place for me
After all it is a big world and in a big world
That means that there's
Lots of people and dangers I need to be
    aware of
Aware of all the dangers of the world
When you're young it's hard to fit in
It's very hard for me to fit in when I try
    to fit in
It turns out worse than I planned it
No one said life was easy.

Michaela Whitmore (age 9)
Aubrey Elementary School

Free

Running through a field of wild flowers,
Makes me feel like I'm filled with
    wild powers.
The wind rushing through my hair,
The grass as green as a pear.
The air smells clean.
There is nothing better than
What I have just seen.
Too bad it was all just a dream.

Taylor Monette (age 11)
École St. Thomas School

~//~

Dogs and Frogs

I like dogs better than frogs.
Dogs are so sweet.
I think they are neat.
Frogs are so icky.
When I think about them it makes me
    feel sticky.
Dogs are so cute.
I like the malamute.
Dogs are so licky.
Frogs are so sticky.

Brittany Klassen (age 8)
Glenmore Christian Academy

~//~

Untitled

Thanksgiving is bonding time...
    with friends and family
Thanksgiving is teamwork...
to make a delicious turkey dinner.

Thanksgiving is a horn of plenty...
    filled with dried fruits and vegetables.
Also Thanksgiving is helping one another...
collecting food of the less fortunate and..

Thanksgiving is a happy time of
    the year!

Hayley Thomas (age 11)
Sherwood Park Elementary School

Under My Bed

Under my bed is a forest of moss and mould
Under my bed stuff goes bad
Under my bed things come to life
Under my bed it is dark and scary
Under my bed I feel something hairy!
Under my bed is where I shall go
With helmet and sword and lunch to go

Crystal Nassichuk (age 12)
Pacific Christian Elementary School

~//~

Untitled

Africa is where I was born

Cameras are for taking pictures
Acorns that fall from trees
Nests for birds to live in
Oliver my spoiled but adorable cousin
Emerald, gold I'll find to be rich

Daring others to do silly things
An artist is what I want to be
Yellow a colour in the bright sky

Rita Oryema (age 9)
Admiral Seymour Elementary School

~//~

God

Every night I pray to God
That things will be okay.
Asking with all my heart
To see another day.

Sometimes I think I hear him.
I think he hears me too.
Some people think I'm crazy,
But what else is there to do?

Every day I grow weaker,
But I'm not afraid to die.
Because I know I'll be with God
In that castle in the sky.

Sara Dyck (age 12)
Dallas Elementary School

138

The Animals' Plea

In the jungle,
The leopards roar.
Our jungle is a bungle,
The birds, the snakes, and some more.
Hissing and cawing with the falling leaves.
Why do we animals have no luck?
Machetes hacking through the trees,
All we want is peace and freedom.
We lost our habitat and you think, "So."
So you can build your mighty kingdom.
We are lost and have nowhere to go.
Do we deserve no respect?
Haven't you wondered what's going
    to happen?
Animals are dying, like thousands of insects.
This is the end; you make us shoo.
Who is going to save us?
Bet it's not you!

Jonathan Hopp (age 12)
Baldwin Junior High School

~//~

I Like That Stuff!

Adults sleep on it
Kids leap on it
Bed
I like that stuff

Moms munch on it
Dads crunch on it
Candy
I like that stuff

Dads sit on it
Grandmas knit on it
Couch
I like that stuff

Dogs pee on it
Boys wee on it
Tree
I like that stuff

Rabbits hop on it
Deer slop on it
Grass
I like that stuff

Stephanie Esposito (age 11)
Children of St. Martha School

Untitled

Dog
big small
run jump walk
near love happy miss
Gunner

Tarin Rhynold (age 7)
Sparling School

~//~

Peace

Peace is love
Because we need to
Care for others
Especially those kids
Who are suffering
Out in the cold
Without food
Without clothing
We need to help them

Amilkhar George Brooks (age 8)
St. Wilfrid School

~//~

The Inner Me

There I sit, in a place of glory and joy,
A place of laughter blossoming bigger
    and bigger
Tiny bright lights dance around me.
A rainbow spreads vibrant colours over
    the land.
An abundant, powerful vulture flies
    briefly overhead,
Striking the air with its screeching call.

Fear and anger creeps its way into me.
Sadness lingers in the heavy air.
Then, all is quiet; the lights start to dance,
And the rainbow once again takes its place.
In the clear, blue sky towering above,
The land gains its joy and glory slowly,
And there I sit, in a place of joy and glory
Once more.

Alyssa Kyllo (age 12)
Silver Star Elementary School

139

Baby Pets

Puppy
Cute small
Playing jumping running
Bone leash toys yarn
Purring climbing sleeping
Fluffy cuddly
Kitten

Deanna Morris (age 10)
Mitford Middle School

~//~

Television

Television is like a drug addiction
Grabs ahold and never lets go
It's like fighting a war with yourself
You seem like you are going to win
You watch again, well that's the end

Brett Webster (age 11)
Pacific Christian Elementary School

~//~

I Hate Gophers

I hate gophers with all my heart;
I wish they would just fall apart.
Gophers are stupid, ugly, and most rude.
That's why I hate gophers
And the principal hates them too!

David Nolan (age 11)
Elizabeth School

~//~

Wild Fires

Like a bully that won't leave you alone...
Fire scars the land.
Fire flashes furiously as it moves through
the forest.
It destroys the memories that you
left behind.

Hayley Thompson (age 10)
Sherwood Park Elementary School

My Cat

I like my cat.
My cat is fat.
My cat can dance.
My cat watches TV.
My cat sits like a human.
Oreo is the best.

Danica Peifer (age 7)
Miller Elementary School

~//~

Paul

There once was a young man named Paul,
Who was just short of six inches tall.
He was so tiny and lean,
That he could never be seen,
And he'd be squashed if he ever did fall.

Pamela Sceviour (age 11)
Calgary French & International School

~//~

Nature Girl

Nature it's where deer roam, birds fly
New life is made in the summer
When I saw her she looked like nature
Beautiful, calm, easy going
I love her
When I get near her I am scared
Shivers down my spine
I wish I can talk to her
She is the missing space in my heart
If she goes the burn in my heart fades away
As she gets closer to me she picks me up
My wounds in my heart, I love her so much
I think she is my soulmate
I can't stop dreaming about her
She is the most beautiful girl ever made
Like nature her heart is pure like water
Her eyes shine like the night sky
Her skin like the polished rocks on the
river's bottom
Her hair blows like the grass in the fields
She walks like the deer, God's girl

Adriel Martin (age 11)
St. Patrick's Catholic School

140

Charm Bracelet

Moons, stars, hearts, and crowns,
Chocolate cake of a rich coloured brown.
Soccer balls, four leaf clovers too!
And symbols of things that I like to do.
Disney characters and letters and tools,
Sparkling colours, and flowers, cool.
And they're all on my bracelet, my lucky
    charm bracelet.
Dolphins and doves, and lots of charms
    that symbolize love.
Balloons and happy faces,
And guitars that would really be
    called basses.
Shells and trees, and birds and bees,
And they're all on my bracelet, my lucky
    charm bracelet.

Stephanie Barnes (age 10)
Miller Park Community School

~//~

Watching War

In the deep trenches water goes cold.
My ankles go numb and begin to fold.
Screams and yells start to fade away,
As I try to curl up and make it go away.
We will remember those who fight that
    will never grow old,
As they fall to the ground and go dead
    and cold.
Friends charge that have the courage to fight,
As I stay behind and watch them take flight.
Planes hit the ground and make me
    duck down.
We are the men that are here for a reason,
To make peace and quiet at a hard season.
As the sun grows old I wait for morning,
As we take night watch and see
    others snoring.
As the enemy comes near,
I have great fear.
I raised my gun and fired,
As the trigger becomes tired.
My friends are dead,
As they stay in bed.
The will have a long rest,
As I am trying my best.
The war is no more,
So I can walk through my house door.

Darren Kolk (age 12)
George Bonner Middle School

Playing at the Beach

Playing, playing, at the beach
Bring a little peach
And at park and with a bark
Said the dog

Abigail Miller (age 8)
James Bay School

~//~

Wild Fires

Like a ferocious beast
Fire spreads its flames
It slithers through furiously
It fights to get its way
Fire kills lives, dreams, and hope.
Fire leaves a mark of destruction.
The animals flee and so should we.
When will it leave?

Halle Huston (age 11)
Sherwood Park Elementary School

~//~

I Like That Stuff

When girls use it
Boys excuse it
Make-up
I like that stuff

When boys leak on it
Girls freak on it
Toilets
I like that stuff

Adults pay with it
Kids play with it
Money
I like that stuff

Boys ride on it
Girls slide on it
Ice
I like that stuff

Billy Young Pine (age 11)
Children of St. Martha School

Shadow

Dog
Cute, hyper
Running, playing, snooping
Curled in a ball
Shadow

Cameron Stel (age 10)
Naramata Elementary School

~//~

Untitled

Cowboys
Men on horses
People roping cows
Proud, excited, happy, high up
Cowboys

Jeff DeLeo (age 9)
Vancouver Christian School

~//~

Grandpa

The time had come, that scary day.
The time to say goodbye, but the words
    I could not say.
I was afraid that night as I lay awake in bed.
I could not sleep with my eyes so red.

My Ma would say things would be fine
As she put her hand in mine.
When the scary time was over would my
    Ma be right?
Then right away my Pa walked in and it
    was a perfect sight.

I was so happy I jumped for joy.
Pa picked my up and swung me 'round and
    said, "You've grown, boy."
I hugged my Pa as proud as could be.
As I said, "I'm glad the war is over and
    you're home with me."

Dedicated to my great grandpa
Clarence Shiels.

Darceelee Brenner (age 9)
Margaret McClumb School

Friend

Friend is a special treasure.
Spending time with them is a great pleasure.
A friend is always there,
To show that they care.
Someone who shares your happiness
    and sorrow,
This bond between two friends is
    never narrow.
A friend is someone who fills your lives
    with beauty and grace,
Which makes this world a wonderful place.
Someone whom you can trust,
Always there to fulfil your lust.
Though friends may not be forever and
    may not be together.
But the memories of a true friendship will
    last forever.

Manpreet Mahairhu (age 12)
Khalsa School

~//~

The War

In Flanders Field they die,
We wonder where they lie.
The war is gone but the thought still stays,
For in Flanders Field a poppy sways,
For each of those who bravely died.

To this very day we think,
And thankfully remember.
The happiness on this day is less
    than slender,
For today we remember those who
    bravely died.

So we thank, through and through,
To those who gave their lives for me
    and you,
This Remembrance Day.

The soldiers fought nonstop,
Even at the fall of a raindrop.

My point is when we think of soldiers,
We should think of them as heroes,
For they fought way before the
    rooster crows.

Megan Urchit (age 10)
Heffley Creek Elementary School

Fun Things

Fun things are good to do.
I hope you like them too.
Playing games is so much fun,
Especially when you're in the sun.
When I'm playing all day long,
I like to sing a nice song.
One thing I like to do,
Is have a great time and be with you.
Do fun things with everyone,
And try not to get a cramp when you're
   having fun.

Sarah Way (age 8)
Glenmore Christian Academy

~//~

The Friendliest Image

Sweet smells of horses and hay
Waft to my nose as I look at the
   friendly image
Etched
In my memory

The lone barn stands as tall as the sky
The roof tickling the bellies of the silver-
   lined clouds

The field is yellow-green dotted with
   Grand prix jumps
Perfect
To the last detail

The familiar smell of grain
I run it through my fingers and I feel the
   tingle of goodness

I gaze admiringly
At the wonderful sight of horses,
   horses, horses

Striding down the aisle, stroking velvet noses
Through the old, rusty bars fitted securely
   on the wooden stall

Leaving now
Leaving the friendly image
That's etched
In my memory

Zahra Mawani (age 11)
Meadowridge School

The Storm

A storm is coming
Now there's rain pouring swiftly
The winds howl loudly
Then as quickly as it came
It disappeared again

Adolina Gawne (age 10)
South Island Distance Education School

~//~

Untitled

Dogs
Friendly, cuddly
Jumping, barking, scratching
Puppies, friend, mammal
Biting, pulling, tugging
Fuzzy, cute
Mutt

Emily Rypstra (age 12)
Parkland Immanuel Christian School

~//~

I Like That Stuff

People rumble in it
Players fumble in it
Football
I like that stuff

Humans play in it
Polar bears stay in it
Snow
I like that stuff

I like to eat it
Teachers treat it
Food
I like that stuff

People drink in it
People sink in it
Water
I like that stuff

Kevin Dietrich Clarke (age 11)
Children of St. Martha School

143

Music

opens up your heart
beautiful beats
relaxing
measures
notes

Jaymee Sluggett (age 9)
R.L. Angus Elementary School

~//~

Crying

Tears are globes
Of happiness
Of love
Of faithfulness
Of loyalty
Of hope
But no, not of sadness.
The sadness stays bottled up
Yet everything that matters is shed,
No more than little droplets of water
But why cry,
When you can laugh?

Jennifer Debroni (age 12)
St. Michael's University Middle School

~//~

Untitled

I saw a rainbow in the sky;
It made me think of cherry pie.
Looking up beneath the sun,
Made me think of a honey bun.
Lying down in the grass,
Made me think of my soccer class.
As I watch the kids run and play,
I could do that another day.
As I remember how the warm sand
Felt against my soft hand.
Gurgle, gurgle, gurgle, crunch.
Oh no, oh no, I forgot my lunch.
And it's almost time for me to go,
But what is this I know,
That a chocolate chip cookie is only a dime.

Katherine Hackett (age 9)
James Bay School

Freedom

Freedom is like the wind,
Drifting swiftly above.
Let me give you a hint,
It's like peace and love.
Freedom is like a butterfly,
Flying high and low,
A butterfly that will decide
Where it wants to go.
Freedom is the key
To happiness and health,
But it doesn't have to be
Having fame and wealth.
It's the power to speak up
For what you think is right.
It could even be some coffee in a cup,
Because freedom is the ability
To witness a peaceful sight.

Alberije Leku (age 12)
Hjorth Road Elementary School

~//~

Untitled

I am as frail as the delicate leg
Of a belittled yet clever long legged spider.
I struggle to hold onto my branch.
My fellow bead-like creatures
Are plucked from weakened strains of grass
Who long to link onto their tiny kernel-
    sized blade,
But the careless wind picks us off
Throwing us into the lush blue sky.
My field dies in the colours crimson,
Lemon, and carrot.
Whoosh!
The agony of the breeze beats against my
    honey-dipped self.
My pond of sparkling nectar sucked by
    many unknown tongues.
I am a wounded soul who will never seek
    the stars.
A droplet of snow will dwell within
    my petals
Destroying my tender shelter
But, in the spring the damp ground
    surrounds me
For I am respouted.
I am the pollen!!

Rachael Moorthy (age 9)
North Poplar Fine Arts School

144

Candy

Candy
Gives sweetness and delight
To excited trick or treaters
On Halloween night

Natasha Turnbull (age 10)
Deep Cove Elementary School

~//~

Snake

Snake, snake, you are so fast, when you
race along the grass.
Snake, snake, you look so great; on the
rock you like to bake.
Snake, snake, how your colours shine;
I wish you could be a friend of mine.
Snake, snake, people fear you here and there,
Whenever you go out to scare.

Nathan Stevens (age 9)
Discovery Elementary School

~//~

Who Are You? I am Me

As I go through this world of wonder and
people ask,
"Who are you?"
I will reply, "I am me, a daughter, a sister,
and a friend,
That's who I am."

As I walk on this road of my life and
people ask,
"Who are you?"
I will say, "I am me, a girl who is loved
and loves
That's who I am."

If you see me in this world,
In this life of wonder and dreams and you
ask me,
"Who are you?"
Again I will say, "I am me, that's who I am."
Who are you?

Amanda F. Gaudry (age 11)
William Grayson School

What am I?

I am different colours, I go on someone.
I can't see, I can't move.
Sometimes I get taken off but usually I
am on a person.
I can travel a long way. I come in all sizes.
What am I?

Shoe

Alexander Stevens (age 9)
Discovery Elementary School

~//~

Death Happens Just Once

Deep in my grave,
I live in peace staring at the sky,
Until the rain gave.
Now I'm alone and wet,
No mice, no birds, no me,
I'm gone.
You see that proves death happens
just once.

Taylor Anderson (age 9)
R.L. Angus Elementary School

~//~

Perfect Me... Or Maybe Not

Me
perfect me
or maybe not

I love spaghetti and meatballs,
But I always get it on my shirt.
I think frogs are really neat,
But both of mine died.

I like writing stories and poems,
But I always make mistakes.
I like reading a lot,
But I have a bunch of books I haven't read.

All my drawers are full of clothes,
But I can't find anything to wear.

Natalie Fair (age 9)
Sunalta School

Ferocious Fires

Like a stampede of elephants making
    everything flee,
fire leaves a scarred path.
It is fast, fearsome, ferocious,
    and frightening.
Fire kills hopes, dreams, and lives.
They bring fear to all of us.

Adam Cottrell (age 11)
Sherwood Park Elementary School

~//~

The Light

Each morning
When you get up
You don't foresee what will happen.
Soon it's too late.
Gazing at the light
Wondering what to do,
Soon you make up your mind.
You are on the other side,
Staring and searching for someone
You lost and miss.

Victor Koshieff (age 12)
Neill Middle School

~//~

Soccer

Soccer is fun.
You have to run.
You hit the pole
Then you get a goal.

Don't go in a crowd
Or else you'll get too loud.
Don't run into the pole;
Then you won't get a goal.

Hit the ball
But then you'll get the call.
Now it's the end,
So you won't have to play defend.

Joshua Ostermeier (age 9)
Parkland Immanuel Christian School

Untitled

Strawberries grow close to the ground
They may be small, but never round
They are very yummy to eat
The taste is much better than meat
On strawberries seeds can be found
You can make strawberry jam
Don't ever put yummy jam on ham
You can make strawberry cheese cake
Tasting almost too good to take
I will give this jam to my school ma'am

David Legge (age 10)
Notre Dame Elementary School

~//~

To My Unborn Child

Have fun, run, and play,
Go to parties, try new things,
But don't get mad at simple things.
Life is too short to be mad.

You listen to songs on the radio,
You hear the singers scream and yell.
They complain that life is so hard,
But you are the person that makes you
    work hard,
You are the person that tells yourself that
    life is hard.
Life is too short to be mad.

My father told me so many times,
Life is too short to be mad.
So I'm passing it on hoping that you'll
    pass my father's words down.
Life is too short to be mad.

Have fun, run, and play,
Go to parties, try new things,
But not be mad; life is too short to be mad,
    have fun while life lasts.
Life is too short to be mad.

Please don't grow up to be a mad person,
Grow up to pass on my wise words that
    my dad told me,
Just go and do no bad, just have some fun
    in life.
Life is too short to be mad.

Vanessa Renneberg (age 12)
Immaculate Conception School

The Soldiers

The soldiers took a shot or two then went
    to a better place,
Thinking how they played a part in saving
    the human race.
Every morning, every night they heard the
    sound of war,
They heard screams of pain and sorrow
    and the sight of blood and gore.
They stood in soggy holes, working hard
    to reach their goals
We should remember them no matter what,
Because of what they have done for us.

Jaskaran Singh Khinda (age 12)
Khalsa School

~//~

On Halloween Night

On Halloween night
You're going door to door
Without a fright

Saying trick-or-treat
Not knowing
The trick is in the candy you eat!

The candy givers all seem very nice
But if you didn't know
They stuff their candy with mice

They have their jack-o-lanterns
Sitting there, smiling as you walk by
And you'd think you'd be suspicious
Then you ask yourself, "Why?"

Because the jack-o-lanterns look so helpless
Being there
With Mr. and Mrs. Selfless

But as you can see
When Mr. and Mrs. Selfless leave
The next kid that's by itself
Is going to scream

Because when the jack-o-lantern sees you
It knows just what to do
As it bites your arm and then *poof*
You're gone!!!

Ashley Deluca (age 11)
Neill Middle School

Gentle Water

A water flutters down the sea
Awakening other sea creatures,
The sea creatures gently
Swim to the breeze of the warm sun,
And life goes on and on.

Yile Lu (age 9)
Charles Dickens Elementary School

~//~

To Mom

Roses are red,
Violets are blue.
If I had to choose one mother,
It would be you.
A mother like you
Is a mother who should,
Have the best thing in the world.
And a mother like you,
Should have a daughter like me.

Katie Cole (age 9)
Sir James Douglas School

~//~

Horses

I love horses when they prance
It almost looks like a dance
Horses are always good
Just like they always should
I love horses when they eat
I love horses; they're so sweet!
I love horses when I ride
It always looks like they're in pride!
I love horses when they sleep
I always take a little peep
Then in comes the new day
Hip hip hip hooray!
Next I look where he lay
Then we go out to play
Then he goes out to graze
Then I go out to praise
Next I go down the lane
Then it starts all over again!

Nicole Herback (age 7)
Glenmore Christian Academy

147

Hallowe'en

Werewolves howling at the full moon.
Bats are flying everywhere.
The smell of candies fill my bag.
People are going boo!!!
Kids are dressing up in costumes.
Pumpkins are everywhere.
Kids are yelling in horror.
It's Hallowe'en.

Oliver Thomas-Powers (age 11)
Sherwood Park Elementary School

~//~

Rolly Polly

I'm very heavy but I'm not a weight.
I have three holes but they aren't eyes.
I am used for a sport but it is not soccer.
I can walk but I need some help.
I can go pretty fast if the person holding
    me is strong.
When I go I hit something.
Strike.
Can you guess me?

Bowling ball

Jake Witt (age 9)
Discovery Elementary School

~//~

A Sticky Thing

I'm really sticky but not sticky to
    begin with.
I come in all shapes and sizes, but I am
    not extra large.
I can come in many designs but I can also
    be plain.
I can even stick on you, but not on furniture.
There are billions of me and teachers like
    to use me.
What am I?

Sticker

Meghan (Meg) Watkins (age 9)
Discovery Elementary School

Sweet

I like sugar. Sugar is sweet.
So are you. Sweet for me. Sweet for you.
Sweet for everyone.
Sweet around the world.

Hannah Kurjata (age 7)
Notre Dame Elementary School

~//~

Follow Me

Follow my lead,
Read
A series of unfortunate events.
Books are a journey
Into your imagination,
Is the willingness to listen.
Follow me,
Smile,
Find a world to explore
In the great outdoors.
Follow me,
Run,
Jump,
Believe in.

Nahanni Balfour (age 12)
Veritas School

~//~

Who Can I Be?

I live in the water,
I swim in the sea,
I live near your house,
Who can I be?
I walk on the ground,
I fly in the sky,
I sing my tunes.
"Tweet, tweet" means "Hi!"
I sing my song morning and night,
I make weird noises,
At night, it's a fright!
So think real hard and try your best.
One more clue:
I live in a nest!

Melissa Bosworth (age 12)
St. Michael's University Middle School

Landscape of Canada

The tall green trees,
Grazing the branch,
The endless free flowing lakes,
The massive mountains decorating the sky,
The glistening slopes of snow and ice,
The flat prairies roll on by,
Back to Vancouver where the city's alive
    by night.
People from all over are different colours
    of light.
Canada is a place filled with many of
    its sights.

Jasmine Kaur Gill (age 12)
Khalsa School

~//~

The Carefree Tree

The great big tree
Stands beautiful and free
A little squirrel hides its loot
By the big tree's root

I look up at a branch
That looks over my ranch
Then a little caterpillar eats its leaf
That little thief!

The little white bud
Sailed slowly like a silly soap sud
The tree stood great and tall
In the winds of fall

It reaches over the driveway
While it holds a little blue jay
Its colours are red and green
Under which to daydream

I found a huge pine cone
That I used as a stepping stone
Up its great big trunk
Ran a cheeky chipmunk!

As it grows dark in the park
It reflects a great landmark
I see a giant limb
In the light that now is dim

Jonathan Cunningham (age 12)
St. Michael's University Middle School

Death

Unexpected,
No one is protected.
Someone you come to love,
Burns away like a feather of a dove.
You cover it up to be a lie,
But inside you are really saying, "Why?"
I do not have an answer to buy,
To tell me why people die!

Patrick Maitwe, Jr. (age 10)
St. Theresa Catholic School

~//~

The Elements

Fire spreads through the forest true
Started by lightning and thunder too
The fire burns through the night
And burns into the morning light

It sneaks into the city as you sleep
But you're awakened by a deafening shriek
Your dad helps with the water spout
First it begins to rain ice then everyone
    will rejoice

Luke Mills (age 12)
Pacific Christian Elementary School

~//~

This Eve's Moonlight

'Tis bright
This Evening
The Dark Side
Of the crescent
Moonlight tonight
Creates a unique
Feeling for all those
Who feel its
Magnificent rays.
But it also magically
And wonderfully creates
A mythical scene
For myself tonight in
The moonlight.

Kevin Ilomin (age 12)
Immaculate Conception School

Peace

Peace is loving your pets a lot
And playing with them.
Peace is sitting under a tree, watching
    the sunset.
Peace is playing sports with a friend.
Peace is helping poor children with no food.
Peace is cleaning parks and beaches.

Stephanie Marschal (age 10)
Topham Elementary School

~//~

Hibernation

The birds are heading south,
The bears are half asleep.
We don't want to wake them,
So shh! Don't make a peep!
The squirrels are collecting nuts,
The wolves are hunting prey.
They better move fast;
They're getting away!
This is called hibernation.
It happens when winter falls.
Glad it's not winter yet.
The animals have lots to get!

Alycia Ammar (age 10)
Ronald Harvey School

~//~

White Circle

I stare up into the sky.
I see a white circle hanging in the night,
Shining so bright,
In the night.
Giving light to the Earth,
Giving light to the people,
Giving light to the animal,
And giving light to nature.
I stare up into the sky once more.
I realize that the little white circle hanging
    in the sky,
Is the moon so bright,
In the night.

Valerie Chan (age 10)
Miller Park Community School

Nature

Nature is a sky of experience
An ocean of learning
A flower of voices
Nature is a busy beautiful place
The bees are collecting nectare
The birds are flying south in the winter
The ants are finding food and bringing it
    home to eat
Nature is the best
The butterflies are flying
The bugs are crawling around
The sky is blue, black, and grey
The bad thing is people are littering
The animals get sick and die because of
    human's waste
Nature should stay around forever
Nature is a part of me

Alexandra (Alley) Braverman (age 10)
Wondertree Centre

~//~

Little Cats

Ten little cats looking very fine
One ran off and now there are nine!
Nine little cats and one was late
He never came so now there are eight!

Eight little cats jumping to Heaven
One jumped too far and now there are seven!
Seven little cats playing with sticks
One was too sharp and now there are six!

Six little cats doing the jive
One got too tired and now there are five!
Five little cats going store to the store
One got stuck and now there are four!

Four little cats swatting at a flea
One ran away and now there are three!
Three little cats gots the flu
One got too sick and now there are two!

Two little cats lying in the sun
One got too hot and now there's one!
One little cat not having fun
He ran away and now there are none!

Jayden Kolesar (age 11)
Children of St. Martha School

150

I, Famous

I have a first name, but not a last.
I have some pictures, but not too many.
I have a front and a back,
But my middle is my most interesting part.
There are lots of me around the world,
But I am unique.
Many people like to look at me, but
few read.
I hold names of famous people, but also
famous things.
What am I?

Guinness Book of Records

Kathleen Doherty (age 9)
Discovery Elementary School

~//~

Useless Things

A boy without a toy,
A two year old without someone to annoy.
A bear without hair,
A stem without a pear.

A TV without a house,
A girl without a blouse.
A clam without a pearl,
A doll without a girl.

An hour without a day,
A horse without a neigh.
A book without a word,
A zoo without a bird.

A desk without a pencil box,
A forest without a red fox.
A washroom without a sink,
A heart without red or pink.

A car without keys,
A dog without fleas.
A road without a car,
A sky without a star.

A clock without time,
A bank without a dime.
A shell without a snail,
A handle without a pail.

Nicholas (Nick) Estergaard (age 10)
Miller Park Community School

Guess Who?

I am black and brown.
Kings and queens use me but they're
not real.
I can only move one space at a time unless
I am crowned.
I like to jump but I can be jumped.
What am I?

Chess piece

Tysen Louth (age 9)
Discovery Elementary School

~//~

Halloween

Witches are around,
Ghosts are about.
I like trick or treating,
And going far out.

I get lots of candy,
And eat it every day.
If I didn't have any candy,
I would starve away.

Gurjot Kaur Dhaliwal (age 11)
Khalsa School

~//~

Time

It's a story
Through generations
It flows, lifting hearts,
It passes, shifting time.
It's around us,
It's beside us,
It's in us.

It shows the way,
As it courses through galaxies,
Through the stars,
Through the moons,
With its wings,
The wings of time.

Jared Johannessen (age 11)
Neill Middle School

Popcorn

Pop! Pop! Pop!
I like popping sound!
Yum! Yum! Yum!
I like yummy popcorn!
But I don't like that smell!
But if you have popcorn
remember to share with me!

Jacqueline Lao (age 9)
Brander Gardens Elementary School

~//~

Dinosaur

Dinosaur, dinosaur, what do you feel?
I feel lots of dirt under my feet.
Dinosaur, dinosaur, what do you taste?
I taste some grass in my mouth.
Dinosaur, dinosaur, what do you smell?
I smell a tyrannosaurus running after me.
Dinosaur, dinosaur, what do you hear?
I hear a stegosaurus roaring.
Dinosaur, dinosaur, what do you see?
I see an anatosaurus swimming in a lake.

Naeemah Imran Khurshed (age 7)
Edmonton Islamic School

~//~

Untitled

I lie on my bed today
Staring at my perfect ceiling
Eyeing my perfect walls
I notice the small greasy fingerprints
And an ocean of pushpin holes

I looked at myself today
Perfectly perky, perfectly happy
With my perfect friends

I looked in the mirror today
Never satisfied with all I have
Obsessed with how I appear to others
You see I'm about as perfect
As the blurry reflection in my mirror

Marianne Jessiman-Perreault (age 12)
Branton Junior High School

Teddy Bears

Oh teddy bears, oh teddy bears
How cute and cuddly they are
With their big black noses
And their small adorable eyes
No one can deny that they are also wise

Oh teddy bears, oh teddy bears
They've got big shaggy ears
And long fluffy coats
Wouldn't you rather hug them then eat
your oats
Unless you're a goat

Julie Bever (age 9)
Mother Mary Greene School

~//~

Thank You!

Thank you for my eyes that see...
The happiness my family brings,
All of my caring friends,
All the teachers that help us learn,
And my loving animals.

Thank you for my ears that hear...
The birds chirping in the trees,
The mighty bang of thunder,
My dad's monstrous laughs,
And a congregation of angels singing.

Thank you for my mouth that tastes...
Wild roses growing in the bush,
The food that is set before us every night,
The milk that was freshly milked,
The freshly made pumpkin pie,
And the turkey roasting in the oven.

Thank you for my hands that feel...
The warm water from the dishes,
My cat's fluffy fur, my mom's
tight embrace,
And the texture of my hair.

Thank you for my nose that smells...
The sweet aroma of my mom's kitchen,
The smell of strawberries, the smell of
wild roses,
And the smell of my hair.

Bethany Friesen (age 11)
Hillcrest Community School

Wildfires

Fires are like a pack of wolves...
Stealth, fast, and unforgiving.
They leave a trail of anger, sorrow,
   and despair...
To all who get in its path.

Jason Margo (age 10)
Sherwood Park Elementary School

~//~

Roars

Around the corner I hear roars and roars.
I look around the corner.
It is just the sounds of cars.
It is so loud I wonder,
If you can hear it all the way from Mars!

Lukus Ray Ali (age 10)
Charles Dickens Elementary School

~//~

Death

Running fast
his heart racing.
Listening
for those voices
those threatening calls
those teasing
words.

He throws himself into
a bush in panic,
Waiting
for them to find him.
He starts to feel ill.

Finally
he passes out
as he hears
his mother's voice
whisper,
"I love you."

*Inspired by a newspaper article on
bullying*

Bobby Busby (age 11)
Neill Middle School

The Duchess of Glen Fir

Duchess is a duchess
Usually friendly
Cuddly with people
Hates most geldings
Eating all food
Sleepy on sunny days
Stubborn to move

Mariah Chapman (age 10)
Naramata Elementary School

~//~

White and Brown

I love to pet your nice soft fur,
I love to cuddle with your nice fluffy fur,
I love the way you lick my face.
You are always cheerful to see me,
You are always happy when you're being
   played with.
You look so cute when you sleep in your
   favourite chair,
I will always love you no matter what.
You're my favourite puppy.
Rufus!

Kendra Keen (age 10)
Miller Park Community School

~//~

The Haunted House

This house is very scary
It is as haunted as can be
No one will go in it now
For it has ghosts and ghouls
It has creaking floors along with the doors
and a leaking pipe
There is a black cat that lays flat on a mat
by a hat
Nobody knows if somebody lives there
It is just very scary
One day Joe, a guy from school
tried to walk in there. Boo!
He was never seen again
and that is the story of the haunted house.

Peter Flanagan (age 10)
Mother Mary Greene School

153

Untitled

Dolphins are nice,
Dolphins are sweet,
They love to play hide and seek.
Dolphins love to twist and curl
And people like to see them twirl.

Aminah Elbaalbaki (age 9)
Edmonton Islamic School

~//~

In the Dark Green Forest

In the dark green forest,
I lie beside a tree.
There is no bee to distract me,
And no animal to see.
Right beside a log,
I see a shaggy dog.
It runs towards me.
It tugs on my clothes,
And barks, "Come play with me!"
And so I ran away with him,
And I am happy now,
And having fun,
Just as happy and bright as the sun!

Jessica Tang (age 9)
Charles Dickens Elementary School

~//~

Costumes

Costumes, costumes,
So much to choose.
And I wonder what everyone else
will dress for this night of fright?

Maybe I should be a witch with a
black gown
Or maybe a ghost not making a sound.

Frankenstein sounds pretty good,
Or maybe a Grim Reaper with a hood?

What should I choose for Halloween?
But of course I need to be scary and mean!!

Kali Mailhot (age 9)
Ronald Harvey School

A Snake

Slithering through the grass
sensing
observing
hearing the hissing from your tongue
devouring
wee mice
Eyes as sunless as a deep hole
body as thin as a rope
tickling while in my hand
protecting your young
while defending your food
a snake what a wonderful creature

Kash McDermott (age 11)
Racette Junior High School

~//~

Extreme Coasters

Rocking, ramming, smashing
Bam!
The rocking ramming roller coaster!
Thrashing fifty miles per hour
Rushing your liver into your throat!
Terrifying, you think?
It was!

The crying of waiting children
Gives a damp frosty feeling,
Creeping its way down, down, down,
Deep into the depths of your terrified
little body!

Closer, closer, closer we get to the entrance,
Heart pounding, body shivering,
tension building.
Wow, what a feeling!

The doors open, dark, gloomy, fearful -
The coaster awaits!
We buckle up, and hold on
Tight as a tiger on its mouth-watering prey.
Ooooo... then silence... then *boom!*
A thrash, firing the coaster like a bullet
Through a dark mysterious world!

Well, what did you expect?
A charming, cheerful, children's ride?
No!

Farzana (Adam) Sidi (age 11)
Meadowridge School

154

Santa

Santa flies
Up in the sky.
He makes the reindeer
Go faster.
He gives toys
To girls and boys.

Jacob W. Boyko (age 6)
Miller Elementary School

~//~

So Fun in the Snow

How gently the snow fell,
On Saturday morning.
Almost every child outside,
Playing in the snow.
The snow was as soft as a bunny.
It tasted like vanilla ice cream.
The snow shimmered like a field
of diamonds.
Every child with a smile on their face,
Having a good time.
How grand it is.
So fun in the snow.

Olivia Hanson (age 9)
Ashley Park School

~//~

Ramadan

Decorate your house.
Inside your house
Sparkles!
Green ones, blue ones,
Silver ones, gold ones.

I like the food
After fasting.
The cakes, the cookies,
And the gum.

Having food
At somebody's house
And at home
Sometimes.

Hamzah Najmeddine (age 7)
Edmonton Islamic School

Broken Silence

The water was still and shining like glass.
The sky grey, remembering winters past.
Only to be heard was the beating of a heart.

Then the snow starting falling
From the clouds with a start
And as the snow hit the ground
The silence broke all around

Jillian Vasko (age 12)
St. Michael's University Middle School

~//~

Night the Cat

Night the cat
Who pounces on houses.
Waiting for gems to fall tonight.

And when night falls
The gems will fall.

And Night the cat
Will start to fight
For all the gems
That will fall tonight.

Christina Trinh (age 10)
Charles Dickens Elementary School

~//~

The Sun Set

Look at the sun, set in the west,
see all the colours shining bright.
This is truly the evening best,
when all around is filled with light.
Birds are flying high in the sky,
the lakes are sparkling, shiny blue.
Why does this all feel like a lie?
Red, oranges, purples, pinks,
and a slight of indigo...
You can't figure out what to think,
the colours just blend in so.
Watch it fast before it's gone,
our wonderful colourful sun!

Karina Pangilinan (age 12)
Immaculate Conception School

155

Birds

When I listen to birds in the moonlight
I hear a nightingale singing, singing for me.
When I listen to the robin, he says to me,
"Chirp! Chirp! Be merry!"
When I listen to the bluebird,
He says to me, "Be happy."
The birds are like a choir of angels,
Singing for me.

Elizabeth (Lillie) Cameron (age 7)
Glenmore Christian Academy

~//~

Candy

Sweet piece of candy
green, sour, smooth,
hard, delicious, juicy,
mouth watering, great
crunch and amazing.
What is it?

Why it's a Jolly Rancher,
all hard and munchy,
short and round,
tasty and a delight,
yum yum.

Alexandra (Alex) Lavalliere (age 10)
Mother Mary Greene School

~//~

Butterflies

Butterflies all in a row
The first one said, "Look, there's a flower
up ahead."
And the second one said, "There are bees
in the air."
And the third one said, "I'm thirsty."
And the fourth one said, "I am ready
to fly."
And the fifth one said, "Let's fly and fly
and fly."
And the last one said, "Fly away!"
And they all flew away.

Jacob Terry (age 8)
James Bay School

Horses

The horses galloping through the
moonlight sky
Little ones cry with tears of steel eyes.
Horses jumping over the waterfall high,
As they run their males must scout out
and spy.
Horses running through the night,
Riding horses is but I will dare try.
Horses blasting to the night sky to fly,
Baby horses born in spring light.

Braydon Switzer (age 10)
Notre Dame Elementary School

~//~

The Great Snowball War

Snow.
As soft as a bale of fluffy cotton.
Crushed into tiny balls of slush.
Thump. What's that?
The enemies have arrived with their
weapons, and they've brought back-up.
My four-year-old cousin leaps by my
side for protection.
They aim.
I know I won't be able to dodge their shots
in time.
I make a quick one for the door. "Plop".
There goes our snow fort. I think twice.
I can't leave my poor litle sidekick in the
palms of my brother and his friends.
I dash back. Too late. They've got him.
I squeeze the circular ball in my hand.
Ready, aim, fire!
Got them! The enemy's been shot in
the leg.
I look up at the rocky Squamish Mountain
and sigh.
Looks like we won today's battle.
"Hot chocolate!" called my grandma.
There was a sound, like one thousand
rhinos stampeding towards me.
The enemies have returned to feast.
I sipped the piping hot chocolate and headed
Towards the blazing fireplace, blanket
in hand.
The smell of victory had never been
so sweet.

Evereet Braitch (age 12)
Panorama Park Elementary School

Birthdays

Birthdays are fun,
As everyone knows.
Supper is good,
While cake is better.

Friends are great,
When we play games.
Games like Twister
Or games like Monopoly.

At parties we sometimes
Go swimming or
Bowling, or even stay home
And play balloon popping games.

I feel birthdays
Are as fun
As getting a new sister
And holding her close to myself.

Jennie Kuntz (age 11)
Parkland Immanuel Christian School

~//~

Sleeping

Please, Mom, just five more minutes.
C'mon, I just want to stay awake.
Yes, my teeth are brushed.
Please, just two minutes.
I'm a big person now.
OK, I'll go to bed.
I'm not sleeping.
Just one minute.
Please, Mom,
No, I won't.
Or maybe
Just a bit
Of sleep.
Must
Stay
Awake,
No,
Can't
Go
To
Sleep,
Zzz
Zzz
Z.

Dylan Callow (age 12)
St. Michael's University Middle School

Christmas

Christmas is such a wonderful thing
It's not just what Santa brings
There's more to Christmas than what
we receive
I know it's extremely hard to believe
The gifts we get are just an added touch
But really they don't mean all that much
So you see what I'm trying to say
There are more than gifts on Christmas Day!

Kayla Oliver (age 12)
Rutland Middle School

~//~

It is Fall

The frosty wind blows through my hair
As the stirring leaves blow across my shoes
It is fall
The wild geese fly up above
As the orange and yellow leaves
Fall from the big oak
It is fall
The buttercups sway as
The last leaf drops
It is fall
But soon to be winter

Savannah Hildebrandt (age 9)
Ronald Harvey School

~//~

Dinosaur

Dinosaur, dinosaur, what do you see?
I see a bee looking at me.
Dinosaur, dinosaur, what do you see?
I see an octopus looking at me.
Dinosaur, dinosaur, what do you see?
I see a bear looking at me.
Dinosaur, dinosaur, what do you see?
I see a tree looking at me.
Dinosaur, dinosaur, what do you see?
I see a pineapple looking at me.
Dinosaur, dinosaur, what do you see?
I see a horse looking at me.

Wahida Abubakar (age 7)
Edmonton Islamic School

157

Untitled

Hamster
Four legs, small
Crawl, nibble, cleaning
Special, happy, miss, love
Teddy

Jordyn Anna Debnam (age 7)
Sparling School

~//~

The Goblins on Halloween

The goblins are so wired on Halloween
The goblins are so scary your hair
Will spike right up on Halloween
Sometimes goblins are so nice on Halloween
The goblins are so funny on Halloween
The goblins are so cool on Halloween

Cole Huber (age 9)
École Joe Clark School

~//~

Shaking

I'm shaking,
Shaking like a leaf.
Traumatized, I run,
Run to Mommy.
I whisper a soft sob,
And she calmly grasps me.
I quickly stumble in bed,
By her side.
Sobbing, I ask,
"Mommy, Mommy!
Where's Daddy?"
In the dark,
I can see her holding back the tears.
"I told you, my dear son,
He went out to sea,
To protect our country."
We are clinging to each other,
Crying a river of prayers.
"Mommy, I had a nightmare,
That he'd never come home."
"Stop trembling, my dear,
For God is near."

Rebeca Pinca (age 12)
British Columbia Christian Academy

Untitled

I am a swimmer
Water is crashing on me
Like never before.

Jessica Laplante (age 11)
Aubrey School

~//~

Time

Time,
What is it?
Is it just a measurement of things gone past,
Or is it a thing that we cannot explain?

It is a thing that most fear.
You may not think so, but you most
    likely do.
Most people fear growing old and dying.
This is fear of time.
Yet, we also wish for it to pass more quickly
    with anxiety,
Sometimes more slowly with grief.

The past dictates the present, and the
    present dictates the future.
What could you have done to change
    the present?
What will you do to change the future?

Time can be as slow as a slug, sliding across
    the bricks of your garden path,
Yet it can also be a falcon streaking through
    the sky, diving for its prey.

But, you will soon realize that time is truly
    a stream of water,
Always slipping through your grasp
    however hard you squeeze,
But always remember, that the time given
    to you is limited.
Always cherish it for you will never be
    able to go
Back to change what you had done.
You will never be able to waste your time;
    all you must do,
Is love the ones you cherish, and do what
    you wish to do,
And you will have not wasted *your* time.

Kingsley Walter Shih (age 12)
Meadowridge School

Rainbow Mountain

There's a place called Rainbow Mountain.
If you want to get there you must use
   your imagination.
It's a place with millions of colours.
The fruit are any colour you wish for.
You see the sun shining with colour.
There's a well of wishing; you only get
   one wish.
This is Rainbow Mountain.

Rainbow Mountain cannot ever end.
It has a beginning but no end.
You can catch falling stars.
You can see the planets flying by.
You can see the world moving.
Wish upon a star with all your love.
This is Rainbow Mountain.

Alexandra Giugliani (age 10)
Aubrey School

~//~

What Love Has In Store For Us

Maybe to love
Is to bloom with one another,
To develop a bond, to unite each other,
Feeling this amazing connection that is
   in store for us.

Maybe to love
Is to realize changes in each other,
To be conscious of, to divide one another,
Sensing this tearful separation that is in
   store for us.

Maybe to love
Is to always hurt one another,
To not just hurt but, to destroy each other,
Knowing this awful farewell that is in store
   for us.

Maybe to love
Is to learn from each other,
To mature our actions, to consider
   one another,
Acquiring this second chance that is in store
   for us.

Carra Pischke (age 11)
École St. Thomas School

Guess Who

I have fur but not hair.
I have a black nose but sometimes brown.
I have a muzzle but not a bear muzzle.
I have a tail but not a short tail.
I have fur on my muzzle but not long.
What am I?

Dog

Lindsay Kornelson (age 9)
Discovery Elementary School

~//~

If I Had a Billion Cats Part Three

If I had a billion cats I would not have
   any friends!
Crash, clang, clang, they would all drive
   me crazy.
Clonk, clonk, clank, clank, broken lamps
   and cracked glasses,
Rip, Rip, zip, zip, ripped curtains and
   torn cushions,
Bark, bark, meow, meow, lots of fights
   held at my house,
Whimper, whimper, boo, hoo, they would
   all be up for sale!

Joy Liira (age 12)
Pacific Christian Elementary School

~//~

The Boy from Spain

The boy from Spain
On his body was pain.
He walked across a lane
And was hit by a train.

Before the bang
He said, *"Oh Dang."*
It started to rain
When he was hit by a train.

He died in pain
The boy from Spain.

Daynon Kellock (age 10)
École Joe Clark School

PlayStation

I have a PlayStation.
I like it.
I play with it.
I play cars with it.
That's it.

Joshua J. Boyko (age 6)
Miller Elementary School

~//~

Red Balloon

"I want a red balloon," she said
"But I don't want to get out of bed."
Then a blue balloon flew in her room.
She got so mad she got the broom.
"I want a red balloon," she said,
Then her mom called, "Get out of bed."

Hailey Stuart (age 10)
Boundary Community School

~//~

My Own Horse

I wish I were a clever and
    swift Thoroughbred;
I would rapidly race and dart towards the
    finish line.
I wish I were a strong and muscular Morgan;
I would carefully pull and heave my load.

I wish I were a brave and colourful Pinto;
I would proudly stray and voyage gracefully.
I wish I were a content and
    enjoyable Hackney;
I would cheerfully trot and canter
    at command.

I wish I were a burly and mighty Shire;
I would joyfully heave and tow carts.
I wish I were a black and white Appaloosa;
I would gracefully trot and gallop around
    my field.

But I'd rather have my own horse than
    be one!!

Nikolai June Cuthill (age 9)
Prairie Elementary School

The Chinese Pond

I was sitting in the front yard
Looking in the pond
Seeing lillies and koi
Thinking
What it would be like
To live in there
But then I look around
I see the willow tree
And all the nightingales
All of a sudden
I'm all full of wonder

Alecia (Ally) Ealey (age 12)
Wix-Brown Elementary School

~//~

The Christmas I'll Never Forget

The Christmas I'll never forget,
Happened just last year.
The stockings were hung by the fire,
Everyone in their beds without a fear.

The children dreaming of Santas
    and presents,
The little babies all sucking their thumbs.
On the Christmas I'll never forget,
Santa still had not come.

There were cookies and milk for Santa,
On the Christmas I'll never forget.
There were carrots for all the reindeer,
But Santa had not come yet.

So Christmas morning when we all
    woke up,
There were no presents under the tree.
No one said a word at all.
There wasn't one smile that I could see.

Then we heard a joyful noise.
It sounded like sleigh bells.
And then out in the town,
We heard happy shouts and yells.

So we all looked out the window,
And what wonderful thing did we see?
We saw jolly old Saint Nicholas,
With presents for you and me!

Aimée Buller (age 11)
Silver Star Elementary School

Halloween

Black cats ran away
Witches flying through the night
Halloween is fun

Malachite Miller (age 7)
James Bay School

~//~

God's Hand

God's hands came down and gave us glory.
For all of us who still stand,
We pray for those who gave their lives.
To remember them in our hearts,
To thank you for your lives.

Tasos Liaros (age 8)
St. Joseph's School

~//~

The Fat Rat and the Cat

There was a rat
It was fat
And it lived under my mat.
There was a cat
Who ate the fat rat
And the cat sat on another fat rat.

There was a rat
Who went under the mat.
And there was a cat
Who saw a fatter rat.

Then the rat saw
A mouse in my house.
Then the fat rat went
Under the mat and the
Cat was looking for the fat rat.

Then the fat rat went back
Outside from under the mat.
Then the fat rat saw a hat.
Then the fat rat brought the cat to see
   the hat.
Then the fat rat got the hat and put the
   hat on the cat.

Muayad Zakkour (age 9)
Edmonton Islamic School

Dinosaur

Dinosaur, dinosuar, what do you see?
I see a stegosaurus looking at me.
Dinosaur, dinosuar, what do you hear?
I hear foot steps in my ear.
Dinosaur, dinosuar, what do you taste?
I taste yummy meat in my mouth.
Dinosaur, dinosuar, what do you feel?
I feel mud under my feet.

Dounya Mouallem (age 7)
Edmonton Islamic School

~//~

Life

I watch the days fly away
As I grow up tall and bright
Smarter everyday
Loving every way of life.

I used to think life was just a joke,
But now I realize life is
Everything that revolves around you.
Life is something you need to cherish
Before you lose it.
Life is special.

Danielle Belyea (age 11)
Lake Bonavista Elementary School

~//~

Night Time

Night time, beautiful, dark, and
without colour
In the great big space,
Gathering all the stars,
Happily coming into the world,
The moon shining, all around,
Taking away the sun,
In the sky,
Making the sky so bright,
Everlasting, until the sun fights its way
back up,
To dawn,
To morning.

Vanessa Rust (age 10)
Mother Mary Greene School

161

Friendship

My friends make me grin.
I like when we play games
Especially when I get to win.
My friends have the prettiest names.
When my friends give me a smile
It makes me run a mile.
My friends have the style down the aisle
And then the doggy pile.

Mackenzie Iredale (age 7)
Glenmore Christian Academy

~//~

Pop Pop Poppity What Could That Be?

Poppity pop, poppity pop.
What's that sound?
Poppity pop pop, poppity pop pop.
It's coming from all around.
Smells real buttery, feels all bumpity.
It looks yellowish-white,
You can eat it day and night.
It's yummy in my tummy,
I know it's popcorn!

Michael Vetsch (age 8)
Brander Gardens Elementary School

~//~

Musical Man

My dad is a musical man
He likes to play guitar
And I always tell him
I'm sure that he'll go far!

One day he was playing
I looked up at his face
He told me to stop staring
And sing *Amazing Grace*!

I took a big breath
To let it all come out
But instead of music
It came out as a shout!

Esther Deuling (age 10)
J.W. Inglis School

Black Cats

Do black cats scare?
Do black cats sit on a chair?
Do black cats get cold?
Do black cats' legs fold?

Kirsten Dahlmann (age 8)
J.W. Inglis School

~//~

Bats

Do bats turn into vampires?
When they fly do they hit wires?
Do they like to sleep upside down
And turn their smile to a frown?

Maygen Culp (age 8)
J.W. Inglis School

~//~

Nothing to Do

Nothing to do,
Nothing to play,
No one is home,
Everyone is away.

I sit in my room,
Nothing in my mind,
Homework's done,
I am ready to cry.

I think and think,
As hard as I can,
Of something to play,
On this rainy day.

Brother gone,
Sister away,
Dad working,
Mom can't play.

I remember something,
Something I can do:
I can draw pictures,
Pictures from the zoo.

Emma Germain (age 9)
Meadowridge School

Who am I?

I don't know who I am and I would like
    to know;
I'll laugh and play, sing and dance, but I
    still don't know who I am.
When it was winter I made a snow angel
    and wondered if it was me,
No, it wasn't me.

When it was spring I picked a flower and
    noticed it was beautiful,
Was that me? No, it wasn't me.

When it was summer I splashed in the
    blue lake;
Was that me? No, it wasn't me.
When it was fall I made a pile of leaves
    and jumped in it;
Was that me? No, it wasn't me.

That I realized I was just me, a normal me.

Jessica Elkin (age 10)
Mitford Middle School

~//~

Ghosts

Very spooky here and here,
    but beware,
they might give you a scare.

Spirits of the dead floating
    with their bed sheets
    over their heads.

Be careful
when they come to your door,
    because they might give
    you a giant roar!

Bang! Boom!
Watch out there,
that little ghost is in the air.

As they fly high
    into the sky
they start to fade away,
    because that's the
    end of their play.

Mason Wong (age 12)
Neill Middle School

Colt

Running and kicking
    biting and jumping
    walking and trotting
eating the sticks off of the trees
He pulls leaves of the twigs
and he eats the grass off the field
I don't care if he bites me
I don't care if he kicks me
He's just being himself
my tall black, white, and brown colt

Patricia (Tricia) Bumstead (age 10)
R.L. Angus Elementary School

~//~

The Spirit of China and Japan

I have wings.
I give good luck but not in Canada.
I am very big but I am almost never seen.
I have scales, claws, and teeth but I am
    not a dinosaur.
I am in books about knights but I am not
    a griffin.
I breathe fire.

Dragon

Rylan Rowe (age 9)
Discovery Elementary School

~//~

Environment

Environment
No littering
Vancouver needs cleaning
I don't like garbage
Rivers need cleaning
Orcas don't like polluted water
Nobody litter in the ocean
Man don't pollute
Everyone come and help
No Nintendos on the beach
Time to clean up

Mathiew Lamontagne Cumiford (age 9)
Topham Elementary School

Untitled

Dog
Black, little
Run, rollover, play
Fun, nice, friendly, laugh
Gypsy

Elizabeth McIver (age 7)
Sparling School

~//~

Thieves

A hummingbird steals nectar from my
mother's prize tulip.
A cow steals the grass in my beautiful
front yard.
A dog steals my cat's food from her bright
orange dish.
A horse steals the golden apples from my
aunt's beautiful apple tree.
A mouse manages to steal the trail-mix
From the cupboard above the stove.

Oh wait a second that was me!

Raene Folden (age 11)
J.W. Inglis School

~//~

Remembrance Day

As I walk into the room
I see a flower that is new.
A bright and red flower, the centre black,
It strikes a memory and I think back
Of the time,
In the war,
The soldiers fought and died,
Just for us, so we'd be free, for the rest
of our lives.
And so when November eleventh
comes around,
Wear the poppy flower true,
And maybe someday you'll do
something special,
Like the soldiers did for you.

Emma Harris (age 11)
Lake Bonavista Elementary School

Untitled

Toys
Small and colourful
Breakable too
Always a new toy
Fun

Bryton James Fortier (age 12)
William Grayson School

~//~

Skateboards

Do skateboards think their wheels are legs?
Or do they think their wheels are pegs?
Do skateboards get hurt when they
are poked
Or when they are choked?

Blane King (age 8)
J.W. Inglis School

~//~

A Lie

The truth must be told; a lie is the worst
Growing bigger and bigger until it bursts
The story changing until it can't be
kept straight
Until a lie is told so many times that people
start to hate
And when you tell the truth nobody believes
They only think you're trying to deceive
People turn their heads, and you are
left alone
And everything you said is cast in stone
When people did believe they thought you
were great
Until lying and cheating became your fate
You thought people would believe you
until the end
But now all you can do is try to defend
Sometimes it might get you out of a
sticky mess
But sooner or later you'll have to confess
The truth be told a lie is the worst
Growing bigger and bigger until it bursts

Emily Reid (age 12)
St. Michael's University Middle School

Opposite

The opposite of palace
Is the ghetto in Dallas
Or it could be the 'hood in Seattle.
Here they freestyle battle.

What is the opposite of sober?
That boozer who drinks over and over.
What is the opposite of smart?
I smelt a fart in K-Mart.

What is the opposite of
Ladianian Tomlinson?
It could be the Spurs' Robinson.

Tyler Edwards (age 12)
Children of St. Martha School

~//~

Useless Things

A dog without a bark
A night without a dark
A school without books
A guy without looks

A boom box without CD's
A house without TV's
A school without a park
A test without a mark

A house without lights
A car without brights
A bedroom without a bed
A person without a head

A table without meals
A skateboard without wheels
A person without a name
A picture without a frame

A book without pages
A war without rages
A pizza without toppings
A deep without droppings

A sewer without pins
A car without rims
A kid without a friend
A book without an end

Mandy Creighton (age 11)
Children of St. Martha School

I Made a Mistake

I went to the kitchen to swat a fly
I made a mistake and swatted my pie
I went to the kitchen to eat a fish
I made a mistake and ate my dish

I went to the guillotine to lose my head
I made a mistake and everything was red
I went to my home to play with dice
I made a mistake; they had lice

I went to my bed to have a sleep
I made a mistake and slept on a sheep
I went to see Duncan at his home
I made a mistake and went to Rome

I went to the store to find my friend
I made a mistake and found the end

Bryce Herba (age 11)
Children of St. Martha School

~//~

A Friend

There once was a girl I knew who was a
    perfect friend
And I'll tell you some of the reasons why
    she was.
She accepts me the way I am; she believes
    me no matter what.
She calls me just to say hi and never gives
    up on me.
She forgives all my mistakes and
    gives unconditionally.
She helps me and invites me over.
She likes to be with me all the time and
    keeps her heart
Close to mine.
She loves me for who I am and makes a
    difference in my life.
She picks me up when I'm down and
    quiets my tears.
She respects me and tells me nice things,
But tells the truth when she needs to.
She understands me and stands up for me.
She never judges me and offers support.
She is the best friend anyone could
    ever have.

Denise Wu (age 11)
St. Paul's School

Untitled

Love is beautiful
It fills you with care
Caring gets you through
Love your brother and sister
Just like me
Love and care
Everyone

Keiffer (Keith) Morel (age 9)
St. Wilfrid School

~//~

Ghosts

Do ghosts live in houses?
Do ghosts make friends with mice?
Do ghosts like to play ball?
Do ghosts like to have fun in a hall
inside the mall?
Do ghosts go to school?
Are ghosts cool?
Do ghosts run?
Do ghosts have fun?
Do ghosts have hair?
Do ghosts sit on a chair?

Casey Heskith (age 8)
J.W. Inglis School

~//~

A Mouse in a House

There was a mouse in a house.
His hole was just like the sole of his shoe.
Who lived alone with a stone.
All he ate was a bone.

One day he saw a very fat rat
So the fat rat ate the mouse
And no mouse was in the house
And the stone was alone.
There was a fat cat who ate the fat rat.

So we never saw the fat cat, the fat rat,
And the skinny like mouse ever again.
Amen.

Farniz Hussan (age 8)
Edmonton Islamic School

Untitled

Hockey
Stick, helmet
Skate, shoot, checking
Cool, happy, sweaty, tired
Kodiaks

Warren Keohane (age 7)
Sparling School

~//~

To Whom it May Concern

Never give up on new things you
haven't perfected
Try your hardest when doing your work
Do your best to the best of your ability
Help others as they would help you
Working hard will amount to your success

Working hard will amount to your success

As you work toward these goals
You will learn more and more as time
passes by
Smarter and smarter you will become
No one has the same determination as
you have
Working hard will amount to your success

Working hard will amount to your success

Sometimes you're frustrated; that's okay
That's why they have erasers on pencils
if you make a mistake
If you put your mind to it, you can achieve
Working can be fun or boring, if you want
it to be
Working hard will amount to your success

Working hard will amount to your success

If you want to succeed to your best
Don't try, *do it!* For yourself and not
anyone else
Today, tomorrow, any day will be fine
You have a lifetime to achieve success
Working hard will amount to your success

Working hard will amount to your success

Chadley (Chad) Abalos (age 12)
Immaculate Conception School

Tangy the Monkey

Tangy was a strange monkey
His hairdo was pink and funky
And his tail curled in like a wadamongdo
And he's coming to get you!!!

Danielle Olafson (age 11)
Patricia Heights School

~//~

The Moon

The moon winked at me
as I rode down the path on my bike.
And just before I went to sleep
it gave me one last smile for the night.

Tanish McMenamie (age 12)
Pacific Christian Elementary School

~//~

The Run

Batter up!
I hear the ump call.
I rush up to the plate,
I look out at the field,
Bases loaded.
I have to hit it,
I just have to.
Come on,
Concentrate.
Here comes the pitch...
Strike one...
Strike two...
I have one strike left...
Whack!
I hit it!
Feet flying,
I made it to
First base,
Second base,
Third base,
Oh no,
Here comes the ball,
Better stay at third.
Yes, we're winning three-zero!

Lana Koehle (age 11)
Neill Middle School

White Stuff

When snow falls down your neck,
It feels like a nice bird's peck...
It sounds like
Crispy, crunchy chocolate bars when you
step in the snow...

When it falls it looks like crystals...
It covers cars with white crystals!

Nicholas (Nic) Brice (age 10)
Ashley Park School

~//~

Angel Dust

Within this little bag,
Placed with loving and care,
Is special angel dust my guardian
placed there.
It is to share among my special friends,
When they are down or feeling blue,
To lift their hearts and show a smile,
Like special friends should do.

Peyton Armstrong (age 11)
Rosevalley Elementary School

~//~

Pets Are...

Pets are...

Funny acting animals like sliding down
a slide,
Playful actions like nudging a ball.
Neat pets are cats, canines, and canaries,
Tricky pets like a rabbit running rapidly.

Pets can be...
Mean if you treat them disrespectfully,
Scary looking figures in the dark.
Fast and slow, animals have speeds of
their own,
A guard barking and growling to warn you.

Pets are a work in progress!!!

Taryn Huszar (age 10)
Ashley Park School

Dogs

Do you think dogs get hot with hair?
Would you think they'd be cooler with
nothing to wear?
Do dogs like to get haircuts?
When they don't, do we call them mutts?

Shaylynn Fey (age 8)
J.W. Inglis School

~//~

Untitled

swimming
chlorine, sweat
cold, warm, heavy
lane ropes, long, diving, board
loud, quiet, kicking, splashing, echoing

Alison MacDonald (age 10)
R.L. Angus Elementary School

~//~

Fall!

Dancing without care
leaves in the air
beautiful wisps of colour.
Sunset orange, crimson red
make a cozy bed.

Robyn Ord (age 9)
Sunalta School

~//~

Train Track

I'm a train on a track
So many boxes on my back, I move
so quickly
As though with fright
Much of the boxes filled with dreams that
I follow
To keep myself on the track.

Brody McRae (age 12)
Wix-Brown Elementary School

Turkeys

Do turkeys run away?
Do turkeys sleep all day?
Where do turkeys go
When there is a foot of snow?

Dillon Roelfsema (age 8)
J.W. Inglis School

~//~

Snow

Nice soft snow
As soft as a fluffy sheep
And as sparkly as a diamond
It's as cold as a freezing ice cube
Nice soft snow

Justin Kehler (age 9)
Ashley Park School

~//~

Just One Chance

Just one chance is all I need,
Just once to be with you.
I'll always be in love with you,
I hope you know that's true.
All I really want,
Is just a single chance
To finally be happy again,
To finally take that glance.
As I really want,
Is for you to be with me.
I'm always crying about you;
It's hard, 'cause you can't see.
Will I be happy again?
I don't seem to know.
I always want to be with you,
But it's hard to let it show.
I'm so afraid to love,
But more afraid to lose.
Holding onto a picture,
It's hard for me to choose.

*Dedicated to a boy that won't give me
a chance...*

Amber Nadeau (age 12)
Clearwater Secondary School

168

Black Cats

Do black cats like to be fat?
Do black cats like to wear hats?
Do black cats like to be on a mat?
Do black cats like to be on a bat?

Jaccob Lariviére (age 8)
J.W. Inglis School

~//~

Pumpkins

Do pumpkins imagine their colour is skin?
Do pumpkins think they have a chin?
Do pumpkins just lay there in the sun?
Do pumpkins have fun?

Jade Schunter (age 7)
J.W. Inglis School

~//~

The Great Red

I heard the sound of thundering hooves
I felt the ground quiver in fear
I smelt the smell of hay and grass
I sensed the herd of the wild, reckless
Red coming
And, then I saw
I saw the flying manes and tails
I saw the mares, the colts, the fillies
Waiting, waiting...
I saw what I had wanted to see
The Great Red
Leading his herd like a shepherd and
his flock
His fiery spirit blazing like an
uncontrollable fire
He was galloping, galloping like the
desert wind itself
They ran by me like I did not exist
Then, they were gone, gone like seasons
And all I had left of the majestic herd
was a simple memory
A memory of the Great Red -
The fire in his eyes
The love for his herd

Katlyn Trainor (age 12)
St. Joseph School

Spring and Summer

Trees, bees, all around,
Flowers blooming, birds chirping,
Sunshine shining everywhere,
Nice fine breeze through the air, nice
and warm
I have to think of more
But as I do I will think of you.

Forrest Johnston (age 8)
James Bay School

~//~

Untitled

I have a cat
That wears a hat.
I have a dog
That doesn't jog.

I have a raven.
His name is Jayden.
I have some ants
That tried to rip my pants.

Anthony Farrow (age 8)
École Joe Clark School

~//~

What Christmas is About

No Christmas is not about presents.
It is about spending time with your family.
It's about getting together on Christmas Day.

No Christmas is not about getting all the
presents in the world.
It is about giving and not receiving.
It is about when Jesus was born.

And who all heard this poem, I hope
you realize
Christmas is not about presents.
It's about family, giving and not receiving
And it is about when Jesus was born.

That, my friend is what Christmas is about.

Allyson Ray Thierman (age 10)
Ashley Park School

When I Grow Up

When I grow up I want to be a teacher
It would also be good to be a preacher
I would not like it when students
    would stare
It might give me a very big scare
I want to teach in Parkland School
I hope the students will think I'm cool

Kevin Bos (age 9)
Parkland Immanuel Christian School

~//~

Gold Rush

Gold shimmering in the sand
Old gold pan shining, sparkling
Long trails through mountains
Dusty, dirty, desperate road

Rockerboxes find precious gold
Usually youth is what you need
Sacrifices are what you make
Hope we get there in one piece!

Joseph (Joe) Esnouf (age 10)
Tyler Wilson (age 10)
Beaver Lake School

~//~

River

Rivers in the day are like shimmering,
    mystical, mysterious pools,
That none can understand.
Animals use it as a drinking source,
While men use it in many different ways.
At night the quiet river
Has a striking reflection of stars in its
    wondrous waters.
Looking up at the night sky,
While the river gurgles as though gasping
    for air,
I see and live in a different universe.
Early morning comes to see my unexplained,
    meandering companion,
Once more with its enchanted glow.

Alicia Currie (age 12)
Heffley Creek Elementary School

A Majestic Evening

Snakes curve up the bruised black sky
Blossoming into exquisite,
Vivid colours.
Angels tap the air,
Leaving screaming pink ripples.
Invisible dancers sprint across a
    darkened sky
Leaving brilliant blue,
Divine red,
Pungent green,
And blissful white ribbons
To momentarily smudge the sky.
A painter's ladder falls, tipping over
Mute gold buckets of paint.
Rich coloured grapes fall
From the bounty of our Lord
With a delicate rain shower
Of rose petals to follow.

Rebecca (Becca) McGuinness (age 10)
St. Cyril School

~//~

If the World Was a Crazy One

If the world was a crazy one,
Homework would always get done.
School would not be every day,
So that kids could skip and play.
You'd need no money to buy a car,
You'd need to be five to get in a bar.
You won't need to wait until you're sixteen,
But drive when you're twelve or
    maybe thirteen.
No one would be against paint ball guns,
After all they're only for fun.
From twelve a.m. to twelve p.m. it is dark,
Mean animals would be nice, such as
    the sharks.
The animals that kill would be rabbits
    and mice,
Catholics would be mean and robbers
    would be nice.
Ice would be hot and hot chocolate would
    be cold,
At the age of twelve you'd be
    considered old.
People would never walk but always run,
If the world was a crazy one.

Stacey Praticante (age 12)
Veritas School

170

I Will Remember

Incredibly brave soldiers, young and
   old, battled

Whatever enemy, any time of day
In boats, planes, or on land.
Little girls and boys hoped their
   courageous fathers
Lived when constantly battling for freedom.

Remembering every tragic moment of
Every miserable day was
Most frightening for families with
   relatives risking
Every second of their lives in war.
Members of the army would
Bravely fly in planes, drive on water or
   on land.
Everyone in Canada has liberty.
Remembering the heroic soldiers who
   passed away is very sorrowful.

Monique MacFarlane (age 11)
École Routhier School

~//~

No

No you can't run,
No you can't jump,
No you can't yell,
No you can't thump.

No you can't scream,
No you can't fall,
No you can't sing,
No you can't call.

No you can't dance,
No you can't spit,
No you can't blink,
No you can't hit.

No you can't hang,
No you can't walk,
No you can't play,
No you can't talk.

"Why not?"
I said you couldn't talk!

Ashley Wilson (age 12)
Pacific Christian Elementary School

Untitled

The skies were blue
And now they're grey
And we have nothing to say.
We pollute, we all know that
And now it's like we are going to attack!!
I love our world but do you?
And now you can show us
By helping with the *North Shore Cleanup!!*

Evangeline Hogg (age 10)
Topham Elementary School

~//~

On Halloween

On Halloween
Everybody goes crazy
And the witches
Get lazy
Well the cat
Picked a daisy
When the vampire was sleepy
The pumpkin went creepy
The skeleton screamed
The sidewalks creaked

Alexis Mary Ludwig (age 9)
St. Wilfrid School

~//~

Untitled

Mom is tired.
I think she is fired.
Dad has the flu.
I think he turned blue.

My brother is nine.
He thinks he's fine.
He likes to eat.
He sometimes says, "Beat."

My sister is five.
She's seen a beehive.
She likes to play ball.
She has a friend named Paul.

Miranda Gray (age 11)
William Grayson School

171

Hay Ride

I'm going on a hay ride;
I hope I don't fall off the slide.
When I'm at the pumpkin patch,
I will light a match,
When the pumpkin is carved
In the pumpkin patch.

Austin Bower (age 10)
Boundary Community School

~//~

War

The piercing sound of many mens' screams,
Many people have dreams,
And hope their fathers will survive,
And hope their fathers will arrive,
At home-sweet-home.

And families captured everywhere,
And many women losing hair,
Because of the powerful armies.

Zachary Mankowski (age 10)
Mother Mary Greene School

~//~

He Was Once a Soldier in War

He was once a soldier in the war,
He fought for property,
And he fought for dignity.
He fought for his country,
Because he loved it so.

He was a soldier in the war,
And as time still goes on,
Remember it as if it were yesterday,
For memories we still need,
Because we loved him so.

He was a soldier in the war,
He was a soldier who gave it all he had.
A soldier whose braveness we wish we
all had,
A solider whom we can call our hero.

Nicole Bordignon (age 11)
St. Helen Elementary School

War

War is
soldiers, guns, and fighting
all through the day
killing other people
to get their own way.

There are psycho ill people
fighting just for fun
hurting lots of people;
their leader is the gun.

Countries try to stop it
by fighting right back;
too bad they just keep on fighting;
I wish they would all

just *stop!*

Zachary (Zach) Anderson (age 12)
Neill Middle School

~//~

The Forest

The forest is green
so lush so free
The forest has animals
so big and so small

Look at its beauty
its lakes so clean
Look at its loveliness
stay here with me

The animals in it
are weak and are strong
The animals live here
and so do we

Some humans destroy it
our forest so green
They built all the cities
so ugly not clean

The mountains and trees
they will always be
the place that I live
with my family

Erica Tippe (age 11)
Pinantan Elementary School

My Dog

My dog is shaggy with lots of hair.
Her name is Kobe. I give her lots of care.
She loves me a ton, so I love her back.
When she walks me, I get plenty of slack.
She works her hardest, a child could see,
To please my mom, my dad, and me.
Kobe is like an eagle in mid-flight,
As she scampers quickly out of sight.
My dog loves to play chase all day.
Sometimes she tries to run away.
I know she loves me but also my dad.
When she sees him she always goes mad!
Every night she runs to the door,
Digging her nails into the floor.
Here she zigs, there she zags,
Her ears fly back and her tail wags.
If you pick her up, you are a fool.
She slobbers, slurps, and always drools.
Stinky dog breath in my face,
But dogs gotta be dogs in any case!

Xaverie MacLennan (age 9)
Swanavon School

~//~

School

Education is fun: it helps you through
   the year,
It helps you get a job when you really
   need it.
School is where you learn to read;
It's also where you learn to; speak, write,
   type, draw, learn French.
You learn, you tell time and spell,
You'll learn that learning is fun!
Science, social, math, spelling, reading, art,
   and computers...
It's all fun!
When school is over you'll go home,
Or you'll have detention and learn lots more.
Then you'll go home and dream about...
The very next day...
Then you'll go to school and have a
   history test.
Sometimes you flunk.
You didn't study, you chewed your
   nails tiny.
You hand it in...
You get an A.

Shelby Warn (age 11)
William Grayson School

Untitled

A knight
Armour and swords
Riding, battle, killing
Strong men who protect a castle
Soldiers

Vanessa A. Martin (age 11)
Pense School

~//~

Don't Litter

Why pollute when you do?
Save yourself and animals too
Pick up once
Pick up twice
Please don't litter, and be nice

Natallie Olszewski (age 10)
Topham Elementary School

~//~

Peace

Peace is hearing the rain against a roof.
Peace is sitting in a bubbly bath.
Peace is playing soccer with friends.
Peace is opening doors for people.
Peace is not killing animals just for fun.
Let's all be peace makers.

Rachel A. Wollenberg (age 10)
Topham Elementary School

~//~

Seasons

Spring, winter, summer, fall.
Everybody loves it all.
Jumping and playing, everyone saying,
   "Good-bye summer, hello fall!"
Sometimes I wonder why we have all
   these things?
It seems like the world is spinning in rings.

Kirstian Fix (age 10)
Pinantan Elementary School

Untitled

Spider-Man
Red, blue
Walls, web, run fast
Cool dude, good, awesome
Rescue

Jordan Guillemette (age 7)
Sparling School

~//~

B.M.X.

BMX
Fast, light
Racing, winning, jumping
Crossing the finish line
Cycling

Jake Haamers (age 10)
Naramata Elementary School

~//~

Untitled

Flowers, flowers, everywhere.
Pink, purple, blue, yellow.
All the colours of the rainbow.
Daisy, tulip, rose.
Flowers, flowers, everywhere.

Meghan Fair (age 6)
Glenmore Christian Academy

~//~

Fall

Fall is the time of year when there is a breeze
And all the leaves fall off the trees.
And for some reason there are no bees;
Maybe they freeze.
Soon the geese will leave and fly
Heading south in the sky.
I know they don't die;
I will soon see them up high.

Hunter Stewart (age 9)
Sunalta School

Life is Wonderful

Look at the birds flying with love,
Look at the sun sweating above.
Look at the butterflies come by with colour,
Look at them take place beside one another.

Look at the big dark and cold night,
Look at it sit there without any light.
Look at the beautiful stars in the sky,
Look at the moon shining so high.

Look at me; I'm almost asleep,
Look at me; I'm too tired to leap.
What's with this? I haven't even read,
But nothing can stop me from going to bed.

Kyle Bliss (age 10)
Miller Park Community School

~//~

The Four Seasons

The four seasons start with spring
the time when swallows begin to sing
The gentle rays melt the snow
Sometimes it's hard to see it go
Yet in my heart I feel no sorrow
as I look towards a bright tomorrow

Summer is now knocking on our door
like it did the year before
In summer time school is out
when all the children run about
The time when skies are bright and blue
This is summer's everlasting clue

Now it is the season of fall
the time when the trees look tall
In the fall it's Thanksgiving
the time we're thankful we're living
In the fall leaves are falling
and the chill of winter comes calling

It's time, it's time, winter is here!
Soon it will be a happy New Year!
At Christmas time you receive many gifts
Winter disappears with the last snowdrift

With a sound of a swallow wing
we again head back into spring

Bianca Dunn-Rydh (age 9)
Aubrey School

Dance of the Faeries

Shining in the bight moonlight
Danced little faeries blue and little
    faeries white
Wings like silk running through
    green meadows
Making the dewy green grass turn to
    golden sorrows

They make the seasons change with the
    swoop of their charming wings
Bluebells explode with the song of their
    "Ring, ring, rings"
The faeries run and jump to hide
Until sunset when the moon makes tide

The skies are blues, lavenders, and reds
The faeries rest safely in soft flowerbeds
Fall has arrived and faeries weep
It's time for their paradise to sleep

Ciara Prosnik (age 9)
St. Vincent School

~//~

Out of Reach

It's out of reach, I can't hold on.
It's leaving me, it's going, going, gone.
I've lost it forever; it'll never come back.
I can't hold on, but then again I can't slack.
I'm lost and I'm lonely, but no
    one understands.
I grip tightly, my cold clammy hands.
I'm leaving my sorrow, I'm leaving my fear.
But when I leave that, I'll leave that I dear.
I'll leave all the poverty; I'll leave all despair.
I'll leave all my wishes, and that evil,
    cold lair.
I cannot remember a time of great bliss,
I cannot remember my very first kiss.
The time I was loved, the time there
    was care.
I cannot remember.
I cannot remember.
    Going,
    Going,
    Going,
    There.

Shawna Lotzer (age 12)
St. Cyril School

Summer Heat

The sun licked through the trees.
The black asphalt consumed the heat.
Tall mirrored skyscrapers laughed
    as the people below squinted at the
    blinding reflection.

Sarah Allan (age 12)
Pacific Christian Elementary School

~//~

Five Little Aliens

Five little aliens standing on the floor;
One fell down and then there were four.
Four little aliens climbing on the tree;
One got stuck and then there were three.

Three little aliens playing with glue;
One got sticky and then there were two.
Two little aliens having too much fun;
And then there was one.

One little alien became a hero
And then there were zero.

Stormy Wells (age 12)
Children of St. Martha School

~//~

Someday I Want to Be

Someday I want to be a tailor,
Or maybe a sailor.
Sailing the ocean blue,
Or making a jacket that is new.
I know what I will be.
I think I will be a bumblebee.
I will fly everywhere,
In the crisp morning air.
Collecting food everywhere I go,
From flower to flower, to and fro.
No, I think I will fly the highest jet up in
    the sky.
I will fly where no man can go.
The Earth's boundaries are below.
Yes, I think I will fly.

Bastiaan Reijm (age 10)
Parkland Immanuel Christian School

175

Spirit Horses

For they are together
Like birds of a feather
Hooves drumming as one in the sand

For years I've wondered
How they could thunder
For hours across the land

For they have been told
By spirits bold
How and where to roam

For they have been set free
And that's fine by me
For now every which way is their home

Rebecca Mlikotic (age 11)
St. Joseph Elementary School

~//~

Ten Big Planets

Ten big planets sitting on a vine...
One went out of orbit and then there
were nine
Nine big planets falling on a gate...
One missed it and then there were eight

Eight big planets trying to see Heaven...
One stared too hard and then there
were seven
Seven big planets eating magic tricks...
One lost its colour and now there are six

Six big planets sitting on a hive...
Bees came out and then there were five
Five big planets going to the store...
One lost its money and then there
were four

Four big planets eating a tree...
One choked and then there were three
Three big planets sitting in goo...
One drowned and then there were two

Two big planets having a lot of fun...
One slipped and then there was one
One big planet sitting on a gun...
He got shot and then there were none

Alex Khourieh (age 11)
Children of St. Martha School

Little Blond Girl

Little blond girl so tiny
In your hands, smiling twenty-four/seven,
Not knowing what lies ahead,
She giggles with her friends.
As she grows she changes;
Her hair goes brown.
But she still smiles twenty-four/seven.
In grade seven her life has changed,
But that little girl still smiles,
And that little girl was me.

Amanda van Egdom (age 12)
Wix-Brown Elementary School

~//~

The Silent Night

After the leaves had fallen and the trees
were bare,
And warm clothes were put on for children
to wear,
South the Canadian geese flew,
While through my hair, a soft wind blew.

But on one starry, silent night,
Through my bedroom window, I saw such
a sight.
Me just staring, me just listening,
"Clink, clink," I hear a soft glistening.

Without a single word or sound,
The clouds laid a blanket on the ground.
The crisp, brown grass changed into a bed
of white,
As stars shone brightly like jewels of
the night.

I ran outside with such great wonder,
Faster and faster, like a strike of thunder.
I fell on that soft, white bed,
As a feeling of pride went through me, toe
to head.

I could see in the glow of a rising sun,
That the white bed was snow and winter
had begun.
I laughed and jumped with all my might,
And I will always remember, forever and
ever, that silent night.

Jasjeet Kaur Sandhu (age 11)
Khalsa School

Untitled

Shiny and high enough
High and above
Out in outer space
Out with other stars
Tall and up with the planets
In the night sky
Nice and high in the night sky
Gives you wishes

Shoots around so people can make a wish
Tough to see in the sky
A nice light in the sky
Rises at night

Christina Haliwyz (age 12)
William Grayson School

~//~

T.V. Trouble

My mom really hates when I watch T.V.
She says it will make my brain turn to mush.
Sitting one day, in my usual way,
Staring into the screen.
When suddenly it went psycho!
Totally berserk!

I was sucked right into a T.V. show
Feeling weird, as I looked up,
There before me was a terrible troll,
Disgusting, stinky, revolting!
As tall as a mountain of garbage and junk,
He picked me up, as light as a pebble.

He tumbled, tossed me around.
I panicked. He thumped over to a rock
And dropped me directly on top.
Grabbing a torch from the dark,
    dingy chamber,
I glared and fired with force. Shwack!
It hit hard on his head... Crash! To the floor.

I peered out of the T.V. screen in time
To see my brother flick the switch to "Off".
Darkness. Pitch black. Nothing else.
I sit and wait till someone... pushes the
    button again.
My mom really hates when I watch T.V.
Now my mush-brain understands!

Meagan Seeley (age 10)
Swanavon School

Untitled

As roses wither and die,
Summer is gone,
And so is its beautifulness.
Alas, it makes me sad,
But I can't wait for the magic,
The magic of fall to begin.

Some people fear the fall.
It announces the nearness of winter.
For me, fall is delightful;
I do not care for the cold.

Fall's colours are bright and cheerful.
Animals scamper for the last bit of food.
Leaves crunch beneath my feet.
And jack o'lanterns are part of the occasion.

As fall draws to a close,
The snow begins to fall.
Fall's magic ends,
And winter's dazzling begins.

Cara Guglich (age 11)
Patricia Heights School

~//~

The Sobberall

Yesterday I met a Sobberall,
While I was heading to the mall.
He was all green;
I'm sure that he was seen.

He made no sense at all;
He said, "Ogal, Bogal, Kall!"
He was a funny little critter,
With two arms, two legs, and a earlitter.

Purple with yellow polka dots and
    two heads,
He said, "Ogal, Bogal, Kall, Gead!"
He had four eyes, two mouths and a nose,
And a tail like a garden hose.

He had big claws and teeth;
A guy walked past named Keeth.
He said, "What is that ugly thing?"
I said, "That's my friend, Ogal, Bogal,
    Kall, Riting!"

Cara Major (age 11)
J.W. Inglis School

Untitled

C - Castles of stone
A - A palace of beauty
S - Slits in the sides
T - Tough as brick
L - Long and high walls around the castle
E - Enchanted palaces
S - Some can be very plain and old

Shelby Fischer (age 10)
Pense School

~//~

My Dog

My dog got a lot of the Thanksgiving turkey
On the celebration holiday.
He had great friendships with his
    doggy friends
Yes, they would not go away!
They helped him eat that turkey
And then they all fell asleep.
We were thankful for the friendship shared
On that hot, hot day.

Jacob Timmermans (age 7)
St. Joseph School

~//~

Ptarmigans

Through the ivory white, a voice is heard
Who calls, with longing shrills and shrieks
I see, through downy drifts of snow,
    a stirring
Thy graceful girl that glances at me
What eyes, black as obsidian, and glistens
Like rain, pitter-pattering on a window pane
Piercing through the snow, stirring in
    the calmness
I am awed by him, who flies away
Therefore, it seems the whole world is
    stilled once again
All he appears to be is a tiny particle
Just drifting, in the sky
I wave goodbye, and close my eyes
Standing in a world of silence

Rachel Fong Johns (age 10)
Patricia Heights School

Sitting on the Beach

Sitting on the beach
Playing in the sand
Eating a peach
With my dirty hands
Listening to waves crashing on the rocks
While children are playing in the sea
By the dock
Seeing a bee
Eating its honey
Near a bush that is small
Where there is a bunny
The sun is shining; I'm having a ball
If only I weren't stuck in my room
Sulking on my bed with my gloom

Kim Damaso (age 12)
Immaculate Conception School

~//~

Hands

Have you ever stopped to think
All the wonders a hand can do?
They can write with pencil and then,
With marker, crayon, or with pen.

They draw pictures, hold a book,
Create charming crafts, and cook.
They throw balls far and near.
Watch out! They like to target your ear!

Your hands have joints, knuckles, and bones.
They come in many different tones,
Like red, light, dark, or yellow.
Hands play instruments like violin or cello.

Balancing, dressing,
Pointing, caressing.
Scratching, itching,
Beckoning, stitching.

Typing, writing,
Playing, fighting,
Loving, folding,
Slapping, holding.

So have you ever stopped to think
All the wonders a hand can do?

Callista MacLennan (age 11)
Swanavon School

Hayride

I am going on a hayride
I hope two don't collide
I am so excited
Ow, I wasn't invited

Landon Weemers (age 10)
Boundary Community School

~//~

Untitled

Castles
Fort for the king
Protecting, attacking
The castle was a strong fortress
Stronghold

Michael Tanner Goetz (age 11)
Pense School

~//~

Untitled

Autumn
Colourful, fun
Jump in leaves with friends
Carving pumpkins with family
October

Winter
Make a snowman
Build a snow fort with friends
Have a snowball fight with friends
Christmas

Spring
All the birds come
Kids play outside all day
Spring is a beautiful season
Colour

Summer
Heat waves, swimming
Swimming, playing, relax
Summer vacation with family
Have fun

Kelton Walters (age 11)
William Grayson School

Untitled

Sneaky
Poisonous
I don't like spiders
Dangerous, tarantulas
Eggs are laid by mothers
Red wolf spider lives at Devin's house

Jordan Samuelson (age 12)
William Grayson School

~//~

Pumpkins

Pumpkins, pumpkins, they're so cute
They are different, they don't hoot.
There are lots of different colours
Some are lighter, some are duller
They sit on your doorstep the whole night
Without getting in one little fight
Their stems are different shapes and sizes
Pumpkins can be won for prizes
Carved pumpkins have a different name
Don't throw pumpkins even with aim

Erin Brassor (age 10)
Notre Dame Elementary School

~//~

Winter!

Winter, winter, freezing below zero
As I lie on my pillow
Waiting to get my hot cocoa
Also waiting for the news to say no school!

Hoping that no one can take me out of bed
Unless I get fed
I got mad when my mother
Got me out of bed
But it was fun when I went sledding
with my brother
On the glistening snow
As I slide down the slippery hill
I crash into an old, big mill
And I get ready to go back home with big
gigantic bruises

Kody Kw Lee (age 10)
Mother Mary Greene School

179

Travel

I went to Rome.
My mother was carrying a dome.
So the travel was long.
The hours were wrong.

I sat and sat
But was scared by a rat!
I slept and slept.
My hair was wrecked!

Khadija Warsames (age 9)
Edmonton Islamic School

~//~

The Monster That Ate a Lobster!

One day I saw a monster
That ate a lobster.
It had a big lump on it.
It was so big his clothes would split.

Then the monster had a fit
Then fell in a pit.
And that was the end of the monster
That ate a lobster.

Jonathon Hamm (age 9)
École Joe Clark School

~//~

I Hear Cruise Night

I hear fast cars racing
I hear others pacing
I hear cops arresting
I hear kids addressing

I hear chrome glisten
I hear the shifting of transmission
I hear old cars rumble
I hear new cars crumble

I hear RPM rising
I hear exhausts diving
I hear tires exploding
I hear asphalt eroding

Duncan Hebenik (age 11)
Children of St. Martha School

Hockey

I hate hockey!
The guys get so cocky!
It's so physical, no gentle nudges.
And they hold terrible grudges.
There is pushing and shoving and hating.
It is more like wrestling than skating.
Then a whistle blows and the game begins!
It shouldn't matter who loses or wins.
It is not sportsmanship they're showing!
No carefree game! Their anger is growing!
Convinced they are the best at the game,
"Champion" must be their middle name.
That is why...
I hate hockey!

Justine Houchin (age 11)
Swanavon School

~//~

Nina

I've always wanted to have a dog -
One cute, cuddly, and sweet.
A big one, small, or in between,
It matters not to me.

One to walk and feed and care for,
One to scold and one to praise.
One to clean up after,
One to lick my face!

One to love who loves me back -
I begged and begged for one.
"You're irresponsible!" said Mom,
"And much much much too young."

They said it's too much work for me,
But still I was determined.
To get a good ol' dog and then...
Mom finally confirmed and...

I love my big black dog
With little bits of white.
Even though she barks and whines
When left alone all night.

She's my *grreat*
Great dane
All the same!

Alexandra (Alex) Georgson (age 10)
Swanavon School

I am Rough and Tough

I am tough and hard, but I can also be smooth.
I can move in water but I don't have legs.
I can get moved by human beings
   and animals
But I cannot move myself.
Wherever you go you can see me
But I cannot see you.
There's millions of me and I can be made
   into a plate
If I'm small enough, but I can also
   be sculpted.
There's only a few of me that can float.
What am I?

Rock

Mitch Knippelberg (age 9)
Discovery Elementary School

~//~

Flowers

Flowers are sweet smelling plants.
Their colours are a beauty to see.
If you lay in a field of flowers, all is quiet
   and still.
You can feel the breeze in your hair, and
   all is a memory,
Because all you can do is relax and smell
   the wonderful smell of dew.

You lie in the beautiful sun, and breathe
   the beautiful air.
You sleep with wonderful dreams and
   feel happy
And alone at the same time.
You feel as if you are in a wonderful land!

All is well for all you can hear is the sound
   of a breeze.
It is peaceful and the sun is setting.
You wish that the day would last forever.
Then, your eyes open.
You are in your own bed and you realize
   it was just a dream.
You can't wait for night to come again so
   you can dream
Of your wonderful place.
The flowers.

Melody Kostamo (age 9)
Gateway Christian School

When I Say I Can't

When I say I can't
I'm really saying I don't want to
Some people say I'm stubborn
But I'm scared
And shy
I know that when I write my feelings
I feel sad and mad

Amanda Borson (age 9)
St. Wilfrid School

~//~

Horses

A pony is phony
A colt can bolt
A foal has a good soul
A mare is a mother that cares
A connemara can wear a tiara
A stallion wearing a gold medallion
A mustang named Boomerang
A filly can be silly

Sabrina Friesen (age 8)
Glenmore Christian Academy

~//~

My Crayon Box

I had a crayon box,
Each colour gleaming in the light,
I had a crayon box with colours,
Of passion, love, and delight.

I had no red for blood,
No white for the dead,
No black for the dust in the air,
And no brown for the desert sand.

I had pink for the flowers,
Blue for the bright sky,
Green for the blowing grass,
And I have orange for love and joy.

I started to draw peace
My dream!

Naomi Krahn (age 11)
Hillcrest Community School

Python

I like snakes and all,
But what do you do
When a twenty-four foot python
Says, "How do you do?"

Derek Carroll (age 9)
Miller Park School

~//~

Bats

Bats are cute, bats are funny.
They like to swim in the pool.
And they fly out at night
And freak people out!
That's why you should like them.

Ashley Berry (age 8)
James Bay School

~//~

Ramadan

When Ramadan comes I am happy
Because I like Ramadan.
I see the moon shining on me.
I wish I could fly to the golden sky.
I hear the people going to the mosque
    to pray
And the people sing, "Welcome Ramadan!'

Ahmad Sherif (age 7)
Edmonton Islamic School

~//~

Winter is

Winter is a time of fun
Snowball fights
Sled races
Building snow forts and snowmen
Sliding down hills until your pants are
    too wet

Winter is joy

Georgia Humphreys (age 9)
St. Joseph School

Ramadan Fasting

Fasting is hard to do,
Fasting to feel like the poor.
Fasting can hurt the stomach
But fasting the whole Ramadan,
You get good deeds,
If you work hard.

Zayd Kharadi (age 7)
Edmonton Islamic School

~//~

Computer Cat

I have a computer cat
Who has a funny mat
Who ate a rat
And chased a bat
He caught a rat
My funny cat
Who has a mat
Laughed so hard
He turned into a bat
Oh my funny cat

Irfan Dhanani (age 9)
St. Wilfrid School

~//~

Space

Now this is only one creation,
But let it spread to all generations.
Space is running its own race;
See the determination on its face.

Always pushing two ways,
Wait, and wait for days on days.
Space is a wondrous thing to see;
It's a thing that is alive in me.

The Seven Sisters stand side by side,
As they're walking life's own ride.
The stars in space make a wondrous face;
Look it's a woman decked in lace.

Space is one of the creations;
Let it spread throughout the nations.

Jennifer Martinoski (age 10)
Redwater School

If I Were a Kite

If I were a kite
I would soar through the air and
Feel the breeze of the cool wind
Against my body
I would hear all the birds sing
Their beautiful song
My coat would fill with air
And lift me higher...
And higher... And higher...
And higher until I could almost
Touch the stars
I would beware of the strong
Winds coming my way
At night I would slowly fall to the ground
When the next day came
I would be ready to soar again.

Calvin Mak (age 12)
R. C. Talmey Elementary School

~//~

Dance Studio

I hear the teachers yelling
I hear my shoes smelling
I hear the tapshoes clapping
I hear my lips smacking

I hear the music blasting
I hear the children laughing
I hear the bars shaking
I hear the trophies breaking

I hear the parents watching
I hear the girls catching
I hear the echoing in my class
I hear a teenager throw out the trash

I hear the horns beeping
I hear the adults sleeping
I hear the drinking fountain
I hear the sound of a mountain

I hear the coaches squeaking
I hear the blood leaking
I hear the people screaming
I hear my heart beaming

I hear the costumes jiggling
I hear the dancers wiggling

Danielle Mueller (age 11)
Children of St. Martha School

Untitled

Santa
Jolly, plump
Caring, loving spirited
Giving presents to children
Warm-hearted

Ellen Hancock (age 10)
Nancock Elementary School

~//~

Untitled

Flowers are pretty.
Flowers are nice,
But soon comes the winter,
But the sun shines.

Bianca Macaraig (age)
Notre Dame School

~//~

War

There's nothing quite like war;
Bodies aching and sore.
People killing, soldiers willing to fight
    in war.
If war could end,
We wouldn't spend our worthy lives in war.

Quinne Miller (age 8)
St. Josephs School

~//~

Jeffrey

Jeff was blind
He didn't mind
The colour of his skin
He wanted to see
The world as it should be

Based on the novel Maniac Magee

Rachael Shelast (age 10)
Redwater School

BIOGRAPHIES
OF
POETS

ABBOTT, KAYLA RAE DAYLE: [b] 03/03/93; [home] Three Hills, AB; [p] Ervin & Sandra; [brothers] Micah; [school] Prairie Elementary; [fav subject] Art, social studies, writing; [hobbies] Crafts; [pets] Maggie (golden retriever/golden lab); [ambition] Illustrator, architectural designer, engineer.

AGAR, HANNAH: [b] 03/04/92 Kelowna, BC; [home] Kelowna, BC; [p] Michael Agar & Candice Schacher; [sisters] Jordan; [school] Rose Valley Elementary; [fav subject] Phys. ed.; [hobbies] Volleyball; [pets] Forrest, Ren, Bode, Ozzy; [ambition] Computer technician.

AL-SEHLY, MOHAMED A.: [b] 10/20/94 Saudi Arabia; [home] Edmonton, AB; [p] Abdullah A. Al-Sehly & Zainab S. Al-Sheban; [brothers] Abdurahman, Rayan, Omar; [school] Edmonton Islamic; [fav subject] Art; [hobbies] Soccer; [pets] Cat; [ambition] Doctor.

AMOS, KELSEY: [b] 09/17/91 Port Alberni, BC; [home] Port Alberni, BC; [p] Dale Amos & Stacie Huot; [brothers] Bryce Huot; [sisters] Caitlyn Huot; [school] Neill Middle; [fav subject] Math; [hobbies] Hip hop, hockey; [pets] Dog, cat; [ambition] Lawyer.

ANDERSON, TAYLOR: [b] 03/25/94 Dawson Creek, BC; [home] Fort Nelson, BC; [p] Tim & Brenda; [sisters] Caitlin, Erica; [school] R.L. Angus Elementary; [fav subject] Science; [hobbies] Soccer; [pets] Mickey, Sarah, some fish; [ambition] Animal biologist.

ARSENAULT, RYKER: [b] 07/25/92 Calgary, AB; [home] Calgary, AB; [p] Rick Arsenault & Janet Fauchon; [brothers] Matthew, Adam, Cole; [school] St. Philip; [fav subject] Science; [hobbies] Martial arts; [pets] Micheal (bearded dragon); [ambition] Play football.

AUBIN, KRYSTIN: [b] 10/15/92 Peace River, AB; [home] Girouxville, AB; [p] Jean & Sue; [sisters] Janisha, Tiana; [school] École Routhier; [fav subject] Art; [hobbies] Gymnastics; [ambition] Hairdresser.

BAILEY, DANIEL: [b] 01/01/92 Regina, SK; [home] Semans, SK; [p] Bruce & Lisa; [brothers] Joel; [school] Margaret McClumb; [fav subject] Song writing, band; [hobbies] Music; [pets] Dog.

BALCE, PAOLO: [b] 08/15/91 Vancouver, BC; [home] Surrey, BC; [p] Valente & Erika; [sisters] Kristina; [school] Immaculate Conception; [fav subject] Math; [hobbies] Tae kwon do, video games, piano, clarinet; [ambition] Video game programmer.

BALDWIN, JEFFREY: [b] 07/02/94 Vancouver, BC; [home] Vancouver, BC; [p] John & Jan; [school] David Oppenheimer Elementary; [fav subject] Art; [hobbies] Soccer; [pets] Citrus, Berry (budgies); [ambition] Professional soccer player.

BALFOUR, NAHANNI: [b] 03/30/91 Creston, BC; [home] Terrace, BC; [p] Willie & Eberle; [brothers] Matthias; [school] Veritas; [fav subject] Writing, lang. arts; [hobbies] Triathalons; [pets] 2 dogs, cat, rabbit, chickens; [ambition] Triathlete.

BAYRAKTAR, MELEK: [b] 08/30/96 Edmonton, AB; [home] Edmonton, AB; [p] Aydin & Sausen; [brothers] Mohammed; [school] Edmonton Islamic; [fav subject] Islamic, art, gym; [hobbies] Drawing, soccer; [pets] Birds, rabbits, cats; [ambition] Doctor.

BELLAVIE, CAMERON: [b] 03/07/91 Calgary, AB; [home] Calgary, AB; [p] Mark & Catherine; [brothers] Andrew; [school] St. Cyril; [fav subject] Phys. ed.; [hobbies] Skiing, mountain biking, guitar; [pets] Austin, Riley, Bristol (cats); [ambition] Criminal lawyer, then judge.

BELYEA, DANIELLE: [home] Calgary, AB; [school] Lake Bonavista Elementary; [hobbies] Soccer; [pets] Sammy, Prince.

BIGIOLLI, NICHOLAS: [b] 05/15/93 Burnaby, BC; [home] Coquitlam, BC; [p] Franco & Sherry; [sisters] Lindsy, Alyssa; [school] Miller Park Elementary; [fav subject] Phys. ed.; [hobbies] Basketball, soccer; [pets] Kira (dog); [ambition] NBA player.

BLACKWOOD, SARAH: [b] 07/01/93 Drayton Valley, AB; [home] Drayton Valley, AB; [p] Robin & Sheila; [brothers] Kyle; [school] Aurora Elementary; [fav subject] Math; [hobbies] Skating; [pets] Tessa (dog).

BLAIN, BROOK: [b] 04/10/93 Red Deer, AB; [home] Fairmont Hot Springs, BC; [p] Brian & Lana; [brothers] Dustin, Beau, Drew, Quinton; [sisters] Lacey; [school] Windermere Elementary; [fav subject] Phys. ed.; [hobbies] Soccer, reading, snowboarding; [ambition] Farmer.

BLYTHE, ROB, JR.: [b] 11/12/93 Abbotsford, BC; [home] Coquitlam, BC; [p] Rob & Carmen; [sisters] Amy, Britney; [school] Miller Park Elementary; [fav subject] Phys ed., library; [hobbies] Family movie night, model building, watching hockey with Dad; [pets] Birds, fish, snake; [ambition] Architect.

BOBADILLA, DANIELLA: [b] 04/04/93 Mexico; [home] North Vancouver, BC; [p] Carlos Bobadilla & Haydee Iglesias; [school] Boundary Community; [fav subject] Art; [hobbies] Figure skating; [pets] Alexander (dog); [ambition] Compete in Vancouver 2010 Olympic Games.

BOJANOWSKI, KRYSTINA: [b] 03/07/91 Burnaby, BC; [home] Belcarra, BC; [p] Dr. Teodor & Belle; [brothers] Nicholas; [school] Meadowridge; [fav subject] Drama; [hobbies] Archery; [pets] Buttons (rabbit); [ambition] Playwrite.

BOMFORD, CHELSEA: [b] 06/07/91 Calgary, AB; [home] Cobble Hill, BC; [p] Bill & Carey; [school] George Bonner Middle; [fav subject] English; [hobbies] Volleyball; [pets] Purrl (cat), goldfish; [ambition] Writer.

BONNETT, ALEXANDRA: [b] 04/28/93 Penticton Hospital, BC; [home] Naramata, BC; [p] Cliff & Deborah; [school] Naramata Elementary; [fav subject] French; [hobbies] Dance, skiing, soccer; [pets] Trouble, Byron, Matilda (cats); [ambition] Designer.

BORSON, AMANDA: [b] 03/25/94 Peter Lougheed Hospital; [home] Calgary, AB; [p] David & Susan; [brothers] Cam; [school] St. Wilfrid; [fav subject] Music; [hobbies] Soccer; [pets] Frosty (cat); [ambition] Wrestler.

BORWEIN, TESS: [b] 01/29/93 Halifax, NS; [home] Burnaby, BC; [p] Peter & Jennifer; [sisters] Alex, Sophie; [school] Aubrey; [fav subject] Drama; [hobbies] Irish dance; [pets] 3 rabbits.

BOYER, ANTOINE: [b] 10/22/92 Calgary, AB; [home] Calgary, AB; [p] Charles Boyer & Lucie Herzig; [brothers] Francois; [sisters] Catherine; [school] Calgary French & International; [fav subject] Science; [hobbies] Scouts, trombone; [pets] Bobinette (cat); [ambition] Travelling.

BRADFORD, JASON: [b] 06/08/91 Hong Kong; [home] West Vancouver, BC; [p] John Bradford & Marivel C. Bradford; [school] Bodwell High; [fav subject] Phys. ed.; [hobbies] Running; [pets] Dog.

BRAVERMAN, ALEXANDRA: [b] 02/18/93 Vancouver, BC; [home] Vancouver, BC; [p] Michael Vick & Susan Braverman; [school] Wondertree Centre; [fav subject] Creative writing; [hobbies] Basketball; [pets] Samuel L. Katz (cat); [ambition] Fashion designer.

BRENNER, DARCEELEE: [b] 07/17/94 Regina, SK; [home] Semans, SK; [p] John & Jerrilynn; [brothers] Levi; [sisters] Jordann, Jamiee, Jaydynn; [school] Margaret McClumb; [fav subject] Novel study; [hobbies] Hockey; [pets] Horse, dog, cats; [ambition] Teacher.

BREUKER, CODY: [b] 05/13/91 Port Alberni, BC; [home] Port Alberni, BC; [p] Adam Cootes & Jennifer Breuker; [brothers] Brendin; [sisters] Chantelle; [school] Neill Middle; [fav subject] Art; [hobbies] Hockey; [pets] Fozzy (dog); [ambition] NHL player.

BRIMMELL, MARIANNE: [b] 01/20/92 Victoria, BC; [home] Victoria, BC; [p] Richard & Andrea; [brothers] Andrew; [school] St. Patrick's Elementary; [hobbies] Running, dance; [pets] Bunny, cat, 3 birds; [ambition] Doctor.

BRLETIC, NICKOLAS JOSEPH: [b] 04/03/93 Vancouver, BC; [home] Burnaby, BC; [p] Don & Lina; [brothers] Michael; [sisters] Vanessa; [school] Aubrey; [fav subject] Math; [hobbies] Soccer, hockey; [ambition] Continue education, athlete.

BROOKS, AMILKHAR GEORGE: [b] 04/03/95 Kingston, Jamaica; [home] Calgary, AB; [p] Allan Brooks & Fedrica Robinson; [brothers] Laurence Robinson, Paul Robinson; [sisters] Sidjae Robinson; [school] St. Wilfrid; [fav subject] Science; [hobbies] Football; [pets] Dog; [ambition] Doctor.

BUCK, LANE: [b] 09/04/92 Lethbridge, AB; [home] Lethbridge, AB; [p] Cameron & Melissa; [brothers] Kane; [sisters] Lauren; [school] Children of St. Martha; [fav subject]

Gym; [hobbies] Hockey, skateboarding; [pets] Speedy, Dolly (cocker spaniels); [ambition] Professional hockey player.

CALLOW, BRENT: [b] 08/15/92 Calgary, AB; [home] Calgary, AB; [p] Brian & Patti; [sisters] Erin; [school] Calgary French & International; [fav subject] Gym; [hobbies] Skiing, mountain biking; [pets] Squeeky, Oreo (cats); [ambition] Mechanical engineer, professional free style skier.

CALVERT, HAYLEY EMMALINE: [b] 01/06/94 Edmonton, AB; [home] Edmonton, AB; [p] Doug James Calvert & Jane Alison Calvert; [sisters] Jillian, Charlotte; [school] Brander Gardens; [fav subject] Art, music, gym, science, lang. arts; [hobbies] Beading, soccer, art; [pets] 7 fish, 2 lizards, 2 cats, frog; [ambition] Veterinarian, landscape architect.

CAMERON, CLAIRE: [b] 02/08/96 Calgary, AB; [home] Calgary, AB; [p] Steven & Brenda; [brothers] Christian; [sisters] Amanda, Sarah; [school] Glenmore Christian Academy; [fav subject] Art, science; [hobbies] Ride horses, basketball; [pets] Laces (dog), Haley (cat), Goldie, Sam, Fred (fish); [ambition] Marine biologist.

CARLSON, NATHAN: [b] 08/15/92 Watrous, SK; [home] Lethbridge, AB; [p] Dean Carlson & Lorna Smith; [brothers] Cory, Colin, Cameron, Kayden; [sisters] Sarah; [school] Children of St. Martha; [fav subject] Math; [hobbies] Hockey, skateboarding; [pets] Dog.

CARNEY, DANIEL: [b] 02/15/93 North Vancouver, BC; [home] North Vancouver, BC; [p] Thomas & Laurel; [sisters] Michelle; [school] Sherwood Park Elementary; [fav subject] Phys. ed.; [hobbies] Soccer, hockey; [pets] Skippy; [ambition] Comedy actor.

CARPENTER-REURINK, ZEBB: [b] 02/15/92 Lethbridge, AB; [home] Lethbridge, AB; [p] Ronald & Marty; [school] Children of St. Martha; [fav subject] Science, social, math, phys. ed.; [hobbies] Hockey, fishing; [pets] Patty, Gracie (dogs), Mouse (cat); [ambition] Dentist, doctor.

CHAU, ANDY: [b] 11/09/91 Vancouver, BC; [home] Burnaby, BC; [p] Albert & Janet; [school] École Sperling; [fav subject] Math; [hobbies] Basketball; [ambition] Grow up successful.

CHEUNG, TIMOTHY: [b] 09/06/94 Vancouver, BC; [home] Burnaby, BC; [p] Paul & Marisa; [sisters] Emily; [school] Vancouver Christian; [fav subject] Phys. ed.; [hobbies]

Hockey; [pets] Hamster; [ambition] Play 1 NHL game.

CHIVERS, JAYLEEN: [b] 03/02/94 Langley, BC; [home] Langley, BC; [p] Nigel & Rachel; [school] Nicomekl Elementary; [fav subject] Lang. arts; [hobbies] Reading, video games; [pets] Lucky (dog), fish; [ambition] Teacher, lawyer.

COSS, ZAKK: [b] 12/07/91 Port Alberni, BC; [home] Port Alberni, BC; [p] Reese & Kimberly; [brothers] Neil, Dallas; [school] Neill Middle; [fav subject] Social studies, history; [hobbies] Family activities; [pets] Tinker, Tuffy, Jigger (dogs), Crackers, Cheese, Sunny (cats).

COSSEY, JASMINE: [b] 05/02/94 Grande Prairie, AB; [home] Shawnigan Lake, BC; [p] Ken & Annie; [brothers] Matt; [school] Discovery Elementary; [fav subject] Math; [hobbies] Dance; [pets] Daisy (dog); [ambition] Singer.

COTTRELL, ADAM GUY: [b] 08/14/92 Melbourne, Australia; [home] North Vancouver, BC; [p] Graeme & Linda; [brothers] Cameron; [school] Sherwood Park Elementary; [fav subject] Phys. ed.; [hobbies] Hockey, soccer, snowboarding; [pets] Lucky (hamster); [ambition] NHL player.

COUZENS, ROBERT LAZARO: [b] 03/21/92 Vancouver, BC; [home] Burnaby, BC; [p] Wayne R. Couzens & Maria Del. Couzens; [brothers] Dean, Henry; [sisters] Jessica M. Couzens; [school] St. Helen Elementary; [fav subject] Art; [hobbies] Basketball; [pets] 9 fish, 3 birds; [ambition] Police officer.

COX, BRITTANI: [b] 04/21/92 Cold Lake, AB; [home] Cold Lake, AB; [p] James & Wendy; [sisters] Randi; [school] Elizabeth Community; [fav subject] Lang. arts; [hobbies] Horseback riding, basketball; [pets] 2 horses, dog, cat; [ambition] University teacher.

CRAIG, JILLENE: [b] 10/30/94 Edmonton, AB; [home] Edmonton, AB; [p] Mike & Joy; [brothers] Kyle; [school] Brander Gardens Elementary; [fav subject] Art; [hobbies] Skating; [pets] Little E (kitten); [ambition] Teacher, nurse.

CRAMER, STEPHANIE: [b] 05/12/94 Maple Ridge, BC; [home] Coquitlam, BC; [p] Owen & Ann; [school] Meadowridge; [fav subject] Lang. arts; [hobbies] Singing, dancing, reading; [pets] 2 cats, dog, 3 fish; [ambition] Veterinarian, always be around animals.

CUMMINS, CAROLYN: [b] 10/18/91 Langley, BC; [home] Delta, BC; [p] John &

Sue; [brothers] Martin; [sisters] Erin Mairs, Kristina Mairs; [school] Immaculate Conception; [fav subject] Art; [hobbies] Horseback riding, soccer, baseball; [pets] Tyson (dog), Nikki (cat), 3 fish; [ambition] Own many horses, event in horse shows (3-day eventing).

DAAB, MOHAMED: [b] 08/17/95 Libya; [home] Edmonton, AB; [p] El-Basheer Daab & Fatima Sweie; [brothers] Adbulmoen; [sisters] Maram; [school] Edmonton Islamic; [fav subject] Math; [hobbies] Hockey, soccer; [ambition] Engineer.

DALEN, MATTHEW: [b] 07/15/92; [home] Grande Prairie, AB; [p] Herb & Michelle; [brothers] Michael; [sisters] Elizabeth; [school] Swanavon; [fav subject] Science; [hobbies] Snowboarding; [pets] Cole, Bailey, Pepper; [ambition] Video game designer.

DALES, MITCHELL: [b] 08/27/97 Melville, SK; [home] Melville, SK; [p] Bernie & Debbie; [sisters] Janelle; [school] Miller Elementary; [fav subject] Computers; [hobbies] Camping; [pets] Beansie (dog); [ambition] Police officer.

DARWICHE, OSAMA: [b] 05/13/96 Edmonton, AB; [home] Edmonton, AB; [p] Mohamed & Ibtissam; [brothers] Anas, Aymen; [school] Edmonton Islamic; [fav subject] Lang. arts; [ambition] Race car driver.

DE LUCA, ROBERT: [b] 06/09/94 Vancouver, BC; [home] Maple Ridge, BC; [p] Pat & Celeste; [brothers] Michael, Francco; [sisters] Lauren; [school] Meadowridge; [fav subject] Lang. arts; [hobbies] Track & field; [pets] 2 fish; [ambition] Writer.

DECK, KALI ARON: [b] 03/31/92 Lethbridge, AB; [home] Lethbridge, AB; [p] Gary & Carol; [brothers] Andrew; [sisters] Chandra; [school] Children of St. Martha; [fav subject] Everything; [hobbies] Gymnastics; [pets] Kelbi, Meiko, Tinker; [ambition] Crime scene investigator.

DEHNEL, ALEXANDRA: [b] 10/22/97 Nelson, BC; [home] Nelson, BC; [p] Morgan & Patricia; [sisters] Grace; [school] St. Joseph; [fav subject] Art; [hobbies] Soccer; [ambition] Nurse.

DELL, CHAYSE: [b] 01/11/94 Kamloops, BC; [home] Kamloops, BC; [p] Brian & Erin; [brothers] Keaton, Aiden; [school] Juniper Ridge Elementary; [fav subject] Art; [hobbies] Soccer; [pets] Dakota (dog); [ambition] Lawyer.

DHALIWAL, GURJOT KAUR: [b] 04/03/91 Grace Hospital, Vancouver, BC; [home] Vancouver, BC; [p] Gian Singh Dhaliwal & Harpreet Kaur Dhaliwal; [brothers] Gurpreet Singh Dhaliwal; [school] Khalsa; [fav subject] Science; [hobbies] Hockey; [ambition] Optometrist.

DOBSON, ASHLEY NICOLE: [b] 09/13/93 Three Hills, AB; [home] Three Hills, AB; [p] Neil & Irene; [brothers] Lyndon; [sisters] Cassandra; [school] Prairie Elementary; [fav subject] Phys. ed.; [hobbies] Badminton; [pets] Cat; [ambition] Chef.

DOMOSLAI, BRANDEN: [b] 03/17/93 Calgary, AB; [home] Morinville, AB; [p] Paul & Melanie; [brothers] Jesse Florkowski, Dalton Domoslai, Jordan Domoslai; [sisters] Ashley; [school] Notre Dame Elementary; [fav subject] Math, gym; [hobbies] Hockey; [pets] Missy (cat); [ambition] Professional hockey player.

DOWAIDI, MIA: [b] 08/08/96 Edmonton, AB; [home] Edmonton, AB; [p] Ziad Dowaidi & Angela Amundson; [brothers] Tarik; [school] Edmonton Islamic; [fav subject] Art; [hobbies] Drawing; [ambition] Teacher.

DUKE, HILLARY: [b] 01/16/91 Port Alberni, BC; [home] Port Alberni, BC; [p] Lawrence & Denise; [sisters] Erin; [school] Neill Middle; [fav subject] Phys. ed.; [hobbies] Swimming; [pets] Dog, 2 cats; [ambition] Lifeguard.

DULKU, BHUPINDER S.: [b] 06/17/91 General Hospital; [home] Victoria, BC; [p] Kulwinder & Amarjeet; [brothers] Baldeep; [school] St. Michael's University Middle; [fav subject] Math; [hobbies] Soccer, basketball; [ambition] Lawyer.

ENNS, SHANOA KENDALL: [b] 09/17/92 Kamloops, BC; [home] Pinantan Lake, BC; [p] Jim & Marlena; [brothers] Matthew James Enns, Luke Williams Enns; [sisters] Hannah Lorraine Enns; [school] Pinantan Lake Elementary; [fav subject] Computers, phys. ed.; [hobbies] Soccer; [pets] Kyara, Nickida, Misty, Dudet, Reba; [ambition] Photographer.

ESPOSITO, STEPHANIE: [b] 02/09/92 Calgary, AB; [home] Lethbridge, AB; [p] Marco & Holly; [brothers] Tyler; [school] Children of St. Martha; [fav subject] Art; [hobbies] Camping, snow skiing; [pets] Casper (dog); [ambition] Zoologist.

FACCHIN, MATTHEW: [b] 07/17/93 Vancouver, BC; [home] Coquitlam, BC; [p] Mauro Facchin & Anna M. Facchin;

[brothers] Anthony, Lucas; [school] Miller Park Community; [fav subject] Science; [hobbies] Writing poetry; [ambition] Creating games for young children.

FAIRWELL, TARAN: [b] 01/14/94 Victoria, BC; [home] Shawnigan Lake, BC; [p] Ian & Phaedra; [sisters] Joisan; [school] Discovery Elementary; [fav subject] Gym, reading; [hobbies] Soccer; [pets] Tillie (dog), Polly, Minuet (cats); [ambition] Make electronic mind-controlled robots.

FEDORAK, KAYLA: [b] 12/30/91 Calgary, AB; [home] Calgary, AB; [p] Randy & Pamela; [brothers] John; [sisters] Angela, Martha; [school] St. Cyril; [fav subject] All; [hobbies] Hockey, playing drums; [pets] Belle (black lab).

FLATMAN, ALEX: [b] 05/18/93 Victoria, BC; [home] Victoria, BC; [p] Trevor & Jody; [sisters] Leah; [school] Beaver Lake Elementary; [fav subject] Phys. ed.; [hobbies] Hockey; [pets] Draco (leopard gecko), 2 cats; [ambition] NHL player.

FLOKSTRA, VALERIE: [b] 11/26/95 Abbotsford, BC; [home] Chilliwack, BC; [p] Dennis & Jennifer; [brothers] Jared, Nathan, Micah; [sisters] Stacy; [school] Home; [fav subject] Math; [hobbies] Gymnastics; [pets] Blue (black lab), Oliver (cat); [ambition] Pan flutist, gymnast.

FORD, DYLAN: [b] 02/26/92 Calgary, AB; [home] Calgary, AB; [p] Trevor & Michelle; [brothers] Tristan; [school] Calgary French & International; [fav subject] Phys. ed.; [hobbies] Snow & skateboarding, wakeboarding, hockey; [pets] Timber (sheltie), Gwynie (chocolate lab); [ambition] Study dentistry, excel in all sports.

FORTIN, JOSÉE: [b] 03/03/95 High River, AB; [home] High River, AB; [p] Richard & Sara; [brothers] Riley, Keefe; [school] École Joe Clark; [fav subject] Library; [hobbies] Skating; [pets] Harley; [ambition] Figure skating coach.

FUNK, NIKKI: [b] 03/22/93 Brandon, MB; [home] High River, AB; [p] Wayne Funk & Betty-Jean MacKay; [brothers] Les Funk, Trevor Funk, Steven Pemberton; [sisters] Elicia; [school] École Joe Clark School [fav subject] English; [hobbies] Cheerleading, tae kwon do; [pets] Sega (dog), Angel (fish); [ambition] Architect.

GALAMBOS, EMILIE: [b] 09/21/94 Langley, BC; [home] Surrey, BC; [p] Peter & Lisa; [school] Pinewood Elementary; [fav subject] Lang. arts; [hobbies] Basketball;

[pets] Whiskers (guinea pig); [ambition] Author, teacher.

GARAND, CHELSEY: [b] 07/12/92 The Pas, MB; [home] Lloydminster, SK; [p] Darin & Susan; [sisters] Peyten; [school] École St. Thomas; [fav subject] Art, phys. ed.; [hobbies] Horseback riding, dance; [pets] Jessie (dog), Raina (horse); [ambition] Nurse.

GARCIA, ALEXANDRIA MARIE: [b] 09/04/93 Victoria, BC; [home] Victoria, BC; [p] John Manuel Garcia & Rosemary Frias-Garcia; [brothers] John M. Garcia, Jr.; [school] Beaver Lake; [fav subject] Reading, writing; [hobbies] Drawing, painting, swimming; [pets] Fluffy Sophia (cat); [ambition] Stop world hunger & all wars, write & illustrate children's books.

GARCIA, MELISSA: [b] 05/14/92 Kelowna, BC; [home] Kelowna, BC; [p] Christian & Sharon; [brothers] Nicholas; [sisters] Caitlyn; [school] Rose Valley Elementary; [fav subject] Phys. ed., art. [hobbies] Baseball; [ambition] Cartoon artist.

GARNETT, HALEY: [b] 07/19/93 Victoria, BC; [home] Sidney, BC; [p] Anthony Garnett & Sandy Lundmark; [brothers] Nils, Andrew, Jonathan; [sisters] Amanda; [school] Deep Cove; [fav subject] English; [hobbies] Soccer, softball; [pets] MiMi (cat), fish, frogs; [ambition] Acting, singing, writing.

GAUDET, PATRICK: [b] 09/18/92; [home] Falher, AB; [p] Jean-Claude & Josette; [brothers] Sébastien; [sisters] Annie; [school] École Routhier; [fav subject] Phys. ed.; [hobbies] Hockey; [ambition] NHL player.

GAUDRY, AMANDA FAYE: [b] 02/17/92 Providence Hospital; [home] Moose Jaw, SK; [p] Chris & Jo Ann; [sisters] Anita, April, Ashley, Kimmy, Tracy; [school] William Grayson; [fav subject] Lang. arts; [hobbies] Hockey, singing; [pets] Odie (dog), Cuddles (cat); [ambition] Singer, guitar player.

GAWNE, ADOLINA JOY: [b] 02/27/93 Victoria, BC; [home] Sidney, BC; [p] Steve & Rebekah; [brothers] Edward, Mathew; [school] South Island Distance Education; [fav subject] Art; [hobbies] Rowing, computers; [pets] 12 chickens; [ambition] Painter.

GEREIN, LAURA: [b] 04/05/92 Victoria, BC; [home] Victoria, BC; [p] Glenn & Thérèse; [sisters] Julie; [school] St. Patrick's Elementary; [fav subject] Phys. ed., creative writing; [hobbies] Competitive running, swimming; [pets] 2 cats; [ambition] Veterinarian.

GERMAIN, EMMA: [b] 07/03/94 Vancouver, BC; [home] Maple Ridge, BC; [p] Robert (Joe) & Diana; [brothers] Bayley; [school] Meadowridge; [fav subject] All; [hobbies] Swimming; [pets] Pebbles, Brutus; [ambition] Olympic gold medal in swimming.

GILL, NEELAM: [b] 11/18/93 Vancouver, BC; [home] St. Albert, AB; [p] Sunny & Nicki; [sisters] Natasha; [school] Ronald Harvey Elementary; [fav subject] Art; [hobbies] Karate.

GILMORE, LAURA: [b] 08/16/91 Hong Kong; [home] Victoria, BC; [p] David S. Gilmore & Anita Gilmore; [brothers] Logan; [school] St. Michael's University Middle; [fav subject] Art; [hobbies] Volleyball, flute, piano; [pets] Soon dog; [ambition] Study art & design, architect.

GLAVES, SAMANTHA: [b] 05/25/93 Fort Nelson, BC; [home] Fort Nelson, BC; [p] Ronald & Marilyn; [sisters] Jasmine; [school] R.L. Angus Elementary; [fav subject] Writing; [hobbies] Reading, basketball; [pets] Muffy (dog); [ambition] Children's books writer.

GOODWIN, ALYSSA: [b] 03/04/95 High River, AB; [home] High River, AB; [p] Jim & Darlene; [brothers] Josh, Levi, Dorian; [sisters] Jerrica; [school] École Joe Clark; [fav subject] Math; [hobbies] Writing, drawing; [pets] 25 alpacas, 5 cats, 4 dogs, 2 fish, snake; [ambition] Poet, artist.

GRAHAM, SALLY: [b] 11/21/93 Victoria, BC; [home] Victoria, BC; [p] Derek & Helen; [sisters] Emma; [school] St. Patrick's Elementary; [fav subject] Art; [hobbies] Soccer; [pets] Meeko, Mishka, Cory, Ashly, Cookie; [ambition] Poet.

GRAY, REBECCA: [b] 10/19/92 Calgary, AB; [home] Edmonton, AB; [p] Dan Gray & Theresa McCallum; [sisters] Theona; [school] Patricia Heights; [fav subject] Phys. ed.; [hobbies] Soccer, horseback riding; [pets] Brenna (dog), Jasmine, Mitzy (cats); [ambition] Herpetologist, professional soccer player.

GREENSHIELDS, KATHRYN: [b] 03/17/91 Saskatoon, SK; [home] Semans, SK; [p] Grant & Callie; [brothers] Tom; [sisters] Charlotte; [school] Margaret McClumb; [fav subject] Art; [hobbies] Dance, 4-H; [pets] Meaghan (dog); [ambition] Kindergarten teacher, mom.

GREGORY, KAITLYNN: [b] 11/22/91 Victoria, BC; [home] Victoria, BC; [p] Eric & Debbie; [brothers] Adam; [sisters] Tara; [school] Pacific Christian Elementary; [fav subject] Drama, lang. arts; [hobbies] Dance, baseball; [pets] Missy (dog), Sprinkles (cat); [ambition] Teacher.

GROPP, DARBY ANN MARIE: [b] 05/26/91 Langley, BC; [home] Langley, BC; [p] Alexander & Darlene; [sisters] Joelene, Keshia; [school] Wix-Brown Elementary; [fav subject] Art; [hobbies] Swimming, skiing; [pets] Tazz (dog), Indee (cat), Bernice (guinea pig); [ambition] Finish high school, lifeguard, swimming instructor.

GRZELAK, PATRICK: [b] 10/30/91 Vancouver, BC; [home] Surrey, BC; [p] Henry & Mira; [sisters] Kathy; [school] Immaculate Conception; [fav subject] Science; [hobbies] Soccer, hockey; [ambition] Lawyer.

HADJIROUSEV, ATAZIA: [b] 06/13/93 Grace Hospital, Calgary, AB; [home] Cochrane, AB; [p] Zachari & Artara; [sisters] Zandrea; [school] Mitford Middle; [fav subject] Art, gym; [hobbies] Soccer, reading, writing; [pets] Tigger (cat); [ambition] Panda scientist, help save pandas, publish & illustrate book about experience.

HAGMAN, MATTY: [b] 06/13/93; [home] Kerry & Laurie; [sisters] Brooklyn, Billie; [school] Ashley Park; [fav subject] Gym; [hobbies] Hockey; [ambition] Hockey player.

HALIM, PATRICIA: [b] 05/15/91 Surabaya, Indonesia; [home] Victoria, BC; [p] Wirajaya Halim & Ratnawati Rusli; [brothers] Patrick Gregory Halim; [school] St. Michael's University Middle; [fav subject] Math, computer; [hobbies] Basketball.

HANDLEY, CAMERON: [b] 05/11/91 New Westminster, BC; [home] Port Alberni, BC; [p] Duncan & Colleen; [sisters] Kiley; [school] Neill Middle; [fav subject] Phys. ed.; [hobbies] Soccer; [pets] Dog, guinea pig, fish; [ambition] Professional soccer player.

HANSON, ARISTA KLEITO: [b] 09/04/93 Grand Forks, BC; [home] Grand Forks, BC; [p] Phillip Hanson & Lizanne Eastwood; [brothers] Io; [school] Distance Education of the Kootenays; [fav subject] Math; [hobbies] Musical theatre, tae kwon do; [ambition] Publish a novel, perform on Broadway.

HARRIS, DEION: [b] 11/21/94 Vancouver, BC; [home] Vancouver, BC; [p] Lydell Harris & Patricia Carruthers; [brothers] Justin; [sisters] Tameka, Kiawa; [school] Captain Cook Elementary; [fav subject] Phys. ed.; [hobbies] Basketball; [ambition] Writer.

HARRIS, STEPHANIE: [b] 11/15/91 Grande Prairie, AB; [home] Grande Prairie, AB; [p] Dwayne & Patti; [sisters] Alana; [school] St. Patrick's Catholic; [fav subject] Gym; [hobbies] Hockey; [pets] Shy-Ann, Scooter, Cuddles; [ambition] College scholarship in college.

HAUCA, SAMANTHA: [b] 09/09/94 Edmonton, AB; [home] Edmonton, AB; [sisters] Kara (8); [school] St. Vincent; [fav subject] Lang. arts, art; [hobbies] Ringette, swimming, piano; [ambition] Architect.

HAWES, ASHLEY: [b] 04/24/91 Victoria General Hospital; [home] Victoria, BC; [p] Mark & Dorothy; [brothers] Colin; [sisters] Jenny; [school] St. Michael's University Middle; [fav subject] English, science; [hobbies] Swimming, flute, crafts; [pets] Ranger (dog), sheep, chickens; [ambition] Interior designer.

HAWES, JAMIE: [b] 05/11/92 Vancouver, BC; [home] Burnaby, BC; [p] Jim & Mary; [brothers] Stefan; [sisters] Joanna; [school] St. Helen Elementary; [fav subject] Math; [hobbies] Swimming; [pets] Finney (fish); [ambition] Orthodontist.

HAYDEN, NEIL: [b] 05/15/91 Toronto, ON; [home] Victoria, BC; [p] Jay Hayden & Kate Ramsden-Hayden; [brothers] Liam; [sisters] Gillian; [school] St. Michael's Universtity Middle; [fav subject] Phys. ed.; [hobbies] Skate & snowboarding, guitar; [pets] Zorro, Ashley (dogs).

HAYNES, NEVIN: [b] 01/07/94 Calgary, AB; [home] Calgary, AB; [p] Graime & Leslie; [brothers] Malcolm; [sisters] Emily, Paula, Elana; [school] Sunalta; [fav subject] Gym (phys. ed.); [hobbies] Indoor hockey; [pets] Rupert (cat); [ambition] Hockey player.

HE, ANGELA: [b] 08/24/94 Burnaby, BC; [home] Vancouver, BC; [p] Siong K. Law & Cassie He; [sisters] Alvina Law; [school] Dr. Anne B. Jamieson Elementary (now), David Oppenheimer (poem written); [fav subject] Art, phys. ed.; [hobbies] Volleyball; [pets] Rabbit; [ambition] Singer.

HENNIG, LISA: [b] 05/13/94 Edmonton, AB; [home] Edmonton, AB; [p] David & Denise; [brothers] Michael; [school] St. Vincent; [fav subject] Art; [hobbies] Soccer, baseball, ballet; [pets] Ricky (dog), 6 fish; [ambition] Artist.

HERBACK, NICOLE: [b] 12/15/95 Ottawa, ON; [home] Calgary, AB; [p] Dean & Angie; [school] Glenmore Christian Academy; [fav subject] Math; [hobbies] Horseback riding; [ambition] Own a ranch with horses.

HERDMAN, VANESSA: [b] 06/05/92 Burnaby General Hospital, BC; [home] Burnaby, BC; [p] Mark & Silvana; [brothers] Michael; [school] St. Helen Elementary; [fav subject] Poetry writing; [hobbies] Dance, soccer, reading mysteries; [pets] Wants a kitten; [ambition] Detective.

HERMAN, ANNA: [b] 03/23/93 Swift Current, SK; [home] Swift Current, SK; [p] Glen & Catherine; [brothers] Marshall; [school] Ashley Park; [fav subject] Computers; [hobbies] Drawing; [pets] Soon kitten; [ambition] Artist.

HILL, VERILY: [b] 04/23/92 Edmonton, AB; [home] Morinville, AB; [p] Doug & Holly; [brothers] Kyle; [sisters] Ronni-Lynn, Daryl-Lee; [school] G.H. Primeau; [fav subject] Lang. arts; [hobbies] Stargazing; [pets] Missy (cat); [ambition] Veterinarian.

HOEKSTRA, KURTIS JORDAN: [b] 05/18/93 Grand Forks, BC; [home] Grand Forks, BC; [p] Otto & Susan; [school] Distance Education of the Kootenays; [fav subject] Social studies; [hobbies] Archery; [pets] Max (German shepherd); [ambition] Computer game designer.

HOLMES, KEARA: [b] 03/28/94 High River, AB; [home] High River, AB; [p] Bill & Cheryl; [sisters] Jade; [school] École Joe Clark [fav subject] English; [hobbies] Swimming, sewing, piano; [pets] Bentley, Jazz (dogs); [ambition] Pre-school teacher.

HOUDE, CURTIS: [b] 04/04/92 Sacred Heart Hospital, McLennan, AB; [home] McLennan, AB; [p] Nicole Parker; [brothers] Kirkland Houde, Dameon Bradshaw; [sisters] Misty-Dawn Bradshaw; [school] École Routhier; [fav subject] Science; [hobbies] Curling; [pets] Cats, rabbits, fish.

HOY, MICHELLE: [b] 02/15/95 Vancouver, BC; [home] Vancouver, BC; [p] Sam & Bobo; [brothers] Samson; [school] David Oppenheimer Elementary; [fav subject] Handwriting; [hobbies] Volleyball; [pets] Queeniey.

HUBER, COLE: [b] 11/03/94 Calgary, AB; [home] High River, AB; [p] Kent & Tara; [brothers] Miles; [sisters] Kendyll; [school] École Joe Clark; [fav subject] Math; [hobbies] Swimming; [pets] Gypsy (dog), Hamtoro (hamster); [ambition] Doctor.

HUSTON, HALLE: [b] 08/11/92 North Vancouver, BC; [home] North Vancouver, BC; [p] Derek & Robin; [brothers] Sam; [sisters] Sydney; [school] Sherwood Park Elementary; [fav subject] Phys. ed.; [hobbies] Horseback riding, soccer; [pets] 2 dogs, 3 cats, 3 fish; [ambition] Professional horse jumper, racer.

HUTCHINSON, MOLLY: [b] 04/07/92 Calgary, AB; [home] Calgary, AB; [p] Grant & Teri; [sisters] Anna; [school] St. Philip; [fav subject] Art; [hobbies] Swimming; [pets] Indigo (dog), Sunny (bird), 7 tropical fish; [ambition] Writer.

HWAYOUN LEE, HEATHER: [b] 08/16/93 Korea; [home] Langley, BC; [p] Sang Yeob Lee & Jeong Ah Lee; [school] Topham Elementary; [fav subject] Math; [hobbies] Horseback riding; [pets] Coco (dog); [ambition] Famous horseback rider.

ISAAC, SHANNON: [b] 07/03/95 Fort St. John, BC; [p] Tim & Penny; [sisters] Jennifer; [school] École Joe Clark; [fav subject] Science; [hobbies] Reading.

JACKSON, TAYLOR: [b] 05/29/94 Victoria, BC; [home] Shawnigan Lake, BC; [p] Tony & Sharon; [brothers] Robby; [sisters] Tonya; [school] Discovery Elementary; [fav subject] Art; [hobbies] Piano; [pets] Hunter, Joey.

JACKSON, WARREN: [b] 08/30/93 Calgary, AB; [home] High River, AB; [p] Doug Jackson & Lauren Dawe; [brothers] Daniel, Josh; [sisters] Mary, Sammi, Amanda; [school] École Joe Clark; [fav subject] Gym; [hobbies] Soccer; [pets] Scamp, Buddy, Tucker, Skittles, Shelby; [ambition] Actor, writer.

JAMAL, MUSTAFA SHAKOOR: [b] 11/24/96 Karachi, Pakistan; [home] Edmonton, AB; [p] Jamal Ahmad Anjum & Munira Jamal; [brothers] Mansoor, Ahmad; [sisters] Taiba; [school] Edmonton Islamic; [fav subject] Science; [hobbies] Painting; [pets] Mitho, Sheree (cockatiels); [ambition] Teacher.

JENNINGS, DEVON: [b] 06/05/92 Kelowna, BC; [home] Burnaby, BC; [p] John & Catriona; [school] École Sperling; [fav subject] Math; [hobbies] Volleyball; [pets] Dog, 3 cats.

JENSEN, DOMINIQUE: [b] 04/15/94 Calgary, AB; [home] Invermere, BC; [p] Mike & Hilda; [sisters] Michelle, Denise; [school] Windermere Elementary; [fav subject] Math; [hobbies] Volleyball, skiing, ballet, tap jazz;

[pets] Honey (hamster), Leo (cat), Pablo (dog); [ambition] Teacher.

JODOIN, DANEA S.: [b] 03/11/91 Edmonton, AB; [home] Spring Lake, AB; [p] Dean & Stacey; [school] John Paul II; [fav subject] Lang. arts; [hobbies] Dance, volleyball; [pets] Memo, Sponge Bob (fish).

JOHANNESSEN, JARED: [b] 04/10/92 Port Alberni, BC; [home] Port Alberni, BC; [school] Neill Middle; [fav subject] Science; [hobbies] Rollerblading.

JOHNSTON, MOLLY: [b] 10/20/92 Quesnel, BC; [home] Maple Ridge, BC; [p] John R. Johnston & Susan A. Loadman; [brothers] Alec; [school] Hammond Elementary; [fav subject] Novel study; [hobbies] Soccer; [pets] Kira (cat), Bobby (dog); [ambition] Actress.

JONES, KEVIN: [b] 04/08/93 High River, AB; [home] High River, AB; [p] Jerry & Sherry; [brothers] Keith; [sisters] Kari; [school] École Joe Clark; [fav subject] Math, lang. arts; [hobbies] Hockey, golf; [pets] 2 dogs; [ambition] Actor.

JONES, TINA: [b] 01/19/94 Winnipeg, MB; [home] Lumby, BC; [p] Ken & Jan; [brothers] Fabian, Keith; [sisters] Kendra, Shaina; [school] Lavington Elementary; [fav subject] Science, writing workshop; [hobbies] Soccer; [pets] Cheyenne, Rocky (dogs), Tigger (cat), 3 fish; [ambition] Write kid's stories.

JOSEPH, ARIANA: [b] 07/23/93 Grande Prairie, AB; [home] Grande Prairie, AB; [p] Ashim & Fiona; [sisters] Marina; [school] Swanavon; [fav subject] Math, English; [hobbies] Dance, reading; [pets] Wants a cat; [ambition] Dentist, continue ballet.

KACZKIELO, KANDRA: [b] 03/19/92 Grande Prairie, AB; [home] Grande Prairie, AB; [p] Curt & Vicki; [brothers] Heath; [sisters] Kara; [school] St. Patrick's Catholic; [fav subject] Lang. arts; [hobbies] Bowling, shopping; [ambition] Writer.

KAPSA, OSCAR: [b] 01/29/94 Vancouver, BC; [home] Vancouver, BC; [p] Miroslaw & Dorota; [school] David Oppenheimer Elementary; [fav subject] Reading, science; [hobbies] Biking, travelling; [pets] Moe (guinea pig), Homer (hamster; deceased); [ambition] Train conductor, scientist.

KAYTOR, KIMBERLY: [b] 04/28/91 Regina, SK; [home] Regina, SK; [p] Barry & Charlene; [sisters] Olithea, Chantel, Danielle, Jessica; [school] Douglas Park; [fav subject]

Writing; [hobbies] Softball; [pets] Fred (cat), Koko (dog); [ambition] Go to university.

KEMPER, MIKAELA: [b] 12/16/94 Vernon, BC; [home] Vernon, BC; [p] Michael & Trudy; [sisters] Mallory, Helena, Julia; [school] Lavington Elementary; [fav subject] Reading; [hobbies] Rhythmic gymnastics; [pets] Sasha (shih tzu), Theo (Himalayan); [ambition] Marine biologist.

KENNEDY, RENÉE: [b] 04/10/94 Langley, BC; [home] Shawnigan Lake, BC; [p] Bruce & Diane; [brothers] Andrew; [school] Discovery Elementary; [fav subject] Math, gym; [hobbies] Soccer, drawing; [pets] Bhoodie (dog), Lucky (cat); [ambition] Actor.

KIM, NAOMI: [b] 08/20/93 Seoul, Korea; [home] Three Hills, AB; [p] Chris & Hannah; [brothers] Daniel, David; [school] Prairie Elementary; [fav subject] Math; [hobbies] Basketball.

KING, KAEL: [b] 06/30/92; [p] Mark & Connie; [brothers] Carter; [sisters] Chelsi, Britni; [school] Aspen Grove Elementary; [fav subject] Science, phys. ed.; [hobbies] Hockey; [pets] Shadow; [ambition] Success.

KING, RHIANNON: [b] 09/03/91 Victoria, BC; [home] Victoria, BC; [p] Ian King & Linda Welling; [school] Landsdowne Middle; [fav subject] Art; [hobbies] Karate; [pets] Blackears, Snowy (cats); [ambition] Animal rights fighter, lawyer.

KNELSEN, DYLANA: [b] 04/07/93 High Level, AB; [home] Three Hills, AB; [p] Rod & Gert; [brothers] Brandon, Dion, Kyle; [school] Prairie Elementary; [fav subject] Phys. ed.; [hobbies] Basketball, highland dance; [ambition] Hairdresser, piano teacher.

KOLK, DARREN: [b] 06/15/91 Duncan, BC; [home] Duncan, BC; [p] Ron & Susanne; [brothers] Kevin; [school] George Bonner Middle; [fav subject] Phys. ed.; [hobbies] Basketball; [pets] Cat; [ambition] Baseball, basketball player.

KOVACS, JORDAN: [b] 08/28/93 Duncan, BC; [home] Victoria, BC; [p] John Kovacs & Karla Willems; [brothers] Graham; [school] Beaver Lake; [fav subject] Reading; [hobbies] Soccer, reading, drawing; [pets] Cat; [ambition] Author.

KOWAL, TRENT: [home] AB; [brothers] Tanner; [sisters] Kayla, Megan; [school] Sparling; [fav subject] Math; [hobbies] Hockey; [ambition] NHL player: Toronto Maple Leafs.

KUDOOS, TAARIQ: [b] 11/25/96 South Africa; [home] Edmonton, AB; [p] Afzal & Zubeida; [sisters] Zakiya, Raeesa; [school] Edmonton Islamic; [fav subject] Art; [hobbies] Computer games; [pets] Snowy (cockatiel).

KUDOOS, ZAKIYA: [b] 08/15/95 South Africa; [home] Edmonton, AB; [p] Afzal & Zubeida; [brothers] Taariq; [sisters] Raeesa; [school] Edmonton Islamic; [fav subject] Art; [hobbies] Swimming; [pets] Snowy (cockatiel); [ambition] Artist.

KUJALA, MATTHEW: [b] 05/29/91 Port Alberni, BC; [home] Port Alberni, BC; [p] Stanley & Carolyn; [brothers] Lance; [school] Neill Middle; [fav subject] Art; [hobbies] Rock collecting, cartoon drawing; [pets] Dog, 2 cats, 1 fish; [ambition] Cartoonist.

KUNTZ, JENNIE: [b] 04/10/92 Edmonton, AB; [home] Edmonton, AB; [p] Jeff & Cynthia; [brothers] Jake; [sisters] Kelsey, Paige, Calista; [school] Parkland Immanuel Christian; [fav subject] Science; [hobbies] Soccer; [pets] Hayley (cat); [ambition] Veterinarian.

LAGUIO, JOEY PERALTA: [b] 11/25/92 Richmond, BC; [home] Delta, BC; [p] Joselito E. Laguio & Janet Peralta Laguio; [school] St. Paul's; [fav subject] Math, lang. arts; [hobbies] Basketball, reading, singing; [ambition] Computer programmer, writer on side.

LARATTA, OLIVIA: [b] 05/08/92 Calgary, AB; [home] Calgary, AB; [p] Aldo & Linda; [sisters] Sofia (8) & Thea (4); [school] Mother Mary Greene; [fav subject] Lang. arts; [hobbies] Singing; [pets] Wants a dog; [ambition] Singer, actress.

LARSEN, JULIA ANNA: [b] 01/23/92 Burnaby, BC; [home] Maple Ridge, BC; [p] Dan Ole Larsen & Shelley Ann Larsen; [brothers] Nicholas Daniel Larsen; [school] Meadowridge; [fav subject] Lang. arts; [hobbies] Horseback riding; [pets] Murphy, Jack (cats); [ambition] Writer.

LARSON, JAIMIE-DEE: [b] 03/14/91 Yorkton, SK; [home] Lethbridge, AB; [p] Jarvis & June; [sisters] Jolyn, Jacey; [school] St. Francis Junior High; [fav subject] All; [hobbies] Hockey, BMX racing; [pets] Jodie (dog); [ambition] Police officer; women's Olympic hockey player.

LAVORATO, LUCA: [b] 09/03/93 Vancouver, BC; [home] Burnaby, BC; [p] Tullio & Teresa; [brothers] Paolo; [sisters]

Sonia; [school] Aubrey; [fav subject] Art; [hobbies] Soccer; [pets] Princess (cat); [ambition] Dentist.

LEBLANC, BLAKE: [b] 12/19/93 Calgary, AB; [home] Calgary, AB; [p] Paul LeBlanc & Karin Klassen; [brothers] Ross; [school] Sunalta; [fav subject] Art; [hobbies] Snowboarding, biking, guitar; [pets] Ruby (dog), Peaches (cat); [ambition] Engineer, artist.

LEE, SOOAH: [b] 11/15/94 South Korea; [home] Port Moody, BC; [p] Yeong-Hoon & Hanna; [sisters] Flora, Jeeah; [school] Meadowridge; [fav subject] Math; [hobbies] Soccer, skating; [ambition] Very good artist, skater.

LEE, STEPHANIE JAEHEE: [b] 04/30/93 Anyang City, China; [home] North Vancouver, BC; [p] Chang Hee Lee & Insook Lee; [sisters] Michelle J.E. Lee & Christine J.S. Lee; [school] Boundary Community; [fav subject] Science, math, French; [hobbies] Soccer, reading; [ambition] Dentist, RCMP.

LEONARD, CASSANDRA MARIE: [b] 05/20/95 Victoria, BC; [home] Victoria, BC; [p] Randy Leonard & Melody Roper; [brothers] Chris B., Chris S., Jeremy S., Josh B., Robert L.; [sisters] Nicole R., Jenny R.; [school] View Royal Elementary; [fav subject] Math; [hobbies] Soccer, computers; [pets] Sassie (cat); [ambition] Nurse.

LEWARNE, BOYD: [b] 04/12/95 Vernon, BC; [home] Lumby, BC; [p] Brent & Athena; [brothers] Austin [school] J.W. Inglis; [fav subject] Math; [hobbies] Soccer, curling; [pets] Jill, Jesse (dogs); [ambition] Marine biologist.

LEWTY, BETH: [b] 10/03/95 Winnipeg, MB; [home] Victoria, BC; [p] Ivar Baird & Cathy Lewty; [school] James Bay Community; [fav subject] Science; [hobbies] Hiking; [pets] Asta (cat); [ambition] Learn sign language.

LIBERTY, SADIE: [b] 07/19/92 Mission Memorial Hospital, BC; [home] Mission, BC; [p] Floyd & Pam; [sisters] Layne; [school] Meadowridge; [fav subject] Lang. arts; [hobbies] Soccer; [pets] 2 dogs, cat, rabbit; [ambition] Veterinarian.

LINDLEY, SAVANNA: [b] 02/20/95 Fort St. John, BC; [home] Taylor, BC; [p] Kim & Terena; [brothers] Mason; [school] Northern BC Distance Education; [fav subject] Lang. arts; [hobbies] Gymnastics, swimming, reading; [pets] 3 cats, dog; [ambition] Veterinarian for large animals.

LOCHMUELLER, ERIC: [b] 10/19/92 Rockeyview Hospital; [home] Calgary, AB; [p] Peter & Deborah; [sisters] Stephanie; [school] Lake Bonavista Elementary; [fav subject] Gym, art, lang. arts; [hobbies] Baseball; [pets] Yoshi (bichon/shih tzu).

LOGGIA, DANIELA: [b] 03/10/91 Montreal, QC; [home] Victoria, BC; [p] Robert & Chiarina; [brothers] David; [sisters] Zita; [school] St. Michael's University Middle; [fav subject] Social studies; [hobbies] Basketball, drums; [pets] Kito (black lab retriever); [ambition] Work with animals (e.g. WWF).

LUCHSINGER, KYLE: [home] Shawnigan Lake, BC; [p] Jarrod & Cheryl; [sisters] Jade; [school] Discovery Elementary; [fav subject] Math, English; [hobbies] Hockey; [pets] 4 rabbits, 2 cats; [ambition] NHL player, doctor.

LUPICK, JACQUELYNN: [b] 07/06/91 Calgary, AB; [home] Kelowna, BC; [p] A. Darryl & Antje; [brothers] Jeremy, Jonathan; [sisters] Justine; [school] Kelowna Christian; [fav subject] English; [hobbies] Drawing; [pets] Misty (mustang).

MACBEAN, CAMILLE: [b] 09/19/94 Calgary, AB; [home] Swift Current, SK; [p] Michael & Isabelle; [brothers] Brady, Samuel; [school] Ashley Park; [hobbies] Hockey, piano, reading; [pets] Bulldog; [ambition] "Be the best that I can be and try as many new things as I can."

MACDONALD, ALISON L.: [b] 06/30/93 Fort Nelson, BC; [home] Fort Nelson, BC; [p] Alexander F. MacDonald & Alice M. Macdonald; [sisters] Alexandria M. MacDonald, Anne Margaret MacDonald; [school] R.L. Angus Elementary; [fav subject] Phys. ed.; [hobbies] Swimming, basketball; [pets] Shadow (dog), Joe (cockatiel), Hulk, Jaws (fish), frogs, snails; [ambition] Police officer.

MAITWE, PATRICK M., JR.: [b] 12/14/93 Brampton, MB; [home] Sherwood Park, AB; [p] Patrick M. Maitwe, Sr. & Annet N. Maitwe; [brothers] PercyM. Maitwe, Arthur I. Maitwe; [sisters] Hope-Annet N. Maitwe; [school] St. Theresa; [fav subject] Math, phys. ed.; [hobbies] Basketball, soccer; [pets] Dog; [ambition] Art, engineering.

MARK, DAVID BUNLING: [b] 01/01/94 Grand Forks, BC; [home] Grand Forks, BC; [p] Bunling Mark & Yvonne Johnston; [school] Distance Education School of the Kootenays; [fav subject] Science; [hobbies] Hiking, gym workouts; [pets] Gizmo (yellow lab), Tigger (shih tzu); [ambition] Photographer.

MARKS, KODY: [b] 12/15/93 Nakusp, BC; [home] Nakusp, BC; [p] Stephen Marks & Jennifer Cliff-Marks; [school] Distance Education School of the Kootenays; [fav subject] Math; [hobbies] Hockey; [pets] Dog, 2 cats, hamster, rat; [ambition] Lawyer.

MARLIN-CONRAD, NIKOLA JOCELYN: [b] 10/22/93 Richmond, BC; [home] Burnaby, BC; [p] Brad V. Conrad & Linda C. Marlin; [school] Aubrey; [fav subject] Art; [hobbies] Soccer; [pets] 2 cats, dog; [ambition] Veterinarian.

MARSCHAL, STEPHANIE: [b] 05/16/93 Burnaby, BC; [home] Langley, BC; [p] Jenö Marschal & Karen Schnackenberg; [brothers] Matthew; [school] Topham Elementary; [fav subject] Art; [hobbies] Soccer; [pets] Midnight (bunny).

MARTENS, TRACY: [b] 07/11/93 Fort Vermilion, AB; [home] LaCrete, AB; [p] John & Helen; [brothers] Jason, Jerry; [sisters] Shawna; [school] Hillcrest Community; [fav subject] Math; [hobbies] Piano; [pets] Cats.

MARTIN, ADRIEL (A.J.): [b] 07/22/92 Edmonton, AB; [home] Grande Prairie, AB; [p] Barry & Nadine; [brothers] Kyren, Callen; [sisters] Lorelle, Tayanne; [school] St. Patrick's Catholic; [fav subject] Math; [hobbies] Building or disecting things; [pets] Wants a dog; [ambition] Crime scene investigator, forensic scientist.

MASON-PENNEY, SIMONE: [b] 01/10/94 Edmonton, AB; [home] St. Albert, AB; [p] Greg Penney & Judith Mason; [brothers] Myles; [sisters] Claire; [school] Ronald Harvey Elementary; [fav subject] Phys. ed.; [hobbies] Volleyball; [pets] 2 dogs, fish; [ambition] "Make a difference in the world."

MATAK-MARKOVIC, ANASTAZIA: [b] 01/05/93 North Vancouver, BC; [home] Burnaby, BC; [p] Kathy Matak; [school] Aubrey; [fav subject] Gym; [hobbies] Soccer, Irish dance; [pets] Smokey, Mickey, Tasha, Madeleine, Seeva, Samantha, Bingo; [ambition] Marine veterinarian, national soccer player.

MCCARTNEY, REBECCA: [b] 06/28/94 Calgary, AB; [home] Edmonton, AB; [p] Ed & Lorna; [brothers] Will; [sisters] Larissa; [school] Brander Gardens; [fav subject] French; [hobbies] Dance; [pets] Amber (dog); [ambition] Teacher, dental assistant.

MCDONALD, CAMERON: [b] 07/09/93 Calgary, AB; [home] Calgary, AB; [p] Robert & Kathryn; [brothers] Derek, Paul; [sisters] Alison; [school] Mother Mary Greene; [fav subject] Math; [hobbies] Soccer, Game Cube games; [pets] Ginny (dog), Hannah (cat); [ambition] Electronic game creator.

MCGREGOR, ALEX: [b] 07/01/93 Pembroke, ON; [home] Morinville, AB; [p] Jim & Shawne; [school] Notre Dame Elementary; [fav subject] Lang. arts; [hobbies] Tae kwon do, reading; [pets] Charlie, Missy.

MCNAIR, DENNIS: [b] Whistler, BC; [home] Calgary, AB; [school] Calgary French & International; [hobbies] Fencing, skiing; [pets] Kayla (boxer); [ambition] Pediatric dentist.

MCRAE, BRODY: [b] 05/01/91 At home, New Westminster, BC; [home] Langley, BC; [p] John Moser & Jamie McRae; [brothers] Chris, Tyson, Nolan, Jeremy; [sisters] Amber, Kiah, Etanna; [school] Wix-Brown Elementary; [fav subject] Phys. ed.; [hobbies] Basketball, chess; [pets] 2 goats, cat; [ambition] Professional basketball player.

MEEKS, CIARRA: [b] 03/04/91 Mission, BC; [home] Mission, BC; [p] Duane & Kelly; [brothers] Josh; [school] Windebank Elementary; [fav subject] Art; [hobbies] Figure skating; [pets] Oliver (cat), Kodi (dog); [ambition] Veterinarian.

MERRILL, REED: [b] 05/22/93 Calgary, AB; [home] Calgary, AB; [p] Christopher & Sonja; [brothers] Christian, Adam; [sisters] Elizabeth; [school] Sunalta; [fav subject] Science; [hobbies] Mountain biking; [ambition] Professional mountain biker, live in Vancouver.

MILLER, ABIGAIL: [b] 06/07/95 Montreal, QC; [home] Victoria, BC; [p] Ian Miller & Tessie Galangco; [sisters] Sarah; [school] James Bay Community; [fav subject] Math; [hobbies] Soccer; [ambition] Teacher.

MINDEK, STEFANIE: [b] 08/25/93 Fernie, BC; [home] Elko, BC; [p] John & Birgit; [brothers] Ben; [school] Distance Education School of the Kootenays; [fav subject] French; [hobbies] Swimming, horseback riding; [pets] Roxie (dog), Sprite (dove); [ambition] Lawyer, go scuba diving in Hawaii.

MOK, JESSICA: [b] 02/07/91 Hong Kong; [home] Burnaby, BC; [p] Alan Mok & Alice Wat; [brothers] Aaron; [school] Parkcrest Elementary; [fav subject] Art, language;

[hobbies] Drawing, reading, writing; [ambition] Art-related, any artist type.

MOLLOY, CHARLOTTE: [b] 02/27/93 Edmonton, AB; [home] Sherwood Park, AB; [p] Ken & Carmen; [brothers] David; [sisters] Petrea; [school] Jean Vanier Catholic; [fav subject] Gym; [hobbies] Soccer; [pets] Jukkie, Morris, JD (cats); [ambition] Professional soccer player.

MONETTE, TAYLOR: [b] 09/24/92 Halifax, NS; [home] Lloydminster, SK; [p] Ron & Rose; [school] École St. Thomas; [fav subject] Art; [hobbies] Hockey; [pets] 2 dogs, cat; [ambition] Doctor.

MOORE, NICHOLAS S.: [b] 12/04/91 Vancouver, BC; [home] Calgary, AB; [school] Calgary French & International; [fav subject] English; [ambition] Fantasy writer.

MOORTHY, RACHAEL: [b] 05/05/93 Abbotsford, BC; [home] Abbotsford, BC; [p] Balan & Shalegh; [sisters] Tiahna, Emily; [school] North Poplar Fine Arts; [fav subject] Phys. ed., lang. arts; [hobbies] Water polo, soccer; [pets] Sachi (dog); [ambition] Be in Olympics.

MOREL, KEITH MARCEL (KEIFFER): [b] 11/24/94 Langley, BC; [home] Calgary, AB; [p] Jimmy & Judy; [sisters] Amanda; [school] St. Wilfrid; [fav subject] Science; [hobbies] Video games; [pets] Maggie (dog); [ambition] FBI member.

MOTANI, MIRA: [b] 10/24/94 Abbotsford, BC; [home] Abbotsford, BC; [p] Mahmud Motani & Anisa Quadir; [school] Meadowridge; [fav subject] Math, computers; [hobbies] Coin collecting, reading, horseback riding; [pets] Cat; [ambition] Competitive horseback rider, wonderful artist.

MUELLER, DANIELLE: [home] Lethbridge, AB; [school] Children of St. Martha; [fav subject] French; [hobbies] Dance; [pets] Sofie, Lola, Winston; [ambition] Doctor.

MUGFORD, JESSICA ANGELA: [b] 10/10/91 Courtenay, BC; [home] Port Alberni, BC; [p] John Mugford & Janice Nielsen; [brothers] Brendon Nielsen; [school] Neill Middle; [fav subject] Writing; [hobbies] Horseback riding; [pets] Joey (dog), Thomas (cat); [ambition] Lawyer.

MURIE, CHRISTOPHER: [b] 08/18/92 Langley, BC; [home] Langley, BC; [p] Randy & Barbara; [brothers] Philip, Michael; [sisters] Leah; [school] Langley Fundamental Elementary; [fav subject] Phys. ed.; [hobbies]

Basketball; [pets] Bird, dog, cat, fish; [ambition] Good basketball player.

MUZZO, MARISSA CARMELA: [b] 11/23/93; Calgary, BC; [home] Calgary, BC; [p] John & Anna; [sisters] Jennifer, Renée, Samantha; [school] Mother Mary Greene; [fav subject] Religion; [hobbies] Dance, rollerblading; [ambition] Veterinarian.

NAKANO, SHAE: [b] 01/25/92 Vancouver, BC; [home] Kamloops, BC; [p] Ken & Joanne; [sisters] Amy; [school] Heffley Creek Elementary; [fav subject] Art; [hobbies] Volleyball, swimming; [ambition] Singer, songwriter.

NICOL, ALEX: [b] 04/12/93 New Westminster, BC; [home] Coquitlam, BC; [p] Derek & Jeni; [brothers] Jacob; [school] Miller Park Community; [fav subject] Math; [hobbies] Soccer; [pets] Mickey (cat); [ambition] Famous soccer player.

NIELSEN, CHELSEA B.: [b] 03/10/92 New Westminster, BC; [home] Langley, BC; [p] David & Jeanine; [brothers] Nolan; [school] Langley Fundamental Elementary; [fav subject] Creative writing; [hobbies] Music, gymnastics, cheerleading; [pets] Simba (cat), Saje (dog); [ambition] Great make-up artist, fashion designer, guitar player.

NOLIN, ELÈNEE: [b] 02/01/94 Lloydminster; [home] Lloydminster, SK; [p] Fayne & Maria; [sisters] Zoë; [school] École St. Thomas; [fav subject] Health; [hobbies] Soccer; [pets] Meeko (dog); [ambition] Explore science.

O'CONNOR, SHANE: [b] 02/21/92 Grande Prairie, AB; [home] Grande Prairie, AB; [p] Ron & Terra; [brothers] Bernie; [sisters] Dani, Rhona; [school] St. Patrick Catholic; [fav subject] Gym, lang. arts; [hobbies] Baseball; [pets] Guinea pigs, cat, newt; [ambition] Work hard.

OLSON, RUSSELL: [b] 05/04/93 Three Hills, AB; [home] Three Hills, AB; [p] Lowell & Joann; [brothers] Dustin; [sisters] Anita; [school] Prairie Elementary; [fav subject] Math; [hobbies] Hockey; [pets] Dogs, cats.

ORYEMA, RITA AMULO: [b] 09/03/93 Kenya; [home] Vancouver, BC; [p] Simon de-Otori Oryema & Selina Lamunia; [brothers] Bruce, Noah; [sisters] Flora, Diana; [school] Seymour Elementary; [fav subject] Math, spelling; [hobbies] TV; [ambition] Doctor.

OUCHAREK, JENNA RAE: [b] 06/13/96 Melville, SK; [home] Melville, SK; [p]

Michael & LeAnne; [sisters] Tianda; [school] Miller Elementary; [fav subject] Gym; [hobbies] Dance, singing; [ambition] Painting.

PASTEGA, ALI: [b] 05/11/92 Burnaby, BC; [home] White Rock, BC; [school] H.T. Thrift Elementary; [fav subject] French; [hobbies] Soccer; [pets] Fish; [ambition] Writer.

PAULSON, SAMANTHA: [b] 03/12/94 Royal Alexandra Hospital, Edmonton, AB; [home] Edmonton, AB; [p] Cliff & Shelly; [brothers] Colton, Corey; [sisters] Amanda; [school] Brander Gardens Elementary; [fav subject] Gym; [hobbies] Singing; [ambition] "Person that does hairs, nails, clothes, shoes, rings, and jacket."

PAYNE, AMANDA J.: [b] 02/22/93 Stony Plain, AB; [home] St. Albert, AB; [p] Scott Payne & Dee-Ann Schwanke (Ken Schwanke, stepfather; Sandy Payne, father's wife); [brothers] Luke, Isiah (stepbrothers); [sisters] Adelle, Andrea (Emily, Anna, Ashley, stepsisters); [school] Ronald Harvey Elementary; [fav subject] Math; [hobbies] Basketball, drawing; [ambition] Artist, basketball player.

PEARSE, SERGE: [b] 11/08/92 Vancouver, BC; [home] Mayne Island, BC; [p] Anthony Dalton Pearse & Tania Godoroja; [brothers] Erin (half-brother); [sisters] Michelle (sister-in-law); [school] South Island Distance Education; [fav subject] Science; [hobbies] Basketball, bushwhacking, reading; [pets] Lucca (wheaten terrier), Schoodle (schauzer-poodle); [ambition] Ornithologist.

PEDERSON, CASSIE DAWN: [b] 06/30/93 St. Albert, AB; [home] St. Albert, AB; [p] Ron & Lisa; [sisters] Jamie-Lynne; [school] Ronald Harvey Elementary; [fav subject] Art; [hobbies] Basketball; [pets] Dogs, horses; [ambition] Fashion designer.

PEEKE, JEREMY: [b] 04/26/91; [home] Semans, SK; [p] Barrie & Melanie; [brothers] Mitchell; [sisters] Tamara; [school] Margaret McClumb; [fav subject] Math; [hobbies] Hockey, golf; [pets] Buddy (dog), cats; [ambition] NHL player.

PERCIVAL, RORY MILES: [b] 08/25/92 New Westminster, BC; [home] Burnaby, BC; [p] Murray & Deborah; [sisters] Haylee; [school] École Sperling; [fav subject] Art; [hobbies] Biking; [pets] Storm, Jetta; [ambition] Mechanic.

PERRAULT, ALEXANDRE: [b] 04/25/91 At home, Montreal, QC; [home] Vancouver,

BC; [p] Barry & Valérie; [brothers] Émanuel; [school] Wondertree Centre; [fav subject] History; [pets] Cat, dog; [ambition] "Help people in any way I can."

PETER: [b] 04/15/93 Fairview, AB; [home] Langley, BC; [p] Joshua & Carol; [sisters] Hanna, Genna, Natanya; [school] Topham Elementary; [fav subject] Social studies; [hobbies] Reading; [pets] Sierra (dog); [ambition] History teacher.

PETERS, ZACHARY: [b] 08/15/91 White Rock, BC; [home] Aldergrove, BC; [p] Henry & Maria; [sisters] Natasha; [school] Wix-Brown Elementary; [fav subject] Phys. ed.; [hobbies] Basketball; [pets] Rocko (dog); [ambition] Architect.

PHILCOX, KYLEE: [b] 01/19/93 Kamloops, BC; [home] Kamloops, BC; [p] Kelly & Corena; [brothers] Brant; [school] Pinantan Elementary; [fav subject] Writers' workshop; [hobbies] Soccer, writing; [pets] Tipper, Cleo (dogs), Milo (cat); [ambition] Horse trainer.

PHILLIPS, TAYLOR: [b] 01/24/92 North Vancouver, BC; [home] North Vancouver, BC; [p] Stephen & Tracey; [sisters] Kaitlyn; [school] Boundary Community; [fav subject] Art, science; [hobbies] Soccer, field hockey; [pets] Tickles, Snuffy (hamsters), Tiki, Licorice (cats); [ambition] Great soccer player.

PIPHER, HAYLEY: [b] 08/30/92 Tansen, Nepal; [home] Kelowna, BC; [p] Bruce & Jude; [brothers] Joel; [sisters] Lauren; [school] Rose Valley Elementary; [fav subject] Writing; [hobbies] Competitive swimming; [pets] 2 dogs; [ambition] Marine biologist.

PORTEOUS, ALEXA: [b] 06/21/92 Kelowna, BC; [home] Kelowna, BC; [p] James & Kathleen; [brothers] Andrew; [school] St. Joseph Elementary; [fav subject] Writing; [hobbies] Soccer, rock climbing; [pets] Q (dog); [ambition] Writer, actor.

POTIÉ, ALEX: [b] 11/15/92 Calgary, AB; [home] Calgary, AB; [p] Alphonse Potié & Jacqueline Martino (Mary Dunford, grandmother); [sisters] Madeline; [school] Calgary French & International; [fav subject] Math, English; [hobbies] Equestrian riding, competitive swimming; [pets] Pudge (fish); [ambition] "Go to school abroad, travel extensively & to love what I do."

POULSEN, ZOEY: [b] 12/11/91 Port Alberni, BC; [home] Port Alberni, BC; [p]

Brian Poulsen & Lisa Davies; [brothers] Drake; [school] Neill Middle; [fav subject] English; [hobbies] Ice hockey; [pets] Luna, Viper, Jo-Jo (cats); [ambition] "Be the best I can be."

PRIOR, JEREMY: [b] 09/08/94 Victoria, BC; [home] Shawnigan Lake, BC; [p] Gary & Shelagh; [sisters] Taryn; [school] Discovery Elementary; [fav subject] Gym; [hobbies] Soccer; [pets] Ruff, Flash (dogs), Stacey (cat); [ambition] Mechanic.

PROST, LIAM: [b] 12/30/91 Calgary, AB; [home] Lethbridge, AB; [p] Gerry & Jeannette; [brothers] Brendan; [school] Children of St. Martha; [fav subject] Lunch, lang. arts; [hobbies] Wakeboarding; [pets] Puzzums, Mimi (cats), Junny (lop-eared rabbit); [ambition] Famous writer.

RAMBARAN, TIA: [b] 10/24/90; [home] Coquitlam, BC; [p] Deeran & Michelle; [sisters] Natasha; [school] British Columbia Christian Academy; [fav subject] Social studies; [hobbies] Piano, ballet, drawing; [pets] Minnie (dog), Daisy (cat); [ambition] Computer graphics, writer, artist.

REARDON, TANIELLE: [b] 11/23/92 Vernon, BC; [home] Lumby, BC; [p] Danny & Sherry; [brothers] Dane, Jayson; [school] J.W. Inglis; [fav subject] Writing; [hobbies] Snowboarding; [ambition] Write poems & songs.

REEGHAN: [b] 07/06/92 Grande Prairie, AB; [home] Grande Prairie, AB; [p] Ken & Shelley; [sisters] Cassidy; [school] Swanavon; [fav subject] Art; [hobbies] Dance; [pets] Kemo (dog), Oh, Henry (guinea pigs), Shy (rabbit), 7 fish; [ambition] Get good career.

REVOY, ENYA: [home] Melville, SK; [p] Sheldon & Teresa; [brothers] Erik; [school] Miller Elementary; [fav subject] Math; [hobbies] Skiing, piano; [pets] Princess Buttercup, Deputy; [ambition] Veterinarian, "tell people about Jesus."

RICHARDSON, HAILEY: [b] 07/09/92 Grande Prairie, AB; [home] Grande Prairie, AB; [p] Laverve & Rhonda; [sisters] Brandy, Brittany, Melanie; [school] Aspen Grove; [fav subject] Art; [hobbies] Soccer, swimming; [pets] 2 dogs, 2 cats; [ambition] Veterinarian.

ROBERTSON, CHANTEL: [b] 03/14/95 High River, AB; [home] High River, AB; [p] Kevin & Melinda; [brothers] Brandon; [sisters] Ashley; [school] École Joe Clark; [fav subject] Gym; [hobbies] Figure skating; [pets] Bailey (dog); [ambition] Take care of & have many animals (esp. dogs).

RODMAN, JUSTIN: [b] 05/01/96 Regina, SK; [home] Melville, SK; [p] Bernie & Carla; [sisters] Katie, Sara; [school] Miller Elementary; [fav subject] Gym; [hobbies] Hockey; [pets] Aimee (dog); [ambition] Mechanic.

RONDPRÉ, STEPHANI ALANNAH: [b] 12/15/91 Grace Hospital, Vancouver, BC; [home] Vancouver, BC; [p] Frederick George & Verna Marie; [sisters] Melinda, Donna, Kylie; [school] Nootka Elementary; [fav subject] Choir, French; [hobbies] Reading, computer role-playing, basketball; [pets] Trevor (hamster); [ambition] Get into good mini school, volunteer when old enough.

ROSSI, ASHLEY: [b] 02/06/93 Edmonton, AB; [home] Fort Nelson, BC; [p] Rick & Jody; [brothers] Brett; [school] R.L. Angus Elementary; [fav subject] Math, lang. arts; [hobbies] Hockey; [pets] Simon (dog), Ebony (kitten); [ambition] World's best author, defenceman.

ROSVICK, MARIA VIOLET: [b] 02/07/92 Calgary, AB; [home] Crossfield, AB; [p] Brian & Brenda; [brothers] Douglas, Henry (older); [sisters] Gina (younger); [school] Our Lady Queen of Peace; [fav subject] Math; [hobbies] Piano, reading, collecting bookmarks; [pets] Bear (dog), Lightning (hamster); [ambition] Teacher, artist.

ROUSSEAU, NOELLE: [b] 12/02/95 Calgary, AB; [home] Calgary, AB; [school] Glenmore Christian Academy; [fav subject] Art; [hobbies] Ballet; [ambition] Writer, ballet dancer.

ROWELL, MICHAEL: [b] 11/27/93 St. Albert, AB; [home] St. Albert, AB; [p] Kim & Petra; [brothers] Thomas; [school] Ronald Harvey Elementary; [fav subject] Phys. ed.; [hobbies] Computer games; [pets] Red (dog); [ambition] Biochemist.

ROY, THOMAS: [b] 09/07/94 Victoria, BC; [home] Shawnigan Lake, BC; [p] Tony & Jennifer; [brothers] Simon, Devlan; [school] Discovery Elementary; [fav subject] Gym; [hobbies] Basketball, hockey; [pets] Lucy (golden retriever); [ambition] Lego designer.

RUSITCH, JESSICA: [b] 07/07/92 Moose Jaw, SK; [home] Moose Jaw, SK; [p] Jamie Passmore & Angela Rusitch; [brothers] Justin, Brandon, Jacob, Jonathon; [school] William Grayson; [fav subject] Social studies; [hobbies] Soccer; [pets] 2 fish; [ambition] Live in Alaska, race dogs.

SAGAL: [b] 07/01/94 Toronto, ON; [home] Edmonton, AB; [p] Deeqa;

[brothers] Sami; [school] Edmonton Islamic; [fav subject] Math; [hobbies] Reading, soccer; [pets] Salem.

SALGADOE, SHENETTE: [b] 11/10/92 Vancouver, BC; [home] Richmond, BC; [p] Shehan & Shermila; [brothers] Shawn; [school] St. Paul's Elementary; [fav subject] Art; [hobbies] Basketball, badminton; [ambition] Artist.

SARICH, REBECCA: [b] 01/04/93 Kamloops, BC; [home] Lethbridge, AB; [p] Jeff & Julie; [sisters] Sarah; [school] Children of St. Martha; [fav subject] Lang. arts; [hobbies] Basketball; [pets] Radar (dog); [ambition] Kindergarten, grade 1 teacher.

SAUDER, ASHLEY: [b] 02/16/94 Swift Current, SK; [home] Swift Current, SK; [p] Randy & Barb; [brothers] Cody, Ryan, Chris; [school] Ashley Park; [fav subject] Math; [hobbies] Skiing, soccer; [pets] Sizzle (horse), Tobin, Badger (dogs); [ambition] Attend university, veterinarian.

SAUER, JAYME: [b] 02/28/97 Calgary, AB; [home] Calgary, AB; [p] Shawn & Shannon; [brothers] Curtis; [sisters] Karlie, Nicole; [school] Glenmore Christian Academy; [fav subject] Gym; [hobbies] Skating; [pets] Fish; [ambition] Writer.

SAUNDERS, MATTHEW: [b] 03/19/91; [p] Rick & Sharon; [sisters] Jen; [school] St. Cyril; [fav subject] Lang. arts; [hobbies] Soccer; [pets] Chester (dog).

SAWATZKY, AMELIEA: [b] 03/26/94 High River, AB; [home] High River, AB; [p] Mark Raymond Sawatzky & Andrea Sawatzky; [brothers] Tristan, Ethan; [sisters] Kira; [school] École Joe Clark; [fav subject] Art; [hobbies] Soccer; [pets] 2 dogs, cat, 2 fish; [ambition] Paleontologist.

SAYAH, SAADIE: [b] 07/24/96 Canada; [home] Edmonton, AB; [p] Mohamad Sayah & Maria Chona Sayah; [brothers] Said, Khaled, Emad; [school] Edmonton Islamic; [fav subject] Lang. arts; [hobbies] Soccer, tae kwon do; [pets] Birds, fish; [ambition] Doctor, teacher.

SCHEIDT, RYAN: [b] 11/24/94 Vernon, BC; [home] Vernon, BC; [p] Rick Scheidt & Christine Sherman; [school] Lavington Elementary; [fav subject] Reading; [hobbies] Hockey, wakeboarding; [pets] Jessie (dog); [ambition] NHL player.

SCHERGER, CHRISTINE: [b] 04/01/92 Edmonton, AB; [home] Lethbridge, AB; [p] Dean & Rosanne; [brothers] Justin; [sisters] Amanda; [school] Children of St. Martha; [fav subject] Lang. arts; [hobbies] Singing, writing stories; [pets] Dog; [ambition] Writer.

SCHMUNK, REBECCA: [b] 10/17/92 Langley, BC; [home] Aldergrove, BC; [p] Bruce & Delyth; [brothers] Ryan; [sisters] Rhianna; [school] Parkside Centennial Elementary; [fav subject] French; [hobbies] Drawing, writing; [pets] Bunny; [ambition] Author, veterinarian.

SCHMUNK, RHIANNA: [b] 07/19/94 Langley, BC; [home] Aldergrove, BC; [p] Bruce & Delyth; [brothers] Ryan; [sisters] Rebecca; [school] Parkside Centennial Elementary; [fav subject] Art, lang. arts; [hobbies] Soccer, cross-stitch; [pets] Siamese fighting fish; [ambition] Artist, writer.

SCIORE, STEVEN: [b] 06/10/93 Calgary, AB; [home] Calgary, AB; [school] Mother Mary Greene; [fav subject] Science; [hobbies] Hockey; [ambition] Be rich.

SCRIMSHAW, JOEY: [b] 01/06/95 Salmon Arm, BC; [home] High River, AB; [p] Tyhson & Leslie; [brothers] Tim (half-brother); [school] École Joe Clark; [fav subject] English; [hobbies] Guitar, swimming, camping; [pets] Muffin (dog), Dotty, Dotty 2, Tiger (fish).

SEELEY, MEAGAN: [b] 04/20/93 Grande Prairie, AB; [home] Grande Prairie, AB; [p] Phil & Carol; [brothers] Kyle; [school] Swanavon; [fav subject] Phys. ed.; [hobbies] Hockey, soccer, reading; [pets] Fish; [ambition] Writer, actress, singer.

SEKULIC, RYAN: [b] 07/30/93 Grande Prairie, AB; [home] Cochrane, AB; [p] Mike Sekulic & Shona Walsh (stepfather: John Penton); [brothers] Tim, Paul-Andrew; [sisters] Kate, Rudie; [school] Mitford Middle; [fav subject] Math; [hobbies] Computer games; [ambition] Scientist.

SHEN, ANITA: [b] 01/14/93 Stuttgart, Germany; [home] Burnaby, BC; [p] Chloé; [fav subject] Math; [hobbies] Ballet, ringette, skiing; [pets] Smokey, Spotty (fish); [ambition] Paediatrician.

SHEPARD, ALEXANDER: [b] 08/16/94 Vancouver, BC; [home] Vancouver, BC; [p] Michael & Sandra; [school] Charles Dickens Elementary; [fav subject] Music; [hobbies] Model building; [pets] Balthazar (Persian); [ambition] Be good at hockey.

SHIN, DAVID (SEUNG YUP): [b] 02/21/95 South Korea; [home] Vancouver, BC; [p]

Kyeung Mok Shin & Sun Kyung Lim; [sisters] Jenny; [school] David Oppenheimer Elementary; [fav subject] Art; [hobbies] Soccer; [pets] Bommy (hamster); [ambition] Martial arts champion.

SIMONSEN, ANNELISE LOUISE: [b] 06/25/93 Penticton, BC; [home] Naramata, BC; [p] Peter Simonsen & Cyndie Salting; [brothers] Anders; [school] Naramata Elementary; [fav subject] Drama; [hobbies] Cheerleading; [pets] Freckles, Smokey (cats), Chester (dog); [ambition] Clothes designer.

SLADE, JAYCIE: [b] 10/25/95 Calgary, AB; [home] High River, AB; [p] Vance & Shari; [school] École Joe Clark; [fav subject] Language; [hobbies] Dance, soccer, music; [pets] Kalvin (dog); [ambition] Work with animals.

SMITH, BAILY: [b] 11/27/94 Nelson, BC; [home] Nelson, BC; [p] Wes & Annette; [sisters] Blaire; [school] St. Joseph; [fav subject] Phys. ed.; [hobbies] Competitive skipping, gymnastics; [ambition] Marine biologist.

SMITH-MORPURGO, CARMEN: [b] 09/18/92 North Vancouver, BC; [home] North Vancouver, BC; [p] Michael Morpurgo & Tracy Smith; [brothers] Jeremy, Tyler; [sisters] Danielle; [school] Boundary Community; [fav subject] Lang. arts; [hobbies] Dance; [pets] Princess Rascal (cat); [ambition] Write rhyming book.

SOMERA, ANTONIO, JR.: [b] 03/25/91 Manila, Philippines; [home] Surrey, BC; [p] Antonio V. Somera, Sr. & Evelyn Somera; [brothers] Chris; [sisters] Anevel & Anya; [school] Immaculate Conception; [fav subject] Science; [hobbies] Basketball, piano; [ambition] Scientist, actor.

SORENSEN, CATERINA: [b] 05/02/93 Calgary, AB; [home] Calgary, AB; [p] Alex & Anna; [school] Mother Mary Greene; [fav subject] Art; [hobbies] Dance; [ambition] Veterinarian.

SORESTAD, BRETT: [b] 01/30/93 Edmonton, AB; [home] Stony Plain, AB; [p] T. Monte & Donna-Marie; [brothers] Mitchel; [school] John Paul II; [fav subject] Math; [hobbies] Kung fu, soccer; [ambition] Black belt in kung fu; FIFA World Cup player.

ST. CYR, NICOLE: [b] 06/13/93 Calgary, AB; [home] Calgary, AB; [p] Willy & Maureen; [school] Mother Mary Greene; [fav subject] Art; [hobbies] Piano; [pets] Dog, hamster; [ambition] Doctor.

ST. GELAIS, DAVID: [b] 05/03/94 Abbotsford, BC; [home] Calgary, AB; [p] Gerard & Lynn; [brothers] Jonathan; [sisters] Judy, Rita; [school] St. Wilfrid; [fav subject] Science, art; [hobbies] Building with Kenex, Lego, creating origami, making things with cardboard & tape; [pets] Rush (dog); [ambition] Engineer, build & invent things.

STARR, GABRIELLE: [b] 03/09/93 Peterborough, ON; [home] Langley, BC; [p] Mike & Jennie; [brothers] David; [school] Topham Elementary; [fav subject] Creative writing; [hobbies] Piano; [pets] Buddy (betta fish); [ambition] Write a fantasy book.

STEELE, PATRICK: [b] 02/21/95 Calgary, AB; [home] Calgary, AB; [p] Ed & Catharine; [brothers] David, Nathan; [school] St. Wilfrid; [fav subject] Phys. ed.; [hobbies] Hockey; [pets] Hulk (hamster); [ambition] Wrestler.

STEIN, ERIC: [b] 12/29/92 Calgary, AB; [home] Langley, BC; [p] Christopher & Lynette; [brothers] Nathan; [school] Langley Fundamental Elementary; [fav subject] Phys. ed., creative writing; [hobbies] Skiing, reading; [ambition] Lego designer, architect.

STEL, CAMERON: [b] 03/24/93 Penticton, BC; [home] Naramata, BC; [p] Bill & Tracey; [brothers] Bradley; [school] Naramata Elementary; [fav subject] Art; [hobbies] Competitive swimming; [pets] Shadow (bouvier); [ambition] Go to Disney World.

STENHOUSE, JORDAN: [b] 07/05/92 McLennan, AB; [home] McLennan, AB; [p] Wayne & Carol; [brothers] Darren; [school] École Routhier; [fav subject] Math; [hobbies] Hockey; [pets] Max (dog); [ambition] NHL goalie.

STEVENS, ALEXANDER: [b] 12/19/94 Duncan, BC; [home] Cobble Hill, BC; [p] Terry & Nancy; [brothers] Nathan; [school] Discovery Elementary; [fav subject] Math; [hobbies] Lacrosse; [pets] Nia (dog), Kitty (cat), Flameboy (toad); [ambition] Truck driver like dad.

STEVENS, NATHAN: [b] 10/20/92 Duncan, BC; [home] Cobble Hill, BC; [p] Terry & Nancy; [brothers] Alexander; [school] Discovery Elementary; [fav subject] Eukelele lessons; [hobbies] Lacrosse; [ambition] Apache helicopter pilot, NLL lacrosse player.

STOKES, TYREL: [b] 08/31/93 Edmonton, AB; [home] Stony Plain, AB; [p] Dave & Brenda; [brothers] Talon; [sisters] Tierra; [school] John Paul II; [fav subject] Math; [hobbies] Hockey, music, baseball; [pets] Tiger (dog); [ambition] NHL player, physicist, musician.

STONE, ROBERT: [b] 05/25/94 Calgary, AB; [home] Calgary, AB; [p] Thomas & Donna; [sisters] Morgan, Chelsea; [school] St. Wilfrid; [fav subject] Art; [hobbies] Go-kart racing; [pets] Maxi, Shade (dogs); [ambition] NASCAR driver.

STUART, HAILEY: [b] 05/29/93 Edmonton, AB; [home] North Vancouver, BC; [p] Tim & Janice; [sisters] Karlyn; [school] Boundary Community; [fav subject] Phys. ed., math; [hobbies] Basketball, tae kwon do, soccer, softball; [pets] Chelsea (dog), Mitzi (cat); [ambition] Actress, teacher.

TANG, JENNY: [b] 04/11/91 China; [home] Burnaby, BC; [p] Ruili Tang & Maggie Xing; [school] École Sperling; [fav subject] Art, math; [hobbies] Swimming, drawing, reading; [ambition] Artist.

THEODORAKIS, NICHOLAS: [b] 04/03/94 London, England; [home] Langley, BC; [p] Michael & Gina; [sisters] Sophia; [school] Topham Elementary; [fav subject] Geography; [hobbies] Hockey card collecting; [pets] 2 fish; [ambition] Design computer games.

THOMAS, COURTNEY RAE: [b] 05/22/90 Calgary, AB; [home] High River, AB; [p] Mike & Bonnie; [brothers] Kurtis; [sisters] Jenn; [school] École Joe Clark; [fav subject] Gym; [hobbies] Gymnastics, dance, singing; [pets] Velcro, Hart, B.J., Wild Thing (cats); [ambition] Nurse, singer.

TITTLE, COLLIN: [b] 06/21/93 Edmonton, AB; [home] St. Albert, AB; [p] Forrest Tittle & Pam North; [brothers] Martin; [school] Ronald Harvey Elementary; [fav subject] Science; [hobbies] Hockey; [pets] Guinea pig; [ambition] Scientist.

TOY, RHEANNA: [b] 04/04/92 Calgary, AB; [home] Calgary, AB; [p] Norman & Sylvia; [sisters] Melina; [school] Woodbine Elementary; [fav subject] Lang. arts; [hobbies] Dance, writing, baseball; [pets] Freckles (gecko); [ambition] Author.

TRAN, TONY: [b] 11/02/93; [home] Calgary, AB; [p] Tran Duc & To Tho; [sisters] Helen; [school] St. Wilfrid; [fav subject] Math; [hobbies] Soccer; [pets] Bird, fish.

TRANFO, ANDREW: [b] 10/17/96 Nelson, BC; [home] Nelson, BC; [p] Pete & Trish; [sisters] Serafina; [school] St. Joseph; [fav subject] Writing; [hobbies] Hockey; [pets] Cat, hamster, fish; [ambition] Crossing guard.

TURNER, CARSON: [b] 03/31/94 Victoria, BC; [home] Victoria, BC; [p] Cameron & Shannon; [brothers] Graydon; [school] St. Patrick's Elementary; [fav subject] Art; [hobbies] Drawing; [pets] Copper (dog), Pumpkin (horse), Rosie (cat); [ambition] Artist.

TYLER, MADDISON: [b] 08/05/95 Calgary, AB; [home] Calgary, AB; [p] Brad & Garbrielle; [brothers] Jackson; [school] Glenmore Christian Academy; [hobbies] Dance, reading; [pets] Fish; [ambition] Dance teacher, children's author.

TYNNING, SHAYLENE: [b] 08/30/93 Swift Current, SK; [home] Swift Current, SK; [p] Ryan & Janice; [brothers] Cory; [school] Ashley Park; [fav subject] Phys. ed.; [hobbies] Gymnastics; [pets] Ginger (dog); [ambition] Teacher.

UBIAL, WILLIAM: [b] 03/25/91 Vancouver, BC; [home] Surrey, BC; [p] Winston & Ana; [sisters] Wendy; [school] Immaculate Conception; [fav subject] Math; [hobbies] Basketball; [ambition] Engineer.

ULRICH, LINNEA: [b] 07/28/92 Regina, SK; [home] Pense, SK; [p] Doug & Shar; [brothers] Taran; [sisters] Sharelle; [school] Pense; [fav subject] Lang. arts; [hobbies] Volleyball; [pets] Licorice (dog), Princess (hamster); [ambition] Hair stylist, make-up artist.

URCHIT, MEGAN: [b] 03/31/93 Kamloops, BC; [home] Vinsulla, BC; [p] Brad & Heather; [school] Heffley Creek Elementary; [fav subject] Art, poetry; [hobbies] Tap dance, guitar; [pets] 2 dogs; [ambition] Lawyer, kindergarten teacher.

VAN AKKER, ALYSHA: [b] 08/29/91 Saanich Peninsula Hospital; [home] Cobble Hill, BC; [p] Egbert & Keri; [school] George Bonner Middle; [fav subject] English; [hobbies] Karate; [pets] Bob, George (female cats).

VERT, JESSE: [b] 02/02/96 Tofield, AB; [home] Camrose, AB; [p] Barb; [brothers] Cody, Justin, Josh; [sisters] Amber, Miranda; [school] Sparling; [fav subject] Gym; [hobbies] Skiing; [pets] Bearded dragon, 2 lizards.

VILLAGOMEZ, ANTHONY THOR: [b] 09/10/91 Philippines; [home] Surrey, BC; [p] Anthony & Teresita; [brothers] Ansley Thom; [sisters] Trish Anne, Ann Therese; [school] Immaculate Conception; [fav subject] Social studies; [hobbies] B-ball, tennis, track, v-ball; [pets] Fish; [ambition] Success in future.

WEBB, VICTORIA: [b] 09/16/92 Edmonton, AB; [home] Edmonton, AB; [p] Darcy & Debbie; [brothers] Anthony, Blake; [sisters] Alannah; [school] Patricia Heights; [fav subject] French; [hobbies] Soccer; [pets] Boo (guinea pig); [ambition] Dentist.

WEBBER, AMANDA MARION: [b] 10/31/91 Sechelt, BC; [home] Terrace, BC; [p] Ian Fraser Webber & Natalie Connie Webber; [brothers] Matthew Alexander Webber; [sisters] Desirée Rose Webber; [school] Veritas; [fav subject] Phys. ed.; [hobbies] Soccer, basketball, volleyball, badminton; [pets] Sammy (cat); [ambition] Lawyer, dentist.

WELCH, PHILIP WILLIAM: [b] 09/26/91 100 Mile House, BC; [home] Victoria, BC; [p] Kenneth Philip Welch & Dana Christine Welch; [brothers] Daniel Stephen Welch (9), Joshua Robert Welch (2); [school] Pacific Christian Elementary; [fav subject] Phys. ed.; [hobbies] Hockey, models; [pets] Dog; [ambition] Actor.

WIGGERS, CHESNEY: [b] 07/04/92 Lethbridge, AB; [home] Lethbridge, AB; [p] Dave & Shannon; [brothers] Brendan; [sisters] Courtney; [school] Children of St. Martha; [fav subject] Gym; [hobbies] Soccer, reading; [pets] Buddy (dog), Cletis (cat), 2 fish; [ambition] Paleontologist.

WILLE, BRONSON R.J.: [b] 03/23/95 Victoria, BC; [home] Victoria, BC; [school] South Island Distance Education; [fav subject] Math; [hobbies] Soccer, golf, tae kwon do [ambition] Nice, happy life.

WILLIAMS, IAN: [b] 11/25/93 Edmonton, AB; [home] Calgary, AB; [p] Scott & Susan; [sisters] Jen, Kate; [school] Mother Mary Greene; [fav subject] Music; [hobbies] Swimming; [ambition] Jazz piano musician.

WILLIAMS, RYAN: [b] 05/08/91 Vancouver, BC; [home] Port Alberni, BC; [p] Joan Williams (grandmother); [sisters] Rosie; [school] Neill Middle; [fav subject] Phys. ed.; [hobbies] Basketball; [pets] 2 cats; [ambition] "To be the best I can."

WILSON, LEVI: [b] 08/01/95 Calgary, AB; [home] High River, AB; [p] Shawn & Sharla; [sisters] Sydney; [school] École Joe Clark; [fav subject] Science; [hobbies] Hockey; [ambition] Fireman.

WONG, TIFFANY: [b] 04/16/93 Hong Kong; [home] Calgary, AB; [p] Sunny & Loretta; [brothers] Andrew; [school] Mother Mary Greene; [fav subject] Art; [hobbies] Skiing; [pets] Puppy; [ambition] Artist.

YAGELNISKI, BRANDY: [b] 04/26/91 Terrace, BC; [home] Terrace, BC; [p] Curley & Chris; [brothers] Travis; [sisters] Kayla; [school] Veritas; [fav subject] Lang. arts; [hobbies] Soccer, travelling; [pets] Tyson (dog); [ambition] Lawyer, veterinarian, teacher.

YORK, CYNDEE K.: [b] 08/03/96 Beaverlodge, AB; [home] Dawson Creek, BC; [p] Curtis & Cathy; [brothers] Andrew; [school] Notre Dame Elementary; [fav subject] Art; [hobbies] Skiing; [pets] Snowball.

YOUNG, ASHLEY: [b] 09/17/92 Moose Jaw, SK; [home] Moose Jaw, SK; [p] Darrell & Karen; [sisters] Ronnie & Tiaunna; [school] William Grayson; [fav subject] French; [hobbies] Singing; [pets] Cat; [ambition] "Family, friends, school, my pet, love of life."

YOUNG PINE, BILLY: [b] 07/22/92 Lethbridge, AB; [home] Lethbridge, AB; [p] Raynard Youngpine & Kim Gravelle; [brothers] Kenny; [sisters] Tania; [school] Children of St. Martha; [fav subject] All; [hobbies] Hockey; [pets] Sasha (cat), Flipper (horse); [ambition] Paleontologist.

YU, JEFFREY: [b] 06/06/91 Vancouver, BC; [home] Coquitlam, BC; [p] Eddie Yu & May Ching Yu; [brothers] Gilbert; [school] Montgomery Middle; [fav subject] Math; [hobbies] Basketball; [pets] Goldfish; [ambition] Computer engineer.

ZACHARIAS, CINDY: [b] 06/29/91 Fairview, AB; [home] Cleardale, AB; [p] Jake & Helen; [brothers] Michael, Cory, Mark, Steven, Phillip; [sisters] Barbara, Maryann; [school] Menno Simons; [fav subject] Math; [hobbies] Volleyball; [pets] Dog; [ambition] Shopping.

INDEX OF POETS